GW00535699

ROYAL COMMISSION

ON

ENVIRONMENTAL POLLUTION

CHAIRMAN: SIR RICHARD SOUTHWOOD

ELEVENTH REPORT

MANAGING WASTE : THE DUTY OF CARE

Presented to Parliament by Command of Her Majesty
December 1985

LONDON
HER MAJESTY'S STATIONERY OFFICE
£12.50 net

Cmnd.9675

ISBN 0 10 196750 0

ROYAL COMMISSION
ON
ENVIRONMENTAL POLLUTION

ELEVENTH REPORT

To the Queen's Most Excellent Majesty

MAY IT PLEASE YOUR MAJESTY

We, the undersigned Commissioners, having been appointed "to advise on matters, both national and international, concerning the pollution of the environment; on the adequacy of research in this field; and the future possibilities of danger to the environment";

And to enquire into any such matters referred to us by one of Your Majesty's Secretaries of State or by one of Your Majesty's Ministers, or any other such matters on which we ourselves shall deem it expedient to advise:

HUMBLY SUBMIT TO YOUR MAJESTY THE FOLLOWING REPORT.

"Most pollution comes from getting rid of wastes
at the least possible cost."

Sir Frank Fraser Darling 1903–79
Member of the Royal Commission 1970–73

Wilderness and Plenty (1969 Reith Lectures)

CONTENTS

CHAPTER I

CHAPTER II

WASTE CONTROLS, CHARACTERISTICS AND QUANTITIES

CHAPTER III

A STRATEGY FOR WASTE

CHAPTER IV

CHAPTER V

GIVING WASTE VALUE

CHAPTER VI

COLLECTION, STORAGE AND TRANSPORT OF WASTES

CHAPTER VII

CHAPTER VIII

CHAPTER IX

CHAPTER X

PROFESSIONALISM : DESIGN, STANDARDS AND TRAINING

CHAPTER XI

RESEARCH AND DEVELOPMENT

CHAPTER XII

OVERVIEW

CHAPTER XIII

CONCLUSIONS AND RECOMMENDATIONS

APPENDICES

FIGURES

TABLES

INFORMATION BOXES

PLATES

1. Domestic refuse collection using wheeled dustbins; examples from (a) UK and (b) the Netherlands. (See paragraph 6.5).

2. A large, well organised civic amenity site, where householders can deliver large items and garden wastes, as well as normal household refuse. (6.22).

3. A smaller civic amenity site with limited opening hours. (6.22).

4. Centralised collection for recycling - textiles and cans can be taken to central 'banks' as well as glass to bottle banks. (5.16).

5. Red bins - used in Germany for the collection of hazardous materials from householders. In this example the bins are for used batteries. (5.19).

6. Refuse left for collection at the kerbside (a) attracts other refuse; (b) can fall into the road and be dispersed by traffic; and (c) can attract animals that may damage the sacks. (6.7).

7. Litter bins which are allowed to become over-full can cause litter to spread in public places ... particularly if the surrounding area is not cleared at the same time as the litter bin. (6.10).

8. Current advice from the Department of Transport is to remove litter bins from lay-bys on trunk roads to prevent the accumulation of rubbish and replace them with notices telling motorists to take their litter home. (6.11).

9. Litter bags for cars are available in some countries (6.13).

10. Construction or demolition wastes fly tipped in a street in London. (6.20).

11. Rural fly tipping is often wastes from the building industry and domestic wastes. (6.20).

12. Local authorities could find more ways of keeping the public informed about waste collection and disposal services. (6.23).

13. Unsatisfactory disposal of waste agro-chemicals and containers. (2.42).

14. An abandoned store of industrial materials (6.33).

15. The Byker waste derived fuel plant: (a) processes crude refuse; (b) separates out incombustible material; and (c) makes pellets from the combustible fraction, which can then be stored (d). (5.21).

16. A schematic diagram of the waste processing plant at Byker, Tyne and Wear, producing pelletised waste derived fuel. (5.21).

17. Old barges with loose covers used to transport domestic wastes to landfill are now being replaced with specially designed fixed cover barges. (6.40).

18. Trains with containers or covered rail wagons are used to transport domestic wastes to remote landfill sites. (6.40).

19. An example, from the USA, of a waste consignment note. (8.36).

20. A well managed landfill site where small cells lead to short advancing fronts of newly tipped waste and allow easy daily cover to be placed. (7.23).

21. A poorly managed site with larger tipping areas, inadequately covered deposits and birds presenting a potential nuisance. (7.23).

22. Leachate liquors are generated in landfills and can contaminate ground and surface waters. (7.5).

23. A schematic diagram of the GLC Aveley landfill site at which methane is collected from the wastes and distributed to fuel a factory's boilers. (7.14).

24. Industrial waste: (a) incineration facilities (note the colour coded waste drums awaiting combustion) and (b) biological waste water treatment at Bayer AG, Leverkusen, Germany. (7.33).

Plates 1 to 12 are located after page 50, and Plates 13 to 24 after page 146.

CHAPTER I

THE PROBLEM OF WASTES

Introduction

1.1 This Report is the outcome of a study announced in paragraph 6.15 of the Tenth Report, published in February 1984([1]):

> 'Many of the problems from the past arise as a result of the pollution of land - from landfill waste disposal (or uncontrolled tipping in former times) and in sites of former industrial activities. We have seen some dramatic instances of the latter in the north of England. From preliminary evidence on these matters which we assembled in 1982, we concluded that there were issues which, although highly relevant to this Report, required more detailed study over a longer period. We were also aware of the recent report by the House of Lords Select Committee on Science and Technology on hazardous waste disposal and it seemed sensible to wait for the issues to clarify before embarking on a further review. We have therefore decided that our next study should be concerned with pollution by wastes, including the problem of land contamination; we are now considering the particular areas for investigation in what is potentially a very broad subject.'

1.2 As with previous studies we initially circulated, in April 1984, a request for written evidence (Appendix 3) to a wide circle of organisations and individuals. We followed that up with visits, meetings and further inquiries. As we record on page 175, we met with a most generous and constructive response, including many unsolicited contributions. A list of those contributing to our study in various ways is at Appendix 2. We also commissioned Environmental Resources Ltd to carry out a review for us of the economics of resource recovery and recycling. Their report *(Resource Recovery: A Report for the Royal Commission on Environmental Pollution)* is being published separately([2]).

1.3 Waste can cause *pollution*, which (as was noted in the Tenth Report) has been usefully defined as:

> 'the introduction by man into the environment of substances or energy liable to cause hazards to human health, harm to living resources and ecological systems, damage to structures or amenity, or interference with legitimate uses of the environment.'([3])

1

In accordance with our terms of reference we concentrate in this Report on questions of pollution and do not explore wider questions of resource conservation, except insofar as they are relevant to pollution avoidance and abatement.

1.4 Much of the evidence we have received relates to good practice. We have tried to assess it and to call attention to aspects which we consider to be particularly valuable in waste management. In this Report we have deliberately avoided repeating all the good advice and analyses which are to be found in the Department of the Environment's series of Waste Management Papers, the reports of various recent committees[4-7] and other readily available publications[8,9].

Definitions

1.5 'Waste' is a term which most people understand, yet a formal definition is far from straightforward. The World Health Organisation defines waste as 'something which the owner no longer wants at a given place and time and which has no current or perceived market value'[10]. It seems to us that waste is best defined by reference to the person who wishes to dispose of it - not to what happens to it afterwards. Material becomes identified as waste when somebody regards it as valueless and wants to get rid of it. This concept is recognised in the definition given in the Control of Pollution Act 1974, which we find helpful and practical for our purposes. Section 30(1) defines 'controlled waste' (i.e. household, commercial and industrial waste) as including:

'(a) any substance which constitutes a scrap material or an effluent or other unwanted surplus substance arising from the application of any process; and

(b) any substance or article which requires to be disposed of as being broken, worn out, contaminated or otherwise spoiled'.

The Act goes on to say that 'any thing which is discarded or otherwise dealt with as if it were waste shall be presumed to be waste unless the contrary is proved'.

Why is waste a problem?

1.6 Waste and the activities associated with it can be harmful or undesirable in a number of respects:

- as a hazard to human beings and other living organisms, e.g. by direct toxicity or through contamination of aquifers, water courses and land;

- as a detractor from amenity and recreation, e.g. through visible, audible or odorous intrusion or through restricting the use of sites by chemical contamination or physical instability;

2

- as a useless consumption of natural resources (this falls outside our terms of reference).

Harm can be caused at any point during the production or disposal of waste - storage, transport, transfer, disposal - and subsequently, after deposition, harm can arise through matter given off or leached out, or where the waste is disturbed in such a way as to bring it into contact with the living environment.

1.7 Because waste is, by definition, of little or no perceived value to the person generating it, there is little financial incentive to handle it in a careful and secure manner, and there is a built-in temptation to relinquish responsibility for it at the earliest opportunity. The continuing problems of fly tipping and litter (see Plates 6,7,8,10 and 11) are examples of what can happen when waste is disposed of without proper care and without a proper framework of regulation and enforcement.

Pollution pathways

1.8 Pollution or contamination of the *ground and soil* can be caused by wastes along four principal routes: deposition in landfills of toxic or hazardous wastes, which can seriously limit the sites' possible after-use; spreading on the ground of some treated wastes (e.g. water and sewage treatment residues), which can lead to a build-up of undesirable contaminants, such as heavy metals, in soils; the deposition of particulate emissions from waste incinerators; and the deposition on industrial sites of potential contaminants used in or generated by industry. Other nuisances or even health risks, such as vermin infestation or litter, can also occur when waste is disposed of to land.

1.9 Damage to the *aquatic environment* can arise through pollution of ground water, surface waters or the sea. The principal ways in which wastes can harm ground water are through contamination by liquids generated in or percolating through landfill sites (leachates) and through contamination from direct contact with liquid or solid wastes disposed of underground. Surface waters also can suffer pollution from landfill site leachates; from water running off landfill sites or mineral waste stock piles; and from spillages, discharges, seepage and run-off of agricultural or industrial effluents to water courses.

1.10 Many types of waste can contaminate or pollute the sea: for example, the direct disposal of sewage or materials thrown overboard from ships; deposits of drill cuttings or drilling muds from offshore oil and gas operations; and unauthorised tank washing by oil tankers.[1,11].

1.11 The *atmosphere* can be polluted by wastes or waste disposal in three main ways: dust and smells may be associated with municipal wastes during collection, transfer or disposal; gaseous or fine particulate emissions may escape from incinerators used to burn wastes; and explosive atmospheres can

3

be generated by the accumulation of landfill gases caused by the anaerobic decomposition of organic materials in landfill sites. The atmosphere is also the pathway for noise from waste disposal operations, which can detract from amenity.

Key characteristics of waste

1.12 As far as their polluting effects are concerned, all forms of waste have one feature in common: waste, being no longer required by its owner, is *consigned to the environment*. By the act of consignment the waste may either find its final resting place, or it may pass into a state of transition - *the waste stream*. In either case, from the moment of consignment, it is a potential source of pollution, and this may largely be attributed to one or more of three features which many wastes share and which distinguish them from, for instance, manufactured products - that *waste is of little or no, or even negative, value*; that there is often *uncertainty about the composition of a waste*; and that many waste streams exhibit a *high degree of variability*, both within and between loads. To prevent pollution from occurring there must be a *secure waste stream*, achieved through the exercise of a proper *duty of care* by producers, handlers and transporters of waste, and the ultimate means of disposal must be the *best practicable environmental option*. The phrases we have emphasised provide many of the themes running through this Report, which we sum up in Chapter XII.

Concerns about wastes

1.13 The Tenth Report commented on public attitudes to pollution and gave some indication of the relative importance of particular aspects of pollution, as perceived by people giving evidence early in 1982. Table 1.1 sets out the results of a recent survey[12] of public perception in the UK of the relative seriousness of six specific issues, two of them relevant to this report. The results of a similar survey[13], comparing attitudes in the Federal Republic of Germany, England and the USA are in Table 1.2. Another recent study, in the United States, shows that public concern over waste disposal is rising[14]. As was noted in the Tenth Report, objective measurements of environmental concerns are very hard to come by; but the data in these Tables are not inconsistent with the broad impression we have formed during our study that, whilst on a general level there is acute concern about certain specific types of waste (notably toxic chemical and radioactive wastes), at the local level nearly every aspect of waste management is capable of becoming an issue of concern. Moreover, there are signs that a greater awareness of the general problems of waste disposal is spreading, partly as a result of the growing international exchange of ideas but also because, as environmental quality steadily improves, the public becomes less tolerant of the problems which remain. We illustrate the main areas of concern about wastes in the box on page 6. In this study we see our task as not only to evaluate and respond to these concerns but also to consider and report on the reforms which we believe are desirable.

TABLE 1.1

BRITISH SOCIAL ATTITUDES
Responses in 1984 to question 'how serious an effect on our environment do you think each of these things has?'

	Very serious	Quite serious	Not very serious	Not at all serious
Noise from aircraft	7	24	50	17
Lead from petrol	45	39	11	2
Industrial waste in the rivers and sea	67	25	6	1
Waste from nuclear electricity stations	69	18	9	2
Industrial fumes in the air	46	40	11	2
Noise and dirt from traffic	20	45	29	4

All figures percentages; 'don't know' responses omitted.
Source: Social and Community Planning Research[12]

TABLE 1.2

1982 INTERNATIONAL ENVIRONMENT SURVEY
Responses to question 'how urgent are the following environmental problems?'

	F R Germany	England	USA
Noise	5.1	4.4	3.8
Air pollution	6.2	5.6	5.4
Water pollution	6.4	5.7	5.8
Over-population	5.2	5.1	4.6
Solid waste disposal	5.0	5.1	5.3
Toxic wastes	6.6	6.0	6.0
Nuclear wastes	6.4	6.2	6.0
Destruction of land and townscape	5.9	5.4	5.3
Depletion of natural resources	6.1	5.9	5.6
Energy	6.1	5.7	5.7

Numbers are the arithmetic mean scores on a seven-point scale, in which 1 = 'not urgent' and 7 = 'very urgent'.
Source: International Institute for Environment and Society[13]

1.14 Because wastes tend to be concentrated (litter being an exception) at particular sites - legally or illegally - they have acquired a 'bad neighbour' image. As with certain other socially or environmentally intrusive developments or activities such as airports, nuclear power stations and prisons, the public tends to be sensitive about the activities associated with waste disposal - particularly where they are on a large scale and are thought to pose risks of the kinds just outlined. The acronym NIMBY - 'not in my back yard' - is widely used to describe the local public opposition to the establishment of new waste disposal sites and other intrusive installations, and on a national level it can lead to pressures for some waste disposal practices to be banned altogether.

MAIN AREAS OF PUBLIC CONCERN ABOUT WASTES

Toxic wastes which have mutagenic, teratogenic or carcinogenic effects, or other latent, slow effects on health;

The tipping of hazardous wastes and the risk of acute poisoning to man and other living organisms;

The spread of toxic or noxious materials placed on the ground to gardens, homes, play areas, etc.;

Irreversible damage to the environment by irretrievable disposal of persistent substances to land or the marine environment;

Contamination of ground water;

The lowering of the amenity value of an area through the presence of wastes - especially litter, but also the noise, smell and other nuisances associated with waste collection and disposal;

The apparent waste of resources which could be recovered from discarded materials[15].

1.15 NIMBY cannot be dismissed as irrational: it is the expression of concern about a risk as perceived by the local inhabitants. But the fact that there is public concern does not necessarily mean that there is a real environmental hazard. A proper evaluation of the risk requires access to the relevant information and its interpretation, and the public will not be reassured by interpretations provided by the putative polluter, who has an interest. In the absence of public confidence in the role of bodies that are both authoritative and independent, interpretations by the press or pressure groups are often accepted, even if they go beyond what an informed expert would regard as justified by the evidence.

1.16 We believe that especially damaging to public confidence are the occasions on which information is not readily provided in response to reasonable requests and the situations in which, rightly or wrongly, the public perceives a failure to observe and enforce proper standards. Once public confidence is lost it can be regained only by a long uphill struggle, which may involve expenditure that is, from the environmental viewpoint, nugatory.

1.17 The question of unnecessary secrecy was dealt with at considerable length in the Tenth Report, and we await the conclusions of the Government's detailed consideration of the Report's recommendations, on which a helpful discussion paper was circulated by the Department of the Environment to interested organisations in August 1985[16]. Needless to say, the recommendations apply as much to waste as to other sources of pollution and, as was said in the Tenth Report, 'secrecy fuels fear'. However it is not just secrecy that undermines confidence: it may be simple incompetence. As the House of Lords Select Committee on Science and Technology said in its report on hazardous waste (the 'Gregson Report')([5]), 'fears about hazardous waste

---

PCBs

What are they?

PCBs (polychlorinated biphenyls) were produced in substantial quantities from the 1930s for applications such as dielectric fluids, solvents, plasticisers and other industrial uses. They are very stable substances and persist in the environment.

How dangerous are they?
Effects on animals
Certain PCBs are carcinogenic to mice and rats([19]) after oral administration, producing benign and malignant neoplasms of the liver.

Effects on man
Commercial PCB products generally contain low concentrations of toxic contaminants such as dibenzo-furans so it can be difficult to attribute particular effects to specific substances.

In groups exposed to high levels of PCBs, either occupationally or accidentally through eating contaminated food, deaths have occurred that have been attributed to PCB poisoning. These deaths have been associated with fatty degeneration, necrosis and cirrhosis of the liver([20-22]). More frequently less severe disorders have been reported in those exposed - most characteristically chloracne, but also skin rashes, nail decay and discolouration, hyperpigmentation of the gums, irritation of the eyes and carious teeth.

In Japan a group of mothers occupationally exposed to PCBs initially showed some clinical signs such as chloracne. They recovered gradually from these disorders but retained elevated PCB levels in the blood, and their breast milk also showed elevated levels. There is a continuing study of the health of the children of these women([23-25]). Those who were not breast fed did not have elevated blood PCB levels; those who were breast fed did, and these persisted for a long time. During this period some of these children showed an increased incidence of the disorders listed above.

Since PCBs are stable, persist in the environment and bio-accumulate, there is also anxiety about possible carcinogenic effects in man. Results of epidemiological studies of workers industrially exposed to PCBs have given inconclusive results.

7

DIOXINS
What are they?

There are 75 different isomers of chlorinated dioxins, each containing between 1 and 8 chlorine atoms and with differing arrangements of these chlorine atoms within the molecule. The isomer which has caused most concern is 2,3,7,8 tetrachlorodibenzodioxin (TCDD).

The dioxins are stable physically and biologically and, in common with other halogenated aromatic hydrocarbons, tend to be increasingly stable with increasing halogen content. They are insoluble in water, but dissolve in organic solvents, fats and oils; they adsorb on to soil particles and do not readily desorb; and they tend to concentrate in the bottom sediments of water bodies and to accumulate in the fatty tissues of fish and other animals.

Chlorinated dibenzo-furans are structurally similar to the dioxins but there are 135 isomers. Sensitive analysis has shown that many PCB samples contain traces of the dibenzo-furans which also appear in many of the samples analysed for dioxins. As analysis has become more precise, so the furans have increasingly been identified.

How dangerous are they?
Effects on animals

The reputation of dioxins for extreme toxicity rests on animal experiments, in which very low dosages of TCDD are lethal to guinea pigs but lethal doses in other rodents were much higher:

TCDD's Lethal Dose Varies in Different Species[26]

Animal	LD_{50} *(µg/kg bw)**
Guinea pig	1
Rat (male)	22
Rat (female)	45
Monkey	< 70
Rabbit	115
Mouse	114
Dog	> 300
Bullfrog	> 500
Hamster	5000

* LD_{50}: dose that causes 50% of the sample to die;
µg/kg bw: micrograms per kilogram body weight

continued

Carcinogenic effects. Animal experiments have shown that when TCDD is given in the diet to rats over a prolonged period at a dose of 0.1 µg/kg body weight/day, there is an increased incidence of cancer in a number of organs. The liver seems to be the organ most affected[27].

Reproductive effects. Animal experiments in which doses of 1-10µg/kg bw TCDD were fed to rats led to foetal loss or abortion. When administered at one tenth of these dose rates, reduction of fertility was observed. Teratogenic studies on mice have associated cleft palates and kidney deformities with dioxins. In both the teratogenic and foetotoxic studies there was only a small difference between dose rates affecting reproduction and those which killed the animal in question[27].

Immunological effects. The limited amount of data from animal experiments indicates that TCDD can have a powerful depressive effect on the immune system[27]. The effect appears to be dose dependent occurring after short term high dose exposures.

Effects on man
Human data all relate to people industrially or accidentally exposed to dioxins in combination with many other halogenated aromatic chemicals. Hence it is difficult to attribute particular effects to specific substances.

Dioxins do not have a record of lethal poisoning in humans. Severe occupational or accidental exposures such as the Seveso incident have resulted in chloracne, minor but reversible nerve damage, and some impaired liver function but no deaths have been conclusively attributed to dioxins.

Carcinogenic effects. Swedish studies have suggested a link between the use of phenoxy-herbicides contaminated by dioxins and the occurrence of soft-tissue sarcomas. These tumours, however, are extremely uncommon. Three cases of soft-tissue sarcoma were also reported in 1981 from small groups of United States workers exposed to TCDD in a manufacturing process. These findings have not been supported by other studies, so no firm conclusions can be drawn.

Reproductive effects. Despite claims concerning adverse effects in Vietnam veterans[28] and other similar claims in the United States, there is no conclusive evidence from the US that dioxins affect human reproduction. Nor have ill effects have been observed in those exposed at Seveso.

Immunological effects. Immunological studies of humans accidentally exposed to dioxins have given inconclusive results.

9

disposal are enormously increased by, if not based on, past mistakes'. A similar message emerges from the First Report of the Hazardous Waste Inspectorate([17]). Much reference will be made to both of these reports in the chapters which follow; and in Chapter XII we return to the problem of NIMBY and offer some practical suggestions for overcoming it.

1.18 As was noted in the Tenth Report, many of today's environmental concerns stem from advances in analytical chemistry, which now enable previously undetected substances to be measured at trace levels in the environment, coupled with heightened public awareness of the risks associated with new or exotic chemicals or with risks newly associated with substances which have been in use for some time. The group of chemicals known as dioxins and furans is a case in point. In fact many of them are widely distributed in the environment as a result of wood fires and the burning of other organic material. Recent concern, however, has centred around the presence of some of these as by-products of the accidental or deliberate incineration of certain chemicals (for example the disaster at Seveso, Italy, in 1976, and the disposal by incineration of waste polychlorinated biphenyls (PCBs)) and as trace contaminants in certain agro-chemicals. In Chapter VII we comment on incinerator operation generally and in particular on the conditions needed for the effective destruction of PCBs.

1.19 In the boxes on pages 7−9 we have summarised what is currently known about the health effects of PCBs, dioxins and furans. There are very wide variations in the reported effects on different species of animals; and so far the only ill effect in man that can be positively attributed to the dioxins is the skin complaint, chloracne. We consider that the available evidence does not justify the current level of public concern. We believe that the hypothesis that man may have acquired a degree of immunity to these toxins from long exposure to wood smoke([18])is at least plausible. Nevertheless, we believe that it is right to err on the side of caution. The aetiology of many illnesses is uncertain and the ability to analyse minute quantities of the very wide range of substances produced has only recently been developed.

1.20 We endorse the need for further research into the toxicity of the dioxins to man. In this connection the work which is in hand, following the initial investigations of the Seveso incident, to study the possible long-term effects of contamination of human populations by dioxins will be of the utmost importance. Public reassurance now largely depends on a reduction in the uncertainty surrounding the health effects of dioxins, furans and their precursors and on visible improvements in the management of industrial and municipal incineration processes of a kind which will command confidence in future. In view of the likely significance of the Seveso studies to all industrial countries, we **recommend** that the Government should seek to ensure that the European Community gives the fullest possible support to this activity and to the proper dissemination of the results of the research.

Scope of this Report

1.21 Whilst waste can be material of many different kinds, in solid, liquid or gaseous form, for the purposes of this study we have decided to draw certain broad boundaries around our area of investigation. These have regard to the fact that many questions of river, marine and atmospheric pollution and the polluting effects of nuclear power and agriculture have already been considered in detail in the Commission's Third[29], Fifth[30], Sixth[31], Seventh[32], Eighth and Tenth Reports. This Report is therefore primarily concerned with containable or packageable wastes, that is to say wastes which are not disposed of by controlled emissions or discharges (as would be, for instance, bulk liquid effluents discharged to sewers and water courses or gases emitted to atmosphere). Sludges and slurries* are therefore included, as are containable liquids disposed of by other means. At the same time we do give consideration, where appropriate, to the wider question of selecting the best practicable environmental options for the management and disposal of wastes, including options in relation to the form in which wastes are allowed to enter the environment. Thus we are concerned, for example, with the decisions that an industrial manager has to make on whether the waste from a particular process is to be disposed of in solid, liquid or gaseous form; and with the original inputs of waste that remain in concentrated form in sewage sludge. But we have excluded from our study the detailed techniques of sewage treatment (on which there is extensive literature and little controversy); and we have not concerned ourselves with discharges and emissions which are sufficiently diluted or dispersed to cause no pollution - for example the discharge of comminuted natural sewage through long sea outfalls, which in the Tenth Report was endorsed as an environmentally acceptable method of disposal.

1.22 Under the heading of solid wastes we have not gone over again in detail the ground which was covered in the Sixth and Seventh Reports (on Nuclear Power and Agriculture respectively), and this was anticipated in the letters we sent inviting evidence from organisations involved in these fields (see Appendix 3). In particular, because of the involvement of other bodies with specific interests and responsibilities in the fields of radiological protection and radioactive waste management, we have not dealt with the technical aspects of radioactive wastes. But we have identified a number of issues in this field which are important for public policy, and we discuss these in the context of parallel issues arising in other areas of our study.

1.23 We came to the conclusion in the course of our study that contaminated land, as a subject in its own right, did not merit extensive treatment in this Report. We appreciate that this may not match the expectations of local authorities and communities who suffer directly from the legacy of past industrial activities and uncontrolled waste disposal practices.

* In materials handling terms, there is a continuum from solids, running through sludges and slurries, to liquids.

11

But we do believe, having studied the evidence, that the problem is largely a historical one, that technical solutions are available in most instances, and that the main difficulties are the identification of contaminated sites and the cost of remedial works. We report on these issues in Chapter II, but we believe the improvements in management practice and regulatory controls which we recommend elsewhere in this Report are the best way of ensuring that the environment suffers no further damage from this particular form of insecure waste disposal.

1.24 Having set, for practical reasons, these boundaries round our study, we have looked at both individual and common characteristics of wastes. Without duplicating or paraphrasing the work of other committees of inquiry or the many practitioners' guides which have been published, our aim has been to offer comments on the state of waste management in this country; to make some comparisons with practice in other countries; to recommend principles and guidelines for current practice and future policy; and to offer advice on issues which are currently the subject of disagreement or uncertainty.

1.25 By waste management we mean the management of waste at all levels of responsibility and at all stages, from production, through handling and transport, to its ultimate disposal.

CHAPTER II

WASTE CONTROLS, CHARACTERISTICS AND QUANTITIES

Introduction

2.1 In this chapter we give an outline of the present legal and administrative arrangements for controlling pollution from wastes, with particular reference to land disposal. We then summarise what is known about the quantities of waste arising in the main categories considered by this Report, with their characteristics. In general statistics are inadequate or lacking altogether, and we make some recommendations for their improvement. We also take the opportunity to discuss at rather more length and to make recommendations on certain problems (agricultural wastes, sewage and water treatment wastes, and contaminated land) which do not readily find a place in the main structure of our Report but which nevertheless we consider important in their own right.

2.2 The management of wastes of all kinds has attracted attention from a wide range of official bodies and others (paragraph 1.4). Waste remains a subject of lively public concern and the present system has evolved against a number of changes over the past decade or so in factors that affect wastes and their handling. These include:

- changes in agricultural practice (e.g. intensive livestock production and increased cereal growing)

- changes in the composition of wastes from various sources (e.g. falling levels of heavy metals in sewage)

- development of new packaging materials (including ever-increasing use of plastics)

- changes in retailing practices (e.g. growth of supermarkets, do-it-yourself stores and garden centres)

- changes in collection methods, particularly increased mechanisation and a reduction in traditional manual methods of handling

- changes in the waste disposal industry (e.g. growth of large private sector disposal contractors and 'privatisation' of local authority services)

- increasing interest in the recovery of materials and energy from waste, including the production of waste derived fuel

- research and development in many areas, including landfill gas, biotechnology and materials separation and recovery

- organisational changes in local government and the water industry

- international influences, notably growing pressures against traditionally practised methods of dispersing pollutants into the environment, especially the sea.

We refer to these changes in more detail as we develop the strategy for waste which we outline in Chapter III.

Legislative background*

2.3 Prior to 1972, the United Kingdom had no provisions on the statute book which dealt with the management aspects of waste disposal in a broad context. Local authorities, however, have for many generations had powers to control waste as a public health problem, and some of the antecedents for these powers can be traced back to medieval times. The Public Health Act 1936, a consolidation of legislation going back to Victorian times, empowers local authorities to remove house and trade refuse and to require the removal of 'any accumulation of noxious matter'. It also imposes on them a duty to inspect their areas for 'statutory nuisances', including 'any accumulation or deposit which is prejudicial to health or a nuisance'; they also have the power to serve abatement notices and to prosecute offenders. A shortcoming of these powers and duties is that they are not sufficient to prevent a nuisance arising; however it does appear that they have ensured that Britain has been spared the uncovering of previously unknown major deposits of toxic wastes (see paragraph 2.51).*

2.4 The first legislation which can be said to have a preventive effect was the Town and Country Planning Act 1947 (since superseded by the Town and Country Planning Act 1971). This requires that any new development, including waste disposal sites or plants, should have planning permission. In the 1960s, however, there was growing concern about the environmental effects of waste. The Government was persuaded by this concern to set up two working groups, one on toxic waste in 1964 (the Key Committee) and the other on refuse disposal in 1967 (the Sumner Committee). The resulting reports[33,34] helped to pave the way for Part 1 of the Control of Pollution Act 1974, which deals comprehensively with domestic and industrial waste. Shortly before this Act was drafted, a series of well publicised incidents relating to the tipping of toxic wastes and the Royal Commission's Second Report[35] alerted the

---

* In the sections which follow, reference is in general made to legislation applicable to England and Wales. The legislation applicable to Scotland and Northern Ireland is not always identical, but it is basically the same in all material respects.

Government to the need to legislate quickly. The outcome was the Deposit of Poisonous Waste Act 1972. The intention was that this Act would be repealed once the more comprehensive system embodied in the Control of Pollution Act was fully in operation. This eventually happened in 1981.

Waste disposal plans and site licensing

2.5 The 1974 Act requires waste disposal authorities (county councils in England, district councils in Wales, and district and island councils in Scotland) to prepare plans for the disposal of all household, commercial and industrial waste likely to arise in their areas (termed controlled waste - see box overleaf), and to review and modify the plans where appropriate. In preparing them, the authorities must consult water authorities, other levels of local government and other relevant bodies, and must make adequate arrangements for publicity and public participation in the draft plans. A waste disposal plan must include information about:

- the kinds and quantities of waste which will arise in the area, or be brought into it, during the period of the plan;

- what waste the authority expects to dispose of itself;

- what waste others are expected to dispose of;

- the methods of disposal, e.g. reclamation, incineration, landfill;

- the sites and equipment being provided; and

- the cost.

The Act requires disposal authorities to consider what arrangements can reasonably be made for reclaiming waste materials. The plan does not require Government approval, but a disposal authority is required to consult any water authority whose responsibilities fall within the area of the plan or any other disposal authority in whose area waste is to be disposed of and, in the latter case, to obtain that authority's consent. If consent is withheld, the Secretary of State is the arbiter. A copy of the plan, when finally determined, has to be sent to the Secretary of State. We discuss progress on the preparation of waste disposal plans, which has been slow to date, in paragraphs 9.8-9.9.

2.6 The Act also introduced a comprehensive licensing system for the disposal of wastes over and above existing planning controls. It makes it an offence to deposit household, commercial or industrial waste on land or to use waste disposal plant unless the land in question is licensed by the waste disposal authority (or explicitly exempted from licensing). A site licence (as it is usually termed) can be issued only if the required planning permission for the site is in force. Applications for site licences have to be referred to water authorities and collection authorities for comment, and the Secretary of State is required to arbitrate in the event of any unresolved dispute between a water authority and a waste disposal authority.

15

WASTE CATEGORIES : SOME DEFINITIONS

Statutory definitions in Part I of the Control of Pollution Act 1974 (COPA) are shown in bold type; paragraph references are given where there is further discussion elsewhere in this Report

Civic Amenity Waste

Under the Refuse Disposal (Amenity) Act 1978, waste disposal authorities are required to provide places where refuse not arising in the course of business may be deposited. Refuse is defined as 'any matter whatsoever, whether inorganic or organic'. In practice it consists of waste arising in households that for one reason or another is not collected with the ordinary dustbin contents - e.g. garden rubbish, old furniture and waste arising from 'DIY' activities. The term derives from the expression 'civic amenity site', which is common in local authority (if not actually in popular) parlance. (6.21)

Commercial Waste (Section 30(3)(c) of COPA)

One of the three components of controlled waste and consisting of 'waste from premises used wholly or mainly for the purposes of a trade or business or for the purposes of sport, recreation or entertainment'. Excluded from the definition are household and industrial waste (q.v.); mining, quarrying and agricultural waste; and any other waste which may be prescribed by regulations. (8.2-8.6)

Controlled Waste (Section 30(1) of COPA)

'Household, industrial and commercial waste or any such waste'. (2.5-2.7; 8.2-8.6; 8.23; 9.8-9.9)

Difficult Waste

A term favoured by some waste disposal authorities and consultants([39]) for referring to wastes which, for whatever reason, require special care in their handling, treatment or disposal. It goes wider than 'hazardous waste' (q.v.) because it can include wastes with 'difficult' characteristics such as quantity, physical form or undesirable attractiveness to scavengers.

Domestic Waste

A term which we use in this Report as being roughly synonymous with 'house refuse' (as used in, but not defined by, the Public Health Act 1936) rather than with the wider definition in COPA of 'household waste' (q.v.), which is not yet operative for waste collection purposes. It would include waste taken by householders to civic amenity sites. (2.28-2.29; 2.31; 5.8-5.10; 6.4-6.9)

Hazardous Waste

An imprecise term which includes all special wastes (q.v.) and other wastes which have harmful effects on the environment, not just on human health. (2.18-2.23)

Household Waste (Section 30(3)(a) of COPA)

One of the three components of controlled waste and consisting of 'waste from a private dwelling or residential home or from premises forming part of a university or school or other educational establishment or forming part of a hospital or nursing home'. Because sections 12-14 of

continued

COPA have not yet been brought into effect, most authorities' regular non-trade collection services cover only domestic wastes (under Section 72 of the Public Health Act 1936): current practice in relation to waste from educational and health care establishments varies. (6.27-6.32; 7.40-7.41; 8.2-8.6; 8.47-8.49)

Industrial Waste (Section 30(3)(b) of COPA)
One of the three components of controlled waste and consisting of waste 'from any factory within the meaning of the Factories Act 1961' or from any industrial premises occupied by a nationalised industry, excluding waste from mines or quarries. Regulation 3 of the Control of Pollution (Licensing of Waste Disposal) Regulations 1976 extends the meaning of industrial waste for certain purposes to include construction waste, dredging spoil and sewage deposited on land. (2.34-2.36; 7.16-7.19; 7.29-7.39)

Municipal Waste
The aggregate of wastes which collection authorities have a duty to collect. These would include: household (domestic), commercial, civic amenity and street cleaning wastes; wastes from municipal undertakings, parks and other amenities; abandoned motor vehicles; the contents of privies and cesspools; and ash from municipal incinerators. (2.28-2.33)

Non-controlled Waste
Wastes excluded from the definitions of household, commercial and industrial wastes - i.e. mine and quarry wastes, agricultural wastes and sewage not disposed of to land. (2.35; 2.37; 2.38-2.42; 2.43-2.45)

Notifiable Waste
Waste which had to be notified under the Deposit of Poisonous Waste Act 1972 (since repealed). (2.8-2.9)

Poisonous Waste
(See Toxic and Dangerous Waste)

Special Waste (Section 17 of COPA)
Waste which it is considered 'is or may be so dangerous or difficult to dispose of that special provision ... is required for (its) disposal'. The detailed definition contained in regulations (see paragraph 2.9) makes it clear that special waste is waste which has the potential to cause acute harm or injury to persons directly exposed to it. (2.8-2.10; 2.20)

Toxic and Dangerous Waste
The words in this phrase are no more precise in their meaning than 'hazardous' (q.v.) or 'poisonous', but taken together they may be used to refer to those wastes (not exactly equivalent to special wastes) which are the subject of the EC Directive on Toxic and Dangerous Waste. (2.13; 2.17)

Trade Waste
Not defined by COPA but by implication a sub-set of commercial waste (q.v.).

2.7 Site licences can be made subject to such conditions as the waste disposal authority sees fit, and may cover the following matters:

- duration of the licence;

- supervision by the licence holder of licenced activities;

- the kinds and quantities of waste, the methods of dealing with them, and the recording of information;

- precautions to be taken (e.g. security of the site);

- the hours when waste may be dealt with;

- the works to be carried out before licenced activities begin or while they continue.

The conditions under which a site licence can be refused are limited and we return to this topic in paragraph 8.41.

Toxic (special) waste

2.8 The Deposit of Poisonous Waste Act 1972 made it an offence to deposit on land poisonous, noxious or polluting waste in circumstances in which it could give rise to an environmental hazard. The Act also required those removing or disposing of such waste to notify the waste disposal authority and the water authority before doing so giving relevant details of its composition, quantity and destination. The 'notifiable' waste was defined on an exclusive basis, that is to say it comprised all toxic or dangerous waste not specifically excluded by regulations.

2.9 One of the criticisms of the 1972 Act was the amount of paper work involved, and the notification system was replaced by the provisions of the Control of Pollution (Special Waste) Regulations 1980, made under section 17 of the Control of Pollution Act 1974, the 1972 Act being repealed in 1981. The section 17 Regulations introduced a new category of 'special waste', defined on an 'inclusive' basis: waste is 'special' if it is a medicinal product available only on prescription or waste containing any of the substances listed in a schedule to the Regulations in such concentrations as to have:

(i) the ability to be likely to cause death or serious damage to tissue if a single dose of not more than 5 cm^3 were to be ingested by a person of 20 kg bodyweight, or

(ii) the ability to be likely to cause serious damage to human tissue by inhalation, skin contact or eye contact on exposure to the substance for 15 minutes or less, or

(iii) a flash point of 21°C or less.

The definition is therefore essentially in terms of the waste's possible effects on human health rather than effects on the environment. The latter, particularly the effects on water, are an important element of site licence conditions and hence the term hazardous waste (see paragraphs 2.18-2.23) is often used to cover the wider category of wastes which pose hazards to the environment.

2.10 The Regulations provide for a control system for special wastes which includes a requirement for waste producers to notify receiving waste disposal authorities of the intention to dispose of special waste; a consignment note system; a record of the dispatch, conveyance and disposal of the waste; a permanent record of the ultimate disposal location; and a power for the Secretary of State to direct a particular site or plant to accept a specified special waste. The Regulations were recently the subject of a review by a joint committee of representatives of government departments, the local authority associations, industrial associations and environmental interests, which reported in April 1985([6]).

Other legislation

2.11 A number of other legislative provisions are relevant to the handling of various kinds of waste, of which the following are the most significant:

- the Health and Safety and Work etc. Act 1974 lays responsibilities on employers in relation to the safety of their workers, and these extend to workers handling waste;

- the Alkali Works etc. Act 1906 requires major industrial emitters to air, including all chemical waste incinerators, to be registered with and controlled by the Industrial Air Pollution Inspectorate;

- the movement of hazardous materials, including waste, is controlled by a variety of specific regulations;

- the Refuse Disposal (Amenity) Act 1978 places a duty on local authorities to provide sites (usually known as 'civic amenity sites') to which residents may bring bulky household refuse free of charge; the Act also governs the disposal of abandoned motor vehicles;

- the Dumping at Sea Act 1974 (shortly to be superseded by Part II of the Food and Environment Protection Act 1985) regulates the dumping and incineration of waste at sea;

- the Radioactive Substances Act 1960 regulates the disposal of all radioactive wastes: these wastes are specifically excluded from the scope of the Control of Pollution Act 1974 and although regulations can be made to bring them within the scope, none have been.

Waste management administration

2.12 We discuss waste management administration in some detail in Chapter IX. The essential point to note here is that waste disposal is very largely a local government function. Central government has reserve powers, including an appellate role (e.g. when an applicant for a site licence appeals against conditions imposed by the waste disposal authority). Central government activity is in other respects confined to the development of broad policy, sponsoring research, issuing advice (for instance the series of Waste Management Papers issued by the Department of the Environment) and negotiating with the Commission of the European Communities over the content and implementation of Directives in the waste field. Recently the Government, in response to recommendations by the House of Lords Select Committee on Science and Technology([5]), strengthened its supervisory role by establishing a small Hazardous Waste Inspectorate within the Department of the Environment.

European Community waste policy and other international aspects

2.13 Besides national legislation, waste management in the United Kingdom has an international dimension, consequent upon various international conventions (notably those relating to the sea - see paragraph 7.47) and membership of the European Community. The two most important EC Directives, the 1975 Framework Directive on Waste([36]) and the 1978 Directive on Toxic and Dangerous Waste([37]), were substantially based on the Control of Pollution Act 1974, and therefore can be said to have had relatively little influence on UK legislation, although some of the details of the Special Waste Regulations might have been different had it not been necessary to comply with the 1978 Directive([38]).

2.14 Whilst the influence of UK policies and practices on European Community activities was important and strong during the formative period, it has been suggested([39]) that this influence has been declining in recent years. If this is so, it is regrettable; and it would be appropriate here to reiterate the comment in paragraph 3.26 of the Tenth Report about the need for the United Kingdom to play a more positive role in the Community. We discuss other aspects of Community waste policy, including the Third Action Programme on the Environment([40]), in Chapter IV.

Legal definitions of waste and their effects

2.15 In order to bring waste disposal within a framework of legal controls, it is necessary to provide precise legal definitions of various categories of waste. However this can give rise to two types of problem (which can be seen repeating themselves in the legal and administrative systems of other countries besides the UK):

  - how to define whether a waste is in fact a waste;

  - how to distinguish between hazardous and non-hazardous wastes.

2.16 As we have said in paragraph 1.5, we find the definition of 'controlled waste' given in Section 30(1) of the Control of Pollution Act 1974 (quoted in that paragraph) to be generally helpful, in that it reflects the point that waste is waste at the moment of consignment. Moreover the passage which says that 'any thing which is discarded or otherwise dealt with as if it were waste shall be presumed to be waste unless the contrary is proved' is useful in that it provides some basis for control over materials abandoned in so-called 'interim' storage depots, although it leaves room for uncertainty over materials which leave one person's hands as waste but which their new owner may wish (or at least claim to be able) to recycle. There is therefore some scope for evasion of current waste control legislation by describing wastes as 'materials in transit', 'stock in trade' or 'material for recycling'.

2.17 The European Community has tried to get round this problem by defining 'waste' as 'any substance or object which the holder disposes of or is required to dispose of pursuant to the provisions of national law in force' and 'disposal' as:

'- the collection, sorting, transport and treatment of waste as well as its storage and tipping above or under ground;

- the transformation operations necessary for its re-use, recovery or recycling'.

These definitions appear in the 1975 framework Directive on Waste[36] and are repeated in the 1978 Directive on Toxic and Dangerous Waste[37]. They are not, however, fully reflected in UK legislation[38], either in the Control of Pollution Act itself or in the Special Waste Regulations (see paragraphs 2.9-2.10).

Categories of waste

2.18 Most - probably all - countries with well-developed waste management policies find it convenient to distinguish in their legislation between wastes which, although undesirable if left in the wrong place or if incorrectly handled, affect primarily the physical environment, and those which are hazardous or harmful to the living environment (cf paragraph 1.3). The latter category is normally known as 'hazardous waste', although the term has no statutory definition in UK law. Similarly, epithets such as 'dangerous', 'toxic', 'poisonous' and 'difficult', all of which are commonly found in waste management literature, are without legal significance and differ little from 'hazardous' in their practical meaning.

2.19 As the Department of the Environment has commented to us, 'hazardous waste' as a term on its own has little meaning since hazard is related to the situation and circumstances rather than just to the properties of the materials. It is significant that the Hazardous Waste Inspectorate, in its First Report[17], does not attempt a definition. Similarly toxicity is an imprecise concept unless target organisms and types of exposure are defined. Most materials have the potential to be hazardous if incorrectly handled. For instance, calcium sulphate (a principal component of plaster-board), normally regarded as an inert material, can if disposed of in inappropriate conditions with domestic waste give rise to the evolution of hydrogen sulphide, a toxic gas.

21

2.20 Section 3(3) of the Control of Pollution Act prescribes higher penalties for unauthorised deposition of waste where:

'(a) the waste in question is of a kind which is poisonous, noxious or polluting; and

(b) its presence on the land is likely to give rise to an environmental hazard'.

In addition, Section 17 requires the Secretary of State to make regulations for the disposal of waste which he considers 'is or may be so dangerous or difficult to dispose of that special provision ... is required for (its) disposal'. As we have seen, the Control of Pollution (Special Waste) Regulations 1980, made under this section, create a category of 'special waste', which essentially is concerned with danger to human health and life. Since its definition excludes wastes which present hazards only to fauna and flora, or which cause other forms of environmental damage, 'special waste' is not necessarily synonymous with 'hazardous waste', although clearly it is a sub-set of the latter. In consequence waste disposal authorities have felt free (and to some extent have been encouraged) to devise their own criteria for and classification of 'hazardous waste' (other than 'special waste'), and this is one of the factors which has contributed to the variability in standards which has been criticised by the Hazardous Waste Inspectorate[17] (see paragraph 7.23).

2.21 Besides the basic distinction in the UK between controlled wastes and their sub-set, special wastes, various other classifications of waste are in current use, for legal or administrative purposes, or may be found in waste management literature. These are explained in the box on pages 16 and 17. Although it is convenient (as may be seen from the box) for waste to be classified for administrative and legal control purposes by source rather than by characteristic, such a classification does not give a true picture of the effect of wastes on the environment and can cause misconceptions on the part of the general public. For example, industrial waste (as defined in Section 30 of the Control of Pollution Act) is often thought of as hazardous in its entirety when in fact a great deal of it is inert and only a small fraction of it comes into the 'special waste' category (see Figure 2.1); while the Confederation of British Industry estimates that only about 12% of industrial waste can be described as toxic or dangerous in a wider sense.

2.22 Similarly, the unqualfied use of the term 'chemical waste' (which has been given some currency in European Community documents) has given rise to the mistaken (and, we think, unfortunate) belief that 'chemical' *ipso facto* means 'hazardous' and that therefore only the chemical industry makes hazardous waste. Even if the argument goes no further than suggesting that hazardous waste is made solely by industry, because only industry makes or uses 'chemicals', it is misconceived. Municipal waste is at least as potentially hazardous to water supplies as much industrial waste. We are inclined to agree with the view[39] that much of the effort which has gone into trying to construct a category of 'hazardous waste', wider than that of 'special waste', has been unproductive.

2.23 Whilst the work of the House of Lords Select Committee on Science and Technology([5]) and the establishment of the Hazardous Waste Inspectorate have helped to ensure that the phrase 'hazardous waste' continues in current usage, we consider that the only useful dichotomy that can be made is the two-tier classification embodied in UK legislation - of 'controlled' wastes (all of which have the potential to cause environmental pollution) and their tightly-defined sub-set of 'special' wastes (confined to wastes which pose danger to human life and health). We feel that public and Parliamentary discussion about 'hazardous waste' has tended to lack precision and may have diverted attention from the need - which we emphasise throughout this Report - to ensure that all controlled wastes are handled in a careful and environmentally appropriate manner.

Waste 'arisings' - historical trends and current data for the UK

2.24 In the following sections we summarise what is known about the quantities of waste arising in the main categories considered in this Report: household; commercial and trade; industrial; mining; agricultural; sewage and water treatment; hospital and health care. Radioactive wastes are for these purposes excluded although we note that details of discharges to land, sea and atmosphere are summarised annually in the Department of the Environment's Digest of Environmental Protection and Water Statistics and the associated Additional Tables; the Statistical Bulletin of the Scottish Office, which details discharges from Scottish sites; and annual reports from the Ministry of Agriculture, Fisheries and Food of monitoring the marine environment([41-43]).

2.25 Although these sources are separately identifiable, the statistics about their arisings are not always so separately collected. We have not been able to determine reliable figures for waste arisings from every sector, but we have compiled, from various sources including many submissions of evidence, an estimate of the total waste arisings in the UK. In Figure 2.1 we show the proportion of waste from each sector that contributes to an estimated total of just under 500 million tonnes per year. In Chapter VII we show disposal routes for these wastes in total, and for selected components of the waste stream.

2.26 Even those statistics that are available are usually qualified. For instance the Chartered Institute of Public Finance and Accountancy (CIPFA)([44]) stresses the importance of treating its figures with caution because only a proportion of the total quantity of waste handled by collection and disposal authorities (37% 1983/4 actuals; 46% 1984/5 estimates) is weighed. Some authorities weigh none: some weigh virtually all their waste. The remaining data are presumably estimated from numbers of collection vehicles with assumed loads and so on.

2.27 In addition waste collection authorities (WCAs) can collect some commercial and trade wastes. The CIPFA waste disposal statistics record the total waste collected by the WCAs, including any commercial waste, and the commercial and industrial waste controlled by the waste disposal authorities

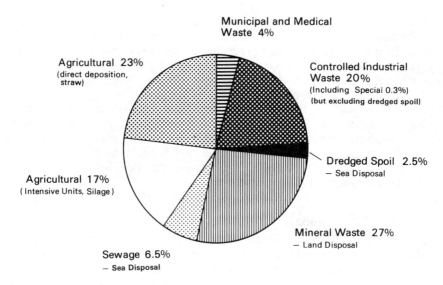

Figure 2.1   Estimated total annual waste arisings in the UK

(WDAs). The waste collection statistics identify the separate collections of household and commercial waste only by individual WCAs and not in summary form.

Domestic, commercial and trade wastes (municipal wastes)

2.28 The waste disposal statistics identify two possible sources of domestic wastes: household wastes from civic amenity sites and waste from collection authorities. Both, but especially the waste from collection authorities, could include trade or commercial waste.

2.29 If the trade or commercial waste included in this way is treated as domestic waste (which it would resemble in many respects), then waste disposal authorities in England and Wales are responsible for disposing of some 19.5 million tonnes of domestic waste each year[44]. Of this total about 15.3 million tonnes are collected by waste collection authorities in the regular door to door collections. The remaining 4.2 million tonnes are taken by the public to civic amenity sites.

2.30 The CIPFA statistics show commercial and industrial waste separately identified by the WDAs in England and Wales to be 27% or 22% (1983/4 actuals; 1984/5 estimates respectively) of the total controlled waste.

2.31 The composition of domestic waste has changed over the past 50 years, reflecting changes in social habits ranging from increasing use of convenience

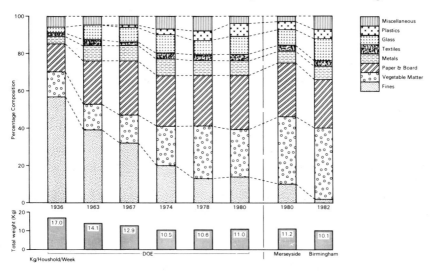

**Figure 2.2   Changes in composition and size of weekly household waste
collections in the UK, 1936-82**

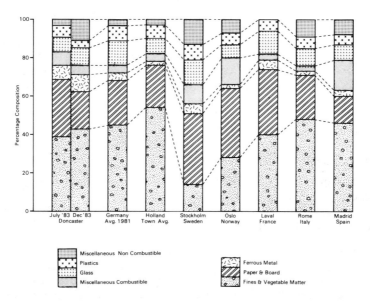

Figure 2.3   Composition of waste entering sorting plants in Europe

Source: Warren Spring Laboratory([90])

25

and pre-packaged food to the reduction in the number of open fires with increasing use of oil, gas and electric heating systems. Figure 2.2 shows the percentage composition of weekly household waste collections for selected years from 1936 to 1982. The figure includes a small graph showing the decline in the weight of waste collected from each household between 1936 and 1974, and the almost constant weight collected in the last decade. The first six columns are derived from the DoE Waste Analysis Surveys and relate to the whole of the United Kingdom. Columns 7 and 8 are regional household waste analyses from Merseyside and Birmingham. The reduction in the proportion of fine particles (smaller than 20 mm) from 57% in 1935 to around 14% in 1980 is clearly shown. Figure 2.3 shows the wide variation in composition of waste arriving as feed stock for sorting plants at several locations in Europe. Neither figure quantifies the observable increase in recent years of hazardous items in the municipal waste stream such as aerosol cans, paint thinners, batteries, pharmaceuticals and garden chemicals.

2.32 Apart from generalisations such as the fact that offices and many shops generate large quantities of paper and cardboard, there is little information about commercial wastes. It should be noted that shops such as greengrocers can generate large quantities of putrescible wastes and that computer paper is often a major proportion of office wastes, although this may be recycled by direct sale to waste paper merchants. Often commercial wastes are collected and disposed of together with household wastes and referred to collectively as municipal wastes.

2.33 Planning waste collection and waste disposal properly requires knowledge of the amounts and composition of wastes in the waste stream, and the currently available statistics about the municipal waste stream do not provide such knowledge. We **recommend** that, pending the bringing into force of section 1 of the Control of Pollution Act 1974, the Government, in consultation with representatives of the local authority associations, industry and others as appropriate, should devise a coherent scheme for the recording of information on arisings, movements and disposals of controlled municipal wastes and should encourage the adoption of such a scheme throughout the country.

Industrial wastes

2.34 This category of wastes includes at least as wide a range of materials as domestic and commercial wastes but, whereas domestic wastes are characterised by the mixture of components they contain, industrial wastes are often produced as relatively large amounts of single materials.

2.35 The quantity of industrial wastes generated in the UK in any year is not known. Not all industrial waste is controlled under the Control of Pollution Act 1974 (COPA) - the Act specifically excludes wastes from mining, quarrying and agriculture - and certainly not all industrial waste is disposed of through WDAs. Estimates vary widely, but in compiling our own estimate of the total annual waste arisings we have identified the industrial wastes listed in

Table 2.1([17,45,46]). Only about 7 million tonnes of controlled waste are recorded in the CIPFA waste disposal statistics - i.e. less than 10% of controlled industrial waste appears in WDA statistical returns. However, section 1 of COPA would require - when it is implemented - that WDAs be aware of all controlled waste streams.

TABLE 2.1

Estimated annual arisings of industrial (including agricultural) wastes

	million tonnes
Controlled wastes	
- special	1.6
- other	94.5
Non-controlled wastes	
- dredged spoil dumped at sea	12
- mineral wastes	130
- agricultural wastes*	
- slurry from intensive livestock units	60
- silage effluent	22
- straw	6
Total	326.1

* In addition there is the waste from livestock deposited directly on to the land: this is estimated at about 110 million tonnes per year and is often included in estimates of total arisings (as in Figure 2.1 and Figure 7.1a).

2.36 We have concluded that there is insufficient reliable information available about industrial waste generation. Without this information we do not consider that waste disposal authorities can properly prepare waste disposal plans for their areas. As in our recommendation for municipal wastes, we **recommend** that the Government should consider ways of improving the quality and comprehensiveness of published statistics on controlled industrial wastes.

Mine and quarry wastes

2.37 Colliery wastes and china clay extraction spoils are the two main contributors to the supply of mineral wastes in the UK, although slate and other stone quarries make further contributions. Each of these wastes normally form spoil heaps in close proximity to the mineral extraction site. Wastes from sand and gravel operations commonly form lagoons in which the clay and silt washed from the gravel is allowed to settle out of suspension; alternatively, they can be used in reclamation of the extraction site. Extensive tailings lagoons are also associated with both china clay and colliery waste. The Reports of the Advisory Committee on Aggregates (the Verney Report)([47]) and the Commission on Energy and the Environment (CENE)([48]) discussed various aspects of mineral wastes. As with other waste materials (and as the Government's response to CENE([49]) implicitly acknowledged), an essential element of future planning is obtaining reliable data on total quantities of wastes already in existence and of those generated each year. These are not at present readily identifiable, and again we **recommend** that the Government should consider ways of improving the quality and comprehensiveness of published statistics on mine and quarry wastes.

Agricultural wastes

2.38 The Commission's Seventh Report([32]) dealt in considerable depth with agricultural wastes and the possible problems of pollution by them. Four categories of agricultural waste can be identified: slurry (excreta); straw; silage liquors; and chemical wastes and containers (for sheep dips, pesticides etc.). The amount of slurry generated was estimated as around 60 million tonnes/year. The principal pollution risks lay with the slurry from intensive livestock rearing, which is held in store in tanks or lagoons prior to disposal by spreading on farm land, where it has beneficial effects as a fertiliser and soil conditioner.

2.39 Although we do not consider this problem in detail in this Report, the risk of overflow, leakage, or accidental discharge of slurry causing pollution of surface water courses, and indeed the increasing number of such incidents, have been repeatedly brought to our attention by the water authorities. Silage effluent is also a continuing cause of incidents of pollution of surface water courses. The high biological oxygen demand of silage effluent makes any pollution incident especially damaging. Table 2.2 gives figures for serious pollution incidents and convictions for pollution from different agricultural sources (excluding straw burning). There can be no doubt that better standards of construction for slurry tanks and silage containment and effluent control systems would make a major impact on the problem. Accordingly we **recommend** that all structures required for the storage or control of slurry, silage and other farm wastes should be made subject to the Building Regulations.

2.40 We are pleased to note that measures under the European Community Farm Structures Regulations have been introduced([50]), which include provision for capital grants on a number of environmentally positive investments including waste disposal systems. While we approve of administrative arrangements encouraging farmers to consult their water authority at an early stage of planning for liquid manure treatment and disposal systems, silage systems, yard washings and dirty rain water collection, we reiterate the **recommendation** of the Seventh Report that such consultation be a requirement, rather than merely advisory, for all grant applications.

2.41 The pollution problems associated with straw and stubble burning were discussed in the Tenth Report but we return to this subject in Chapter VII.

2.42 A final category of agricultural wastes - chemicals and their containers (Plate 13) - has obvious affinities with the types of industrial wastes with which

TABLE 2.2

**Serious pollution incidents from agricultural sources
and convictions, 1983 and 1984**

Pollution source	1983		1984	
	Serious incidents	*Convictions*	*Serious incidents*	*Convictions*
Silage effluent	362	28	359	32
Cattle yard runoff	344	3	328	4
Slurry storage	338	16	320	42
Pig yard runoff	164	21	100	5
Manure stores	48	2	26	19

Source: Reports of the 1983 and 1984 surveys of water pollution incidents caused by farm wastes in England and Wales([51,52]).

this study is particularly concerned. The arrangements for regulation or supervision of disposal of these wastes were considered in the Commission's Seventh Report, and we would endorse the remarks and recommendations made at the time (1979). We note the Government's view, in its response to the Report([53]), that Section 18(2) of COPA (which makes it an offence to dispose of uncontrolled waste which is poisonous, noxious or polluting and is likely to give rise to an environmental hazard) already provides waste disposal authorities with powers to take action against those who dispose of farm wastes irresponsibly, whether on or off the farm site. Nevertheless, we consider it anomalous that agro-chemical wastes which are disposed of away from farm sites, and therefore outside the terms of the guidelines and code of practice which apply to disposal on site, should be subject to less stringent controls than similar wastes from industrial sources. Whilst we have not collected new evidence on the matter, we believe that there is still a case, notwithstanding the resource implications([53]), for bringing this category of farm wastes fully within the scope of COPA and thus making it subject to normal site licensing controls and, where appropriate, to the provisions of the Special Waste Regulations. On the latter point, we note that the joint review committee (see paragraph 2.10) agreed that the question of inclusion in the Regulations of farm wastes meeting the 'dangerous to life' criteria merited further consideration([6]).

Sewage and water treatment wastes

2.43 Sewage sludge, the residual sludge from sewage treatment plants, is probably one of the most consistent categories of waste arising in UK. About 1.2 million tonnes of dry matter are disposed of each year of which 45% is used as fertiliser and soil conditioner on agricultural land, 30% is dumped at sea as sludge (about 10 million tonnes wet weight), and 25% is disposed of to landfill sites or by incineration([46]). The comparative figure for the EC in 1979 was 6 million tonnes. Current disposal routes for sewage sludge in the EC are estimated as 40% to landfill, 12% to incineration, 9% dumped at sea and 39% used in agriculture. The present low EC figure may possibly be because of the widespread use of septic tanks for immediate discharge, rather than sewage treatment plants: this is expected to change with increased use of sewage treatment plants.

2.44 Although sewage sludge, like farmyard slurry, can be used both as a fertiliser providing nitrogen and phosphorus and as a soil conditioner it contains trace elements, particularly heavy metals, which derive largely from industrial wastes and which can cause unacceptable concentrations of heavy metals in agricultural soils with risks of subsequent uptake by plants. However the levels of heavy metals found in sewage sludges have been decreasing in recent years (see paragraph 7.49 and Figure 7.2), partly through the rundown of some older heavy industries and the generally lower level of industrial activity, but more especially because water authorities are imposing and enforcing more stringent conditions on industrial effluents destined for sewers and industry is co-operating in meeting these conditions. In Chapter VII we refer to the opportunities made possible by technological advances for industry to improve the quality of its effluent, for instance by removing heavy metals, and thereby to discharge cleaner wastes and to recover re-useable materials.

2.45 Despite these advances each of the three major disposal routes for sewage sludge faces some resistance to its use. There is currently a proposal before the Council of the European Communities([54]), the effect of which might be to limit the use of sewage sludge in agriculture, although such limitation is not the primary aim. The proposal seeks to control the rate of spreading by limiting the concentration and total amount of specified elements (heavy metals) in the sludge and soil. While we agree that heavy metals should not be allowed to increase in concentration, especially through the use of sewage sludge on farm land, we would prefer to see the heavy metals removed from sewage rather than the use of sewage sludge restricted, and we make recommendations accordingly (paragraph 7.49). Several EC Member States would like to reduce the quantities of waste, including sewage sludge, dumped at sea, and there is increasing pressure for such reductions. The third option, landfill, meets with some resistance from some waste disposal authorities because of uncertainties about its influence on landfill gas generation and on leachate generation and composition. Some research into co-disposal of sewage and domestic wastes in landfill is being carried out and should result in guidelines for WDAs to follow.

Hospital and health care wastes

2.46 Hospitals, health centres and clinics, and surgeries (medical, dental and veterinary) generate several different types of waste. General wastes from these sources are essentially similar to domestic or commercial wastes and do not differ from these in the risks they pose and the methods by which they can be disposed of, but other types of waste regularly arise which carry risks of infection (both known and unknown) as well as injury. 'Sharps' (discarded syringes, needles, broken glass and any other sharp instrument)([55]) are a variety of waste that arise from medical premises and increasingly from patients at home which can present specific hazards in collection, and concern has been expressed by collection authorities about the risk to collection workers when such wastes are improperly wrapped. Pathological wastes (tissues, organs etc.) and infectious wastes (from laboratory work, surgery and other treatments of infectious patients) can also present serious risks. Separate collection and incineration of such wastes is the usual treatment and disposal route. Chemical, pharmaceutical and radioactive wastes are also categories of wastes generated at hospitals and other health care sites which are also normally subject to separate collection and incineration. Data on the amounts of health care wastes generated in the UK are not available, but the risks to the environment arise more from improper disposal management than from inadequacies of technology. We discuss these questions further in Chapters VII and VIII.

Contaminated land

2.47 For the reasons explained in paragraph 1.23, we have decided that contaminated land, as a legacy of past practices, most of them already obsolete, falls largely outside the scope of a report which is principally concerned with ways of improving waste management in the future. Nevertheless, having gone into various aspects of the matter in the course of taking evidence, we wish to draw attention to certain problems relating to the use and redevelopment of contaminated land. Later, in Chapter IX, we make some comments on ways of preventing, or mitigating the effects of, future contamination.

2.48 Land may become contaminated for a variety of reasons, but the following are the most common categories:

(i)   derelict former industrial sites (e.g. gas works and sewage works);

(ii) former waste tips within the boundaries of defunct processing plants;

(iii) abandoned stores of materials (not necessarily wastes during the active life of the stores); and

(iv) disused waste disposal sites.

2.49 Technical advice and guidance on problems associated with the development of contaminated land - both site-specific and general - is provided by the Interdepartmental Committee on the Redevelopment of Contaminated Land (ICRCL), serviced by the Department of the Environment. ICRCL has now been in existence for nearly 10 years and has produced a series of guidance notes[56], mainly aimed at local authorities and consultants, on various aspects of the problem. Whilst struck by the slenderness of the staff resources devoted to this task in DoE, we are satisfied that the advice provided is technically sound[57,58] and is backed by an adequate programme of research (see paragraph 11.17)[59]. We also note that the British Standards Institution has been working on a possible code of practice for those engaged on the identification and assessment of contaminated land and, although we understand that this has run into practical difficulties, we consider it is a worthwhile objective (see paragraph 10.13).

2.50 The scale of the problem is difficult to estimate. There are considerable practical difficulties in establishing whether or not a particular site is contaminated and, if so, how seriously. Analysis of the contaminants can also be difficult unless former uses are well documented. It is therefore not easy to decide whether the contamination presents any risk to the reuse of the land. Only rough estimates exist of the total area of contaminated land, and there has been no survey of the whole of the UK. On the basis of the sample of sites referred to ICRCL, it has been estimated by DoE that sites totalling at least 10,000 hectares in England alone, and currently available for reclamation or redevelopment, may be contaminated.

2.51 Despite this lack of firm data, there is a consensus among all those from whom we have had evidence that the United Kingdom does not suffer from the legacies of past malpractices to anything like the extent of the United States or some countries in continental Europe, and that the possibility that the UK may yet contain undiscovered horrors on the scale of Love Canal* can be altogether discounted. The reasons for this seem to lie partly in differences between the UK and other countries in relation to land availability and demand, and partly in differences in legislative and administrative procedures.

2.52 In the UK, the emphasis has been placed mainly on the importance of reusing land for economic and social reasons, because 'new' land suitable for development is scarce, especially in and around our urban areas. By contrast, in the USA such pressures are less important. Moreover, the procedures governing land use in the USA differ markedly from those in the UK: until recently they appear to have been less effective, for example, in exercising proper control over activities such as the disposal of hazardous waste. It has been suggested to us that the same was broadly true of the period of rapid industrial reconstruction in the areas of Europe worst affected by the Second World War. In consequence, many waste disposal sites were badly located and operated in an unsatisfactory way. In the USA it has been estimated that there may be as many as 20,000 abandoned hazardous waste disposal sites. Their existence is regarded by the authorities as the most important problem of land contamination in the USA, and substantial financial and technical resources ('Superfund' see box on page 34) have now been allocated to cleaning them up. There is no evidence that in the UK waste disposal sites have, either in the past or at present, been operated in a way likely to cause similar problems - certainly not on such a scale - and the need for emergency action is therefore much less likely. This is not to suggest, however, that there have been no examples of bad practice.

---

* In 1977 an exceptionally wet spring caused toxic chemicals to leach from a waste tip contained in an abandoned canal near Niagara Falls, New York State. After several decades of tipping the site had been covered and built over, and the contamination affected a large number of houses and a school. Eventually several hundred residents had to be permanently relocated.

2.53 A summary of the main powers currently available to local authorities in relation to contaminated land is in the box on page 35. The principal problem, as we see it, is one of ensuring that local authorities, in their planning capacity, are furnished with adequate information and advice when considering planning applications from developers. Because of the uncertainty about whether particular sites are contaminated or not (paragraph 2.50), it has been suggested by some local authority witnesses that additional legislation is needed to provide local authorities with a right of entry to premises suspected of being contaminated and a power to serve notices requiring the provision of information about possible contamination*. Whilst this suggestion might merit further examination in any general review of the law on statutory nuisances, we believe that what is needed is more coherent guidance and better administrative procedures within local authorities, rather than additional powers.

2.54 Provided that contaminated sites are identified at an early stage in the planning process and, in accordance with current advice from the Department of the Environment([60]), taken into account during the preparation of local plans and structure plan alterations, existing powers appear sufficient for the planning and other authorities to deal with them adequately. Knowledge of local history and familiarity with local topography will generally ensure that areas of potential contamination are identified for further investigation as part of the planning process. What are lacking are adequate awareness and reliable co-ordination within and between local authority departments responsible for planning, developing the area and the site, and environmental health.

2.55 Since the critical point of decision is the granting or withholding of planning permission, we consider that the right vehicle for consolidating advice to local authorities is a planning circular. A useful precedent for this is the Department of the Environment's 1973 Circular 'Planning and Noise'([61]), which (although now in need of updating) gives guidance on how to assess a noise problem against what standards and, more importantly, contains model conditions which may be used or adapted by local authorities at the planning application stage. We believe that an analogous circular on contaminated land, building on and consolidating the advice of ICRCL, would be of value to all authorities (including inspectors at public inquiries) who have to decide or advise on questions of planning, land use and acquisition or sale of land, and would enable better use to be made of existing powers. Such a circular would define the circumstances in which contamination would be a material consideration in refusing planning permission, in requiring modifications to a development, or in making permission dependent upon a site investigation and assessment or on other factors. The latter could include ensuring that when an industrial site goes out of use, the buildings and plants are demolished safely

---

* The powers in Sections 91-93 of the Control of Pollution Act 1974 (rights of entry and inspection etc. and power of authorities to obtain information) would apply where the contamination can be linked to the presence on the land of controlled wastes.

SUPERFUND

Superfund was established by the Comprehensive Environmental Response, Compensation and Liability Act (CERCLA), which Congress enacted in December 1980. The United States Environmental Protection Agency (EPA) is responsible for managing the Superfund program. Until this law was passed, the Federal Government lacked the general authority to clean up old hazardous waste sites.

When a dumpsite is old and abandoned it may be impossible to find anyone responsible for the problem - or anyone able to afford the cost of a clean-up. Moreover, many releases of hazardous substances demand prompt attention to avert serious damage. There may not be enough time for legal proceedings before action must be taken.

CERCLA authorizes the Federal Government to respond directly to releases (or threatened releases) of hazardous substances and pollutants or contaminants that may endanger public health or welfare. Costs are covered by a $1.6 billion fund (Superfund), 86 per cent of which is financed by taxes on the manufacture or import of certain chemicals and petroleum, the remainder coming from general revenues. This fund is reimbursable: the government generally can take legal action to recover its clean-up costs from those subsequently identified as responsible for the release. Anyone liable for a release who fails to take ordered actions is (under specified conditions) liable for punitive damages equal to three times the government's response costs.

The Superfund program is built on the recognition that responses and clean-ups must be tailored to the specific needs of each site or each release of hazardous substances. EPA's enforcement efforts seek to ensure that private responsible parties finance clean-up actions when possible. Direct government action, when called for, can take the following forms:

Immediate removals, when a prompt response is needed to prevent harm to public health or welfare of the environment.

Planned removals, when an expedited, but not necessarily immediate, response is needed.

Remedial actions, which are longer term and usually more expensive, aimed at permanent remedies. They may be taken only at sites identified in a National Priorities List, compiled by the EPA.

An important part of the Superfund program is to encourage voluntary clean-up by private industries and individuals when they are responsible for releases. At present, private parties handle about 90 per cent of all releases that would otherwise require a removal action.

Before a remedial action or planned removal can be taken, States must agree to pay 10 per cent of project costs (at least 50 per cent if the site was owned by the State or a local government). State governments must also agree to maintain the site after response work is completed and provide for off-site disposal if necessary.

Adapted from 'Superfund: What It Is, How It Works' (US Environmental Protection Agency, 1983)

MAIN POWERS AVAILABLE TO LOCAL AUTHORITIES IN RELATION TO CONTAMINATED LAND
Paragraph references relate to further discussion in the Report

Town and Country Planning Act 1971
Town and Country Planning Act (Scotland) 1972
Where land has been identified as contaminated, any limitations on its future use should normally be reflected in development (structure or local) plans. (2.54)

If a local planning authority regards land contamination as a 'material consideration', it may refuse planning permission for a particular development or it may grant permission subject to conditions. (2.55)

Public Health Act 1936
Public Health (Scotland) Act 1897
Local authorities' powers to require abatement of or (if necessary) to deal with 'statutory nuisances' may be applicable to certain types of existing contamination (broadly those which are prejudicial to health), provided that a nuisance can be demonstrated to have effects outside the confines of the site. (2.3)

Control of Pollution Act 1974
Control of Pollution (Special Waste) Regulations 1980
The deposit of controlled waste on land is an offence unless licensed by the waste disposal authority, and offenders can be required to remove or otherwise render harmless the materials in question. These provisions, with the additional safeguards that apply to 'special waste', should in principle ensure that no major new incidents of contamination occur. (2.5-2.10)

Health and Safety at Work, etc., Act 1974
Employers have a duty under the Act to conduct their business in such a way as to minimise risk to the health and safety of their employees and the public. The Act is therefore relevant to the prevention of contamination by industry in the course of its operations.

Other Powers
Building regulations: local authorities have powers under the Public Health Acts to reject applications under Building Regulation controls where polluting material is present on a site. (2.56)

Derelict land grant: Under the Derelict Land Act 1982, local authorities in England and Wales may be paid grants for the reclamation (including prior survey) of derelict land (which may include contaminated land). (In Scotland the reclamation of derelict land is a function of the Scottish Development Agency.)

Restrictive covenants: Under Section 52 of the Town and Country Planning Act 1971 (Section 50 of the Scottish Act) and Section 126 of the Housing Act 1974 local authorities may enter into agreements with land owners which, inter alia, may prohibit inappropriate uses of contaminated sites or specify remedial measures.

and in a way which does not disperse the contamination still further; and that the site is left in a tidy and safe state awaiting proposals for reusing and restoring it. It would be valuable for the cost-effective development of contaminated land if the circular could also include guidance as to conditions that are likely to be acceptable to the statutory bodies concerned with water quality (water authorities and water companies). Accordingly we **recommend** that the Department of the Environment, the Welsh Office and the Scottish Development Department, after consultation with relevant parties, should issue planning circulars containing comprehensive advice for local authorities, other statutory bodies and developers on the redevelopment of contaminated land or land which may be suspected to be contaminated. These circulars should reiterate the recommendation which the Commission made in its Fifth Report, and which the Government has accepted in principle([62]), that local planning authorities should ensure that environmental health officers are consulted on all relevant planning applications.

2.56 Some problems may, however, remain once planning permission has been granted, since the powers available to planning and pollution control authorities to require changes in the form of a development in the light of later information are limited. We note that a recent extension in the scope of the Building Regulations([63]) has removed some uncertainties surrounding local authorities' powers under Section 54 of the Public Health Act 1936 to prohibit the erection of buildings on land containing putrescible, noxious or polluting material; but the powers apply only to the site of the building, not to the curtilage. Nevertheless, we suspect that here again it is not so much powers that are lacking as the information necessary to ensure that the site is developed in a cost-effective way by the developer, despite the belated discovery of contamination, and that the advice contained in a circular would be helpful in this context too.

CHAPTER III

A STRATEGY FOR WASTE

Introduction

3.1 The creation of waste and the need to dispose of it have been essential features of human civilisation from earliest times. The twentieth century, however, has seen particularly rapid developments in the nature and quantity of waste for disposal. Whilst critics of the 'throw-away society' may be unduly pessimistic in painting a picture of an ever-growing sea of rubbish (except in so far as waste goes hand in hand with population growth), there can be no doubt that waste management is in a state of rapid evolution, with much needing to be done both to improve current practices and to anticipate future problems. This is due partly to changes in the nature of wastes, partly to changes in our understanding of the hazards from wastes, and partly to the increasingly high standards which the public expects.

3.2 Throughout our present investigation certain common strands have emerged in relation to the generation, storage and disposal of wastes. In particular, whilst in some fields there may be clearly defined mechanisms governing the collection and disposal of certain categories of waste, there appears, nevertheless, to be no definitive legal framework governing the subject as a whole. Indeed it can be argued that the multiplicity of organisations responsible for handling or disposing of wastes or for overseeing these operations serves to add to the confusion and compounds the problems of setting standards as well as assessing performance.

3.3 Because of the particular characteristics that distinguish wastes from manufactured products and other articles of value (paragraph 1.12), it may be necessary to change the constraints which govern the fate of wastes in the environment, if we wish to see a reduction in pollution. This will involve, in various permutations, changes in attitudes and patterns of behaviour, changes in professional and technical standards, changes in financial and economic impacts, and changes in the law. The objective of such changes must be to ensure the *long-term integrity and security of the waste stream* - a term which we use to mean the life history of an item of waste from the point at which it originates to the point at which it ceases to be waste or is finally disposed of. In the remainder of the chapter we discuss the various aspects of this task of changing the constraints.

A duty of care

3.4 The first task is for society to identify where the responsibility lies for ensuring that wastes are properly handled and disposed of. In our judgement this must rest with the individual or organisation who produces the wastes. The producer incurs a *duty of care* which is owed to society, and we would like to see this duty reflected in public attitudes and enshrined in legislation and codes of practice.

3.5 Employers already have such a duty under Section 2 of the Health and Safety at Work etc. Act 1974 in relation to the health, safety and welfare of their employees. In addition, in Section 3, the Act states that 'it shall be the duty of every employer to conduct his undertaking in such a way as to ensure, so far as is reasonably practicable, that persons not in his employment who may be affected thereby are not thereby exposed to risks to their health or safety'. What we are proposing is that a parallel principle should be applied to the general care of the environment.

3.6 We are pleased to note that the Confederation of British Industry, in its guidelines for producers of industrial waste, advocates a wider responsibility very much on these lines:

> 'As a producer of waste *you* are responsible for making proper arrangements for it to be disposed of safely and without harming your employees, the public or the environment. This basic responsibility cannot be ignored or palmed off on someone else.'[64]

We have also noted the recently published guidelines on industrial waste management by the European Council of Chemical Manufacturers' Federations (CEFIC)[65], which under ten headings (see box opposite) set out a series of generally applicable principles. These principles are wholly consistent with the recommendations in this Report and we highly commend them as ground rules for sound waste management.

3.7 Whilst the CBI's advice is based on the law as it stands, we believe that the waste producer's or handler's legal obligations towards the environment need to be clarified and strengthened, with particular reference to the requirement to satisfy himself, when passing on waste to somebody else, that it will be correctly dealt with. For reasons developed in Chapter VIII, we do not support the concept of US-style 'cradle-to-grave' producer responsibility, as has been advocated within the European Community and OECD in relation to the movement of certain hazardous wastes[66]. We believe that, within the framework of the duty of care, a waste producer may assign responsibility to a person who he has good reason to believe is competent to handle the waste safely, and we endorse the recommendation by the joint review committee on the Control of Pollution (Special Waste) Regulations 1980[6] that waste producers' responsibilities should be enhanced along these lines (paragraphs 8.16-8.21).

CEFIC : SUMMARY OF PRINCIPLES OF INDUSTRIAL WASTE MANAGEMENT

1. **Waste reduction** : Take all economically and technically justifiable measures to minimise generation of waste through process optimisation or re-design.

2. **Waste recovery** : Seek every opportunity for the economic recovery of residues as feedstock, for energy production, or any other purpose.

3. **Characterisation** : Obtain an adequate knowledge of the composition and characteristics of the wastes generated.

4. **Disposal methods** : Select a disposal method that is appropriate, considering the characteristics of waste.

5. **On site management** : Take appropriate steps to ensure proper management of wastes at production sites.

6. **Use of contractors** : When outside transport or disposal contractors are employed, satisfy oneself that they can deal with waste materials safely, effectively and legally, and confirm that waste consignments reach the specified final disposal site and are disposed of in the agreed manner.

7. **Management plans** : Review waste management plans periodically.

8. **External relationships** : Make all necessary communication with the relevant authorities.

9. **Information to customers** : Provide customers or processors with adequate information about potential hazards in disposing of the products they buy or handle.

10. **Research and development** : Foster the exchange of technical, scientific and economic information about safe disposal of wastes and, where appropriate, support studies to find more effective methods.

Source: CEFIC[65]

3.8 Outside the scope of legislation, we see the duty of care playing a key role in public education and codes of practice. It is as implicit in the message which anti-litter campaigns seek to instill in school children as it is in the special responsibility which we believe the chemical industry has for ensuring that technically appropriate and well managed facilities exist for the destruction of hazardous chemical wastes (see Chapter VII). We would like to see the pace at which attitudes change quicken. As the Tenth Report commented, regulatory pressures can act as a helpful stimulus to technological innovation.

Minimising and giving value to waste

3.9 There are a number of ways in which the creation of waste, and hence the ultimate disposal requirements, can be reduced. These include new processes, low-waste technology, longer product life, recycling and resource recovery. All of them help to reduce the size of the waste stream and the risk of pollution through inadequate disposal.

3.10 Any way of giving value to waste has a positive effect on the security of the waste stream. Waste reclamation schemes tend to be only marginally profitable, and are therefore especially vulnerable to disruption by changes in the economic climate, as discussed in Chapter V. High environmental standards can however act as a stimulus to recycling, converting waste into energy, or using waste for another purpose such as compost or for land reclamation.

3.11 In most commercial transactions, successful suppliers take care to ensure that their products reach customers safely, expeditiously and up to specification. The dissatisfied customer can seek redress or at least take his future custom elsewhere. But when the product is waste this normal commercial pressure does not operate. The consignee in this situation is the environment, and must be protected against the careless and uncaring by regulations and control. The aim must be to ensure that disposal costs are not externalised but remain coupled to the original processes, operations and transactions which lead to waste generation. Despite its misuse as a slogan, we support the 'polluter pays' principle in this context because its application leads to environmentally sound policies.

Maintaining a secure waste stream

3.12 A secure waste stream is one which ensures that there is no abandonment before proper disposal. The requirements will vary according to the nature of the waste. Much depends on adequate enforcement and on the dissemination of information about best practice, design, construction, maintenance and operation of plant and storage facilities; the preparation of accurate consignment notes; transport in registered and properly marked vehicles (see Chapter VIII); and the retention of documentation including plant records for specified periods. In the case of special wastes, much of this is already provided for in regulations.

Setting suitable standards

3.13 Proper exercise of the duty of care requires a clear understanding of what is the 'proper' way of handling waste, and that must in turn depend on the nature of the waste. At one end of the spectrum the duty may be said to have been discharged if, for instance, domestic waste is consigned in the prescribed manner to the waste collection authority. At the other extreme it may be exceedingly difficult and onerous to show that the duty of care has been properly discharged, for example where nuclear waste is concerned. Between these extremes there is a huge range of different wastes, with differing characteristics, differing in their potential to pollute the environment and differing in requirements associated with their safe disposal.

3.14 We consider that it is insufficient to introduce the duty of care without at the same time providing the waste producer with objective standards which apply throughout the country and which contain a uniform mechanism for ensuring the security of the waste stream on a countrywide basis. In Chapter X we make recommendations about the need to develop new standards. Since we are arguing that it is for the polluter to pay for the disposal of waste he produces, clearly it is necessary that standards should be accepted as reasonable in relation to economic factors and the risks of environmental damage.

Ensuring disposal by BPEO

3.15 The selection of the Best Practicable Environmental Option (BPEO), a concept developed by the Commission in its Fifth and Tenth Reports, involves an analysis of the costs and benefits (in the widest sense of those terms) of different options for pollution control in a given situation[67]. The aim is to find the optimum combination of available methods of disposal so as to limit damage to the environment to the greatest extent achievable for a reasonable and acceptable total combined cost to industry and the public purse. The benefit component of the analysis - the limitation of pollution - involves the consideration of three variables: the polluting potential of the materials released, the quantities released and the sensitivity to the pollutant of different sectors of the environment. The smaller the combined effect of these variables the greater the benefit. Thus BPEO may lead to the decision to discharge a large quantity of a slightly toxic material to a sector of the environment where it is rapidly degraded, in preference to the emission of a much smaller quantity of a somewhat more toxic material to a sector of the environment where it accumulates. As the definition above implies, the extent of the benefit from pollution abatement has to be traded off against its cost. This process must take account of local conditions and the current state of technical knowledge. The level of costs considered acceptable and reasonable may therefore come to be adjusted in the light of evaluation of benefits. Because of the magnitude of the costs it may be necessary to opt for a degree of pollution abatement that is less than that which is technically achievable, without of course abandoning the latter as an ultimate goal. Progress toward this goal can often be facilitated by setting a timetable for increasing levels of abatement. The term Best Environmental Timetable (BET) was used in the Tenth Report to describe this approach.

3.16 In selecting a BPEO for a given case one must take into consideration all the relevant factors: those operating at a distance as well as those close at hand, in the longer term as well as in the present, and loss of amenity as well as actual damage. We must also stress the importance of timely research to provide an adequate basis of knowledge on the effects of a pollutant and on the efficacy of methods of dealing with it, in order to permit confident selection of a BPEO.

3.17 In the context of waste disposal (but excluding the special case of radioactive waste), and assuming that steps have been taken to minimise the amount of waste that has to be disposed of, the following are the principal applications of BPEO:

(i) The waste is treated so that its potential for pollution is substantially reduced (e.g. by incineration or chemical reaction). These treatments will produce residues which may be ash, solid chemicals, slurries or liquids from a scrubber. The disposal of these secondary wastes must be taken into account in selecting a BPEO for the process overall.

(ii) The waste is contained in a location from which it cannot escape into the surrounding air, land or water whilst either natural microbiological or chemical weathering processes, or both, convert the pollutants into relatively innocuous substances (e.g. properly sealed landfill).

(iii) The waste is sealed into a matrix, from which escape (if any) is very slow, and is buried.

(iv) The waste is dispersed into the environment so that it is immediately diluted to a concentration at which it causes negligible local harm. The composition of the waste must be such that its pollutants are degraded, neutralized or immobilized by the natural microbiological and chemical environmental processes and their rate of addition to the environment must not be such as to overload its capacity.

EXAMPLES OF APPLICATION OF BPEO TO CERTAIN TYPES OF WASTE

Anything which goes to landfill should either be degradable or be in a stable or solid state. The concept of 'dilute and disperse' is justified only if the natural media into which the waste is emitted may be considered to break down organic materials, neutralise any extreme pH and immobilise heavy metals at a sufficient rate to prevent concentrations reaching a threshold (if it exists) for damage.

Heavy metals and mineral materials, such as asbestos, should be immobilised, for instance by adsorption into clay or by vitrification, and returned to the earth's crust.

Physically dangerous materials (e.g. broken glass, old refrigerators and countryside litter, which can be a fire hazard) can simply be removed to where they have no further potential for causing harm.

Volatile, flammable or oily wastes should preferably be burned.

3.18 Wastes should be disposed of by the appropriate option without undue delay, for so long as the waste is held in its original form its potential for pollution remains unabated. Some examples of the general application of BPEO considerations to specific wastes, and a flow diagram illustrating how decisions may be taken on waste disposal methods within the chemical industry, are in the boxes above and opposite. We would however stress that every case must be evaluated in the light of its own particular circumstances and that BPEO may depend on factors which are external to the industry in question.

AN ILLUSTRATION OF HOW WASTE DISPOSAL METHODS MAY BE SELECTED IN THE CHEMICAL INDUSTRY

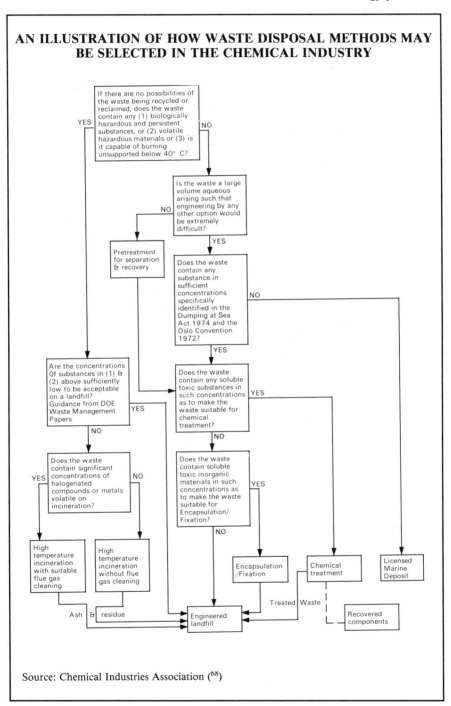

Source: Chemical Industries Association ([68])

43

Chapter III

Enforcement and monitoring

3.19 Finally, we consider that an appropriate mechanism must be established to audit the waste producer's observance of his duty of care by meeting the standards to which we have referred. In most instances appropriate bodies are already in being and we see no case for adding new bodies to the organisations which already exist. We do, however, in Chapter IX suggest a number of ways in which the functions of these organisations might be strengthened and brought closer together in the interests of consistency and greater efficiency. With a clear set of ground rules the waste producer will know with precision how to discharge his duty; the authorities will be able to monitor his performance; and the public will know and see that the duty is being properly fulfilled.

3.20 We also discuss in Chapter IX the question whether a balance needs to be struck between the costs which it is reasonable to impose on the waste producer (and therefore reflected in disposal charges) and those which should be borne by taxpayers at large through the activities of central government. We conclude that Government has a clear duty to ease the transition to higher standards and to ensure that there is continued compliance with them. It is therefore right that, without implying any diminution of the powers of local waste disposal authorities, the Government should make a direct input to the setting and enforcement of standards to nationally acceptable levels.

CHAPTER IV

REDUCTION OF THE WASTE STREAM

Introduction

4.1 This chapter is concerned with the avoidance of waste, considered under two headings. Process waste arises in the course of manufacture and may be thought of largely as the residual raw or process materials or by-products that are not utilised in the finished product. Product waste is the waste entering the stream from the purchase, use, and ultimate disposal of the product.

Process waste

4.2 It has been put to us that there is little further opportunity to reduce waste in factories[68]. Whilst we accept that in many cases it may be difficult to reduce waste we do not accept the impossibility of the task. Indeed numerous cases have been cited to us which demonstrate that there is a continuous flow of new ideas and initiatives in this field both in this country and elsewhere[69-71]. Experience in many companies has shown that once attention is focused by senior management on reduction of waste, possibilities are uncovered which are both commercially and environmentally acceptable.

4.3 Low and non-waste technology is a phrase currently in vogue which emphasises this aspect of production. There are industries which have effectively been practising low and non-waste technologies since the industrial revolution, but use of the modern phrase might succeed in bringing consideration for the waste stream to the forefront of the minds of others. Avoiding waste can bring increased commercial benefit by altering a process, by changing from one process to another which might cost less in itself, or by decreasing disposal costs by generating less waste[72-75]. (See boxes overleaf).

4.4 If the costs associated with waste disposal were properly allocated we consider that the waste stream would be brought to the same status as other processes. This approach would include the costs of cleaning up after a breach in the security of the waste stream, and should ensure that the funds allocated to waste disposal are not too restricted.

4.5 As a member of the European Community the UK is party to the Third Action Programme[40] which includes among other items provision for action: to reduce pollution and nuisance at source where possible; in waste management including treatment, recycling and reuse; and in the development

45

**An example of one company's approach to
POLLUTION PREVENTION PAYS**

WASTE STOPPER: PUMICE ON COPPER

Problem

3M's electronic products plant
in Columbia, Mo., makes flexible
electronic circuits from copper
sheeting. Before sheeting can be
used in the production process,
it has to be cleaned.

Formerly, the metal was sprayed
with ammonium persulfate,
phosphoric acid and sulfuric acid.
This created a hazardous waste that
required special handling and disposal.

Solution

Cleaning by chemical spraying was
replaced by a specially designed
new machine with rotating brushes
that scrubbed the copper with pumice.

The fine abrasive pumice material
leaves a sludge that is not hazardous
and can be disposed of in a conventional
sanitary landfill.

Payoff

40,000 pounds a year of hazardous
waste liquid prevented.

$15,000 first year savings in raw
materials and in disposal and labor
costs.

In the third year of use the new
cleaning machine had saved enough to
recover the $59,000 it cost.
Because of increased production each
year, costs saved and volumes of
pollution prevented continue to
rise.

Source: 'Ideas'. A compendium of 3P Success Stories. Environmental Engineering and
Pollution Control Department
3M, St Paul, Minnesota

An example of low waste technology in the steel industry

DESCALING OF HOT ROLLED STEEL.

The old technology - acid pickling

Wastes produced - depleted hydrochloric and sulphuric acid

- acidified rinse water.

Reasons for change - to achieve greater control over waste disposal

- to reduce rising waste disposal costs.

Options for on-site waste reduction:

- neutralising acid liquors - requires additional chemicals

- residual sludges need disposal

- recovery of acid for reuse - possible especially with modern ion exchange systems to recover both acids

- shot blasting - physical rather than chemical process

- leaves smaller volumes of inert wastes

- allows savings of up to 50% of original descaling costs.

Options adopted:

- shot blasting is now the preferred method for descaling drawn steel

- acid recovery still used in plants producing steel bars in a variety of shapes and sizes, for which shot blasting is not suitable.

Source: Aston University[76]

of clean technologies. In an annex to the declaration it is stated that environment policy must be concerned (among other things) with the reduction of any form of pollution, nuisance or interference with the environment or resources which create waste. There is thus positive support for industries that wish to develop and invest in low or non-waste technologies.

47

We commend this approach to reducing the waste stream and thus reducing the potential for waste to pollute the environment.

Product waste

4.6 In examining product waste two aspects must be considered: the product itself, and peripherals associated with it, such as packaging. It is essential that the potential environmental impact of a new product should always be assessed and taken into account during the product's design. This assessment should include the manufacture, packaging, labelling, normal use, potential for re-cycling after the normal working life has been exhausted, and subsequent final disposal of the product. We discuss this further in Chapter X when we consider design.

4.7 The same design approach should also be applied to packaging. Packaging made of biodegradable materials is less likely to cause permanent environmental damage (even paper litter will rot) but the problems of reduced strength and different costs must also be considered. We note that despite these potential and probable disadvantages the Italian Government has now decided to ban plastic bags and non-biodegradable packaging[77], and paper packaging will have to be made of recycled fibre. This ban is to be implemented on 1 January 1991, giving sufficient time for manufacturers and distributors to adjust their practices, and hence is an example of applying the principle of Best Environmental Timetable[1].

4.8 In addition to using raw materials that encourage environmentally satisfactory disposal of products and packaging, manufacturers and retailers can encourage their customers to dispose of products and packaging thoughtfully. Labelling is one obvious route (some food packages, for instance, carry the international 'Tidyman' symbol or requests to the purchaser to dispose of the wrappers carefully but, too often, in small print). It would help to identify packaging that could be recycled readily by marking or tagging it in some standard way. At present tin cans (i.e. those made of tinned steelplate) can be recovered from the waste stream by the use of magnets. Looking to the future, magnetically coded labelling may permit the development of new sorting systems: steel tags could be used to distinguish PET bottles from other plastics, and in the longer term we can envisage the use of computer controlled identification and sorting systems.

4.9 The EC has adopted a Directive on Containers of Liquids for Human Consumption[78] (see extract in box opposite) which provides for Member States to encourage, by legislation, administrative action or voluntary agreement, the restriction of beverage containers entering the waste stream, or remaining there for final disposal. Thus the EC is promoting a waste reduction policy for specific items, as well as the general policies contained in the Third Action Programme.

4.10 We consider that a reduction in the number of cans entering the waste stream would make a significant difference to the amount of litter generated, and that a change to all aluminium drinks cans would make recycling practicable (see paragraph 5.16). PET (polyethylene terephthalate) and high density polyethylene (HDP)* can both be reprocessed([79,80]), and it is therefore worth recovering PET bottles either by preventing them entering the waste stream or by recovering them from it. Even though return schemes (to retailer, reverse vending systems†, central collection points)([2])are to be preferred as the most cost-effective ways of recovering these bottles, if they get into the bulk waste stream separation in resource recovery plants (see paragraphs 5.20-5.21), could be achieved if these bottles could be tagged to allow mechanical recognition and extraction from the waste stream.

FROM ARTICLE 4.1 OF DIRECTIVE 85/339/EEC ON CONTAINERS OF LIQUIDS FOR HUMAN CONSUMPTION

Member States shall take measures designed:

(a) to develop consumer education in the advantages of using refillable containers, recycling containers and eliminating used containers from household waste;

(b) to facilitate the refilling and/or recycling of containers of liquids for human consumption;

(c) as regards non-refillable containers:
- to promote the selective collection of containers,
- to develop effective processes for retrieving containers from household waste,
- to extend the outlets for materials recovered from containers,
in so far as this is economically feasible;

(d) to encourage the technical development and placing on the market of new types of container, with the aim in particular of reducing the consumption of raw materials, facilitating recycling and the final disposal of container waste and achieving overall energy savings;

(e) to maintain and, where possible, increase the proportion of refilled and/or recycled containers and/or to decrease the proportion of non-recycled or non-refillable containers where the conditions of industrial activity and the market so permit.

4.11 The trend for packaging to form an increasing proportion of domestic rubbish was identified in Chapter II. This not only reflects the change in fuel usage, and the reduction in the ash content of domestic wastes, but also the changes in retailing practice, in particular the growth of supermarkets where,

---

* HDP is used to make the black base cups on PET bottles.
† Reverse vending machines offer tokens, coins or filled cans in return for a certain number of used cans or bottles.

for reasons of cost, efficiency, hygiene, consumer preference and attractiveness the majority of the goods are pre-packaged. The growth in packaging reflects the popularity of self-service shopping, with its requirements for branded and quality controlled products, and the loss of the specialised retailer. We have been told that an experimental study in Germany, in which consumers were asked to try to reduce the packaging they put into the waste stream, showed that even when they tried to buy goods with minimum packaging the amount entering the waste stream could be reduced by only 10-15%. However, there is also the question of public preference: attitude surveys in the UK and Australia have suggested that the British and the Australians, at least, like their products prepackaged([81,82]).

4.12 It is probable that there is no feasible method for reducing the extent of packaging, although changes in its form and composition could reduce the size of the waste stream. We therefore **recommend** that the Department of the Environment should continue to support and put into practice the objectives of the EC Third Action Programme in relation to waste management and in particular those concerning the encouragement of low or non-waste technologies; and we further **recommend** that the Department of Trade and Industry should seek the active co-operation of the Department of the Environment and of industry itself in finding appropriate ways of implementing Article 4 of the Directive on Containers of Liquids for Human Consumption.

(a) (Municipal Journal)

(b) (Municipal Journal)

Plate 1   Domestic refuse collection using wheeled dustbins; examples from (a) UK and (b)
the Netherlands. (paragraph 6.5).

(West Midlands County Council)

Plate 2   A large, well organised civic amenity site, where householders can deliver large items and garden wastes, as well as normal household refuse. (6.22).

(RCEP)

Plate 3   A smaller civic amenity site with limited opening hours. (6.22).

(Greater London Council)

Plate 4   Centralised collection for recycling — textiles and cans can be taken to central 'banks' as well as glass to bottle banks. (5.16).

(RCEP)

Plate 5   Red bins — used in Germany for the collection of hazardous materials from householders. In this example the bins are for used batteries. (5.19).

(a)

(b)

(c)

(RCEP)

Plate 6   Refuse left for collection at the kerbside (a) attracts other refuse; (b) can fall into the
road and be dispersed by traffic; and (c) can attract animals that may damage the
sacks. (6.7).

(RCEP)

Plate 7   Litter bins which are allowed to become over–full can cause litter to spread in public places . . .

(RCEP)

. . . particularly if the surrounding area is not cleared at the same time as the litter bin. (6.10).

(Keep Britain Tidy Group)

Plate 8   Current advice from the Department of Transport is to remove litter bins from laybys on trunk roads to prevent the accumulation of rubbish and replace them with notices telling motorists to take their litter home. (6.11).

(RCEP)

Plate 9   Litter bags for cars are available in some countries. (6.13).

Plate 10   Construction or demolition wastes fly tipped in a street in London. (6.20).

Plate 11   Rural fly tipping is often wastes from the building industry and domestic wastes. (6.20).

(West Midlands County Council)

Plate 12   Local authorities could find more ways of keeping the public informed about waste collection and disposal services. (6.23).

CHAPTER V

GIVING WASTE VALUE

Introduction

5.1 Waste has no value to its owner, and may even have the negative value of causing costs to be incurred in its disposal. Hence one way of reducing the waste stream is to impart some value to the waste. It then becomes a useful product or raw material - for someone else, if not to its original owner.

5.2 If material in the waste stream can be used without significant alteration it may then be considered suitable for *reuse*. Returnable bottles are an example. Alternatively waste materials may be *recycled* as raw materials for the same sorts of products: waste paper for paper manufacture; cullet for glass manufacture; oil for re-refining, and so on. A further option is that the waste material can be *reclaimed* as the raw material for some new product or use, such as the manufacture of compost or waste derived fuel; the recovery of energy as heat or electricity from the mass incineration of wastes is also a form of reclamation.

5.3 As we explained in Chapter I, we are concerned in this Report with ways of reducing the potential of wastes to cause pollution. We therefore commissioned the report from ERL ([2]), which has informed much of this chapter and will be published separately. The reuse, recycling and reclamation of waste materials are advocated for other reasons too, for instance to conserve energy and other resources or to create jobs, and many people would regard these reasons as more important than the ones we have considered. Such concern about the apparent waste of valuable materials is reflected in the recent report 'The Wealth of Waste' by the House of Commons Trade and Industry Committee([15]), the activities of the Warmer Campaign* and in some of the evidence submitted to us. Nevertheless, these aspects fall outside the scope of our study.

Waste exchange schemes

5.4 Most of the examples in paragraph 5.2 come from the domestic waste stream. But the industrial waste stream also provides opportunities for reuse, recycling and reclamation. By and large, if a particular product or tool can be

---

* A privately sponsored organisation founded in February 1984 to provide exchange of information on the use of refuse as an energy resource.

reused in industry, it will be; and it will not enter the waste stream until its useful life can be prolonged no further. There is however widespread untapped potential for recycling and reclamation in the industrial sector[71]. An individual company or factory should make maximum use of any raw materials entering the site, though we were glad to learn that significant improvements in efficiency of raw material usage continue to be made.

5.5 The possibility that one enterprise might be able to use another's apparently waste materials may not always be thoroughly explored. One means by which such possible uses could be identified is through waste exchange schemes. As part of the materials recovery programme at Warren Spring Laboratory* the UK Waste Materials Exchange[83,84] was set up. This was funded from the Department of Trade and Industry's research budget and initially was free to participants. Companies with waste arisings could have them listed; other companies who thought they could use the wastes were put in touch with the originator. Scrap metals and secondhand equipment, for which there were already recognised commercial markets, were not listed. Table 5.1 shows the quantities and types of waste successfully exchanged. The initial research phase of this project demonstrated that the Exchange provided a useful service to participants. It was then decided that it should be financially self-supporting. In the event support from industry for the project fell away. One factor which may have contributed to its lack of success is the fact that it was a passive waste exchange, with action required by originator and potential user, and with WSL acting solely as a post box instead of actively seeking possible outlets for waste arisings. We have had evidence[85] of one locally operated scheme, in which the organisers, the waste disposal authority, have played an active part in seeking out potential users for waste arisings. This scheme is also free to participants - the authority's expenditure being justified by the reduction in the amount of waste ultimately requiring disposal.

5.6 There are also trade associations in the reclamation industry that promote the recycling of industrial materials. One example is the Chemical Recovery Association[86], which has nearly 40 companies as members and whose business is the recycling (by cleaning) of used solvents and oils. Although waste residues arise from the cleaning process, their volume is very much smaller than that of the original feedstock. CRA thus operates, through its members, as a kind of specialised waste exchange, but one of its major problems is reported to be the low priority which even the chemical industry gives to waste disposal.

5.7 While specialised or local schemes clearly have the potential to work effectively, we consider that wider exchanges of information could lead to greater exchanges of waste materials and thus to a greater reduction in the volume of material sent for disposal. We believe that it would help to demonstrate a responsible attitude to waste, as part of the duty of care, if

---

* WSL: an industrial research establishment of the Department of Trade and Industry.

TABLE 5.1

Quantities and types of waste exchanged through the UK waste materials exchange, 1974-79

Type of waste	No. of items advertised	Quantities available as		No. of transactions reported	Quantities disposed as	
		Continuous arisings (tonnes/yr)	Single arisings (tonnes)		Continuous arisings (tonnes/yr)	Single arisings (tonnes)
Acids and alkalis	138	421,550	420	19	102,350	23
Catalysts	31	2,270	780	14	930	750
Inorganic chemicals	405	1,635,880	18,570	76	22,400	2,508
Organic chemicals and solvents	481	41,120	970	118	10,314	318
Food processing	74	247,300	570	17	1,963	264
Metals	110	62,730	10,120	7	12	26
Minerals	165	679,220	700,560	23	3,070	185,029*
Oils and waxes	138	56,496	895	33	2,738	112
Paper and board	153	48,650	520	29	960	40
Rubber and plastics	495	25,990	2,130	92	8,503	875
Textiles and leather	187	27,500	240	22	555	60
Miscellaneous	422	293,970	7,300	55	3,500	6,878
Totals	2,799	3,542,680	743,070	505†	157,295	196,883

* This includes one item of 120,000 tonnes.
† This excludes 34 items of which weights were not known.
Source: The United Kingdom Waste Exchange[83]

industry were to play a more active role in this field. We do not favour a national exchange being funded or administered by central government. But we consider that the Government should explore with bodies such as the CBI, chambers of commerce and trade associations the arrangements that would be needed for publishing lists of available wastes on a country-wide basis. We **recommend** that the Government should engage in discussions with appropriate bodies with a view to encouraging the exchange of information about industrial wastes.

Separate collection at source

5.8 The highly heterogeneous nature of domestic and commercial waste means that the success of recycling or reclamation depends on how easily materials can be separated from the waste stream. Waste paper, glass, cans and oil are examples of waste materials which can most readily be recycled for the manufacture of equivalent products, provided that contamination is minimal. These are therefore the items for which separate collection schemes have principally been introduced - through local authority collection systems, through voluntary group collections or through centralised collection banks.

5.9 Separate collection of waste paper by local authorities has declined drastically over the past 15 years. In 1970, 451 local authorities were collecting 360,000 tonnes of waste paper, but in 1982/83 the number had declined to 53 and the quantity of paper collected was under 48,000 tonnes([2]). The reduction in activity reflects, primarily, the instability in the price of waste paper although changes in the method of waste collection and pressure upon local authorities to streamline activities have been contributory factors. Most collection of waste paper from domestic sources is now undertaken by voluntary groups (such as scouts or school parent-teacher associations) who are ready to subsidise the collection and transport costs and can store paper until a marketable quantity has been accumulated. By contrast the commercial sector still affords the best source of recyclable material. The volumes available combined with the incentive to reduce disposal costs provide an economically viable framework within which waste paper merchants can recover substantial quantities of clean, non-contaminated paper and board. A stable market for waste paper and board is the touchstone for an efficient recovery system. Government procurement could play a valuable role in this field.

5.10 Separate collection of materials that have potential for recycling has been tried in several locations in Europe (principally in the Netherlands and Germany, but also on a smaller scale in France and in one location in the UK)([2]). When we visited Germany we saw one system which depended on householders having a variety of different coloured dustbins for different materials - the 'green bin' system([87]). Materials remained mixed either because a significant proportion of the householders failed to segregate their wastes adequately (up to 40% in one German town) or because the number of bin types was limited. But even two or three bins per household present a formidable storage problem in many urban areas, and a high capital cost. Moreover there are either greatly increased collection costs or less frequent emptying of each individual dustbin. If the latter is allowed to apply to bins containing putrescible materials, smells and possible health risks will result. We noted that, for efficient recycling, each material (paper, plastic, glass, non-ferrous metals, steel, etc.) needed to be collected quite separately. Refuse that was only partially separated, but still to some degree mixed, was in practice as difficult to sort as refuse coming from a single bin, and in one sorting station we observed material from different coloured dustbins being recombined. The post-collection sorting of mixed refuse presents difficulties and we noted that some of this was often undertaken manually: it seemed to us a particularly disagreeable task. Complete removal of plastic from paper is especially difficult. Whilst segregated collection schemes for domestic waste may help to increase public awareness and satisfy a political demand for the conservation of materials, we do not consider that the adoption of these schemes in the UK would significantly reduce pollution.

Centralised separate collection

5.11 Separate collection can take a different form: instead of doorstep collection by a central agency (whether local authority or voluntary group) some materials can be separated from the rest of the waste stream by the householder and then taken by him to a central collecting point. Beverage containers appear to be especially well suited to this type of collection, whether they are made of glass, metal or PET (see paragraph 4.10). In the following paragraphs we review current initiatives and make recommendations which we believe will not only help to remove these items from the waste stream by enhancing their value but which will also reduce a significant and persistent form of litter.

5.12 The recently adopted European Community Directive[78] on Containers of Liquids for Human Consumption (see paragraph 4.9 and box on page 49) is also relevant. Although our recommendations in this field are directed specifically towards reducing and, if possible, avoiding environmental pollution nevertheless we consider they may also be valuable in formulating the policies required by the Directive.

Glass bottle banks
5.13 As in many other European countries, substantial quantities of glass bottles are recovered in the UK through the medium of bottle banks for use as cullet*. The national bottle bank scheme established by the glass container industry in conjunction with local authorities in 1977 contributed to the 100,000 tonnes of glass removed from the waste stream in 1983. Some comparative statistics for Germany, the Netherlands and France together with information on the numbers of bottle banks are set out in Table 5.2. In the United States in 1982 727,000 tonnes of waste glass was collected, twice the figure for 1980 and this appears to be part of an upward trend[88].

TABLE 5.2

**Glass recycling through bottle banks:
comparative data, 1983**

	UK	Germany	Netherlands	France
Waste glass collected				
- tonnes	100,000	704,000+	150,000+	400,000
Bottle banks				
- total number	2,500	35,000+	6,500+	20,000
- average density	1 per 22,250 people	1 per 2,000 people		1 per 2,000 people (target)

Source: ERL Report[2].

5.14 Compared with Germany, France or the Netherlands lower quantities of waste glass are collected in the UK: there are fewer bottle banks both in absolute terms and in proportion to glass container usage. We believe that bottle banks are important and, at least in areas where the costs of transporting waste glass to the glass manufacturer are not too high, provide a satisfactory method of recycling.

* Cullet is glass fed to furnaces together with raw materials.

5.15 We received evidence that bottle banks operate most effectively where costs, particularly those associated with the provision of the containers, are met through commercial sponsorship. We commend these co-operative initiatives between the waste disposal authorities and the private sector as a sensible, as well as economical, method of reducing the waste and litter streams, and also of achieving recycling. However, we believe the siting of bottle banks (at any rate the larger types) needs careful planning. This is likely to be still more important if other recovery schemes (for instance, for cans and PET) develop significantly. We consider that there should be more bottle banks in the UK but they need to be sited to avoid adverse effects on amenity (e.g. intrusive appearance and source of noise). It is preferable that they should not be located in predominantly residential areas, and this may mean that in towns it will be difficult to achieve the ideal, which is that householders should not have to travel further to bottle banks than to their local shopping centre*. The most suitable locations would appear to be car parks near existing supermarkets and, with the development of larger retailing establishments with their associated infrastructure including car parking, we consider that adequate provision should be made for siting bottle and other recycling banks at the design stage and when planning permission is granted. The choice of any location should allow for the accumulation of other waste or litter, notably cardboard cartons, which inevitably occurs alongside and which the local authority must arrange to pick up efficiently and regularly. We **recommend** that local authorities, in their capacity as planning authorities, should consider requiring the provision of bottle banks in large retail and other appropriate development schemes; and that as waste collection or disposal authorities they should investigate the scope for increased provision of bottle banks at existing suitable sites.

Can recovery

5.16 Various initiatives have been taken in the United Kingdom to recycle beverage cans. For example, the 'Save-a-Can' scheme, run by the Can Makers Institute, is based on recovery banks (Plate 4) similar to bottle banks but a contribution is made to a local charity rather than a payment to the local authority as with bottle banks. Another scheme, operated by the East Anglian Metal Company, has concentrated upon aluminium cans, which are purchased for a guaranteed flat rate: collection of cans is organised primarily by local groups, especially charities. We have come to the conclusion that so long as a variety of different metals continue to be used in the manufacture of beverage cans in the UK (75% of soft drink cans are made entirely from aluminium, while 75% of beer cans are made from mixed metal)[2], the opportunities for adding value to the waste stream through recycling will be marginal. However, we understand that the trend is toward a higher percentage of aluminium cans (as in the USA and Sweden, where most cans are 100% aluminium[71]). If this continues it will be possible through collection schemes or reverse vending

---

* Not more than 300 metres on foot was suggested in Germany and not more than $1\frac{1}{2}$ miles by car in urban areas was suggested in the West Midlands.

machines to achieve recovery in the UK closer to the 50% rate claimed in the USA and the 75% which is the target in Sweden. We conclude that there would be clear advantages if beverage cans could be constructed of a uniform material which was readily recyclable (see paragraph 4.10) in order to reduce the risk of pollution from this source.

Recovery of PET and other materials

5.17 The recovery of PET bottles (paragraph 4.10) through central collection systems has been the subject of initiatives by the British Plastics Federation and, more recently, by a company in the chemical industry. As with cans and glass bottles we believe these initiatives should be encouraged, since here too an increased level of recovery will reduce the volume of the waste stream and significantly reduce litter.

5.18 Other materials for which similar but localised schemes have operated are textiles (Plate 4), aluminium foil and waste oil (see also paragraph 5.25-5.27). All of these materials are collected in the Save Waste and Prosper Scheme in Leeds[2]. Our impression of these initiatives is that they appear to have been a good deal less successful than the recycling of glass from the point of view of adding value to the wastes. We do, however, share the view that they may have assisted in the reduction of litter and to that extent have contributed to the reduction of pollution.

5.19 Central collection schemes have also been used for hazardous items from households. In Germany we saw red bins, which could be adapted to particular applications - for example for collection of spent batteries at retailers' premises or drugs and pharmaceuticals at chemists' shops (Plate 5). In France and Japan separate collection of mercury batteries is encouraged, although it would appear that the French scheme is not yet successful[2]. We have also heard of collection authorities making special arrangements from time to time to collect, at central points, materials such as pharmaceuticals and household solvents. Besides restricting the entry of these hazardous materials into the waste stream, and thus their spread through the environment, collection or disposal authorities are able to accumulate them to the point where specialist disposal becomes possible or where reprocessing or recycling becomes an attractive proposition. Clearly neither of these would be possible if the materials had remained part of a mixed waste stream. The European Commission has initiated investigations, due to be completed at the end of 1985, into the collection and recycling of mercury and nickel-cadmium batteries in Member States[89].

Mechanical separation from the waste stream

5.20 As we have seen earlier, even materials which have been segregated from the waste stream by various separate or central collection methods may require further sorting at transfer stations or disposal sites. This may involve a combination of manual and mechanical sorting. Manual sorting can achieve good selectivity and even in plants which are predominantly mechanised may be justified where the municipal waste stream contains a sufficient quantity of good quality paper. We saw this happening at a mechanical sorting plant in Germany, where several grades of paper can be produced. Manual sorting is used to extract the better quality grades; the remainder is sorted mechanically. However, complete separation of plastic from paper, or ceramics from glass, is not possible. The experience of this plant demonstrates the problems of trying to segregate clean materials for recycling once the waste stream has been bulked.

5.21 There is also a question of scale: in Germany it was suggested to us that the optimum catchment population for a recycling plant was in the region of 300,000. In addition, social conditions in small towns or suburban areas may be an important factor behind the success of recycling schemes which depend on some segregation of materials by the householder. By contrast the problems of major conurbations call for different solutions. To separate the waste from a large community would require either an army of manual pickers or mechanical sorting; and except for ferrous and non-ferrous metals mechanical sorting seems unable to achieve high grade products. Some plants designed to produce waste derived fuel (see paragraphs 5.23 and 5.24) have incorporated equipment to reject cans and glass (the major non-combustible components) which has successfully achieved separation, although there has not been a satisfactory market for the products. Research plants in South Yorkshire and Tyne and Wear (Plates 15 and 16) are now being followed by the construction of two new plants in the West Midlands and Merseyside, in which many of the research and marketing lessons from the early plants should be implemented. Waste sorting by mechanical means is probably best suited to circumstances where the required product is a source of energy rather than clean recyclable components. These circumstances are more likely to arise in large cities, with large unsegregated waste streams.

Conversion of waste to energy

5.22 Energy can be recovered directly as heat when waste is incinerated in bulk. The heat can be used to serve district heating schemes, or to provide process heat for manufacturing or space heating for factories. Often in mass incineration plants there is no preliminary treatment of the wastes, but ferrous metals may be separated from the residues magnetically. Given the high capital costs of incineration plant it seems unlikely that any future plant would be constructed without provision for some energy recovery: this means that any incineration plant must have a customer for the recovered energy[2].

5.23 A more flexible way of recovering energy is by the production of waste derived fuel* (WDF)[90], in that it does not depend on tied customers to the same extent as direct supply of energy and can be stockpiled. WDF can be produced in either of two forms: pelletised or shredded. The former can be

---

* Also known as refuse derived fuel (RDF).

burnt in many conventional boilers, but shredded fuel is most appropriate for large combustion units - especially cement kilns. WDF has about half the calorific value of coal and customers require some financial incentive to use WDF and are unwilling to pay the equivalent price for the same calorific value of coal. This means that WDF producers often find it difficult to achieve an adequate margin after recovering production costs, and this places the viability of WDF production in the balance. Other influences, however, such as a restriction on the availability of landfill sites, could sway an authority's decision in favour of WDF production in order to reduce the volume of waste requiring landfill.

5.24 We are concerned that there is still uncertainty about the possible polluting emissions from WDF combustion([91,92]). The high plastics content of the fuel makes emission of gases with high chlorine content likely; there is also the possibility that precursors of dioxin (see Chapter VII and the box on page 92), other organic compounds or heavy metal particulates may be emitted or concentrated in the ash residues. Although WDF is not a fuel approved under the Clean Air Acts for smoke control areas([93]), it has been suggested in some quarters that it can be burnt on any grate, and even in domestic fires. In our view this would be extremely unwise. We **recommend** that until more is known about emissions from WDF combustion it should be burnt only in units where good control can achieve high temperatures, with good oxygen mixing and with sufficient residence times. This would point to exclusively industrial applications.

5.25 Another source of energy from waste is the methane recovered as a by-product from landfill sites (Plate 23). Although we welcome initiatives that exploit landfill gas effectively, we consider that the first priority should be to deal with it as a hazard requiring proper control. If at the same time it is possible to use it as a resource, that is a bonus. We do not advocate the deliberate creation of methanogenic conditions in landfill sites. We discuss this matter further in Chapter VII.

5.26 Waste oils may be re-refined or burnt in their existing state. Table 5.3 compares the proportions re-refined, burnt or dumped in six European countries. All of these countries are party to the EC Directive on Waste Oils([94]), which requires, *inter alia*, that:

- countries take measures to ensure that, as far as possible, waste oils are recycled;
- records are kept of the quantity, quality, origin and location of waste oils; and
- undertakings which dispose of waste oil must obtain a permit.

5.27 In both France and Germany measures have been introduced to recover oil by re-refining. No such action however has been taken in the UK([2]), although existing legislation provides some control over the dumping or unrestricted burning of waste oils (which may, for instance, be contaminated

TABLE 5.3

Disposal of waste oils in Europe: 1983 estimates

Country	Estimated volume arising as waste (000 tonnes)	Burnt on site or used as fuel (%)	Re-refined (%)	Dumped (%)
Denmark	80	85	5	10
F.R. Germany	500	40-50	50-55	negligible
France	400	10-15	55-60	25-30
Italy	300	30	30	30
United Kingdom	350	60	15	25
Netherlands	110	90	10	0

Source: ERL Report[2]

with lead). We are concerned, however, that there may be a continued risk of air pollution arising from the burning of waste oils with inappropriate equipment[95] or of pollution from oils dumped on land. We note that the House of Lords Select Committee on the European Communities is currently examining a proposed EC amending Directive about burning waste oils only in large burners.

5.28 The disposal of used tyres presents particular problems. Tyres can cause unstable voids in landfill sites, and there are only limited outlets for reclaimed products (rubber and steel) from them. This makes energy recovery from used tyres attractive, and we have noted several initiatives in this field:

- burning of whole tyres in cement kilns[2];
- burning in smaller combustion units after shredding[2,96];
- transformation by pyrolysis into oils and solids which can be used as fuel[2,97,98].

5.29 Another innovative idea is the production of oil from wastes containing cellulose[99]. Through research carried out at the University of Manchester Institute of Science and Technology and Salford University Industrial Centre at the instigation of the Greater Manchester Council, a process has been developed to treat either prepared municipal refuse or straw to produce oil which is virtually sulphur free and suitable for subsequent refining. This project has successfully proved the technique at a small scale, but industry has been reluctant to participate in the scaling up to pilot and then to full-scale plants, despite encouraging economic analysis of the system's commercial potential.

5.30 Although the environmental impacts of the technologies referred to in the last two paragraphs have not yet been fully explored, we consider that further development should be encouraged.

Reclamation for new products

5.31 Waste derived fuel (paragraphs 5.22-5.23) is one example of a valuable new product being recovered from the municipal waste stream. Another example is the manufacture of compost. For most uses compost should have only limited amounts of glass, plastic or metal in it, but these requirements are difficult to meet when bulk municipal waste is composted. So far in England only one major waste composting plant (in Leicester) has been constructed, and this has since been closed down, owing to difficulties in marketing the composted products*. In France, however, one hundred plants are in operation([100]). In Germany we saw a plant which produced compost with a relatively high glass, metal and plastics content and therefore not suitable for general use: its principal use was as covering material for the company's landfill sites. (We understand that other plants exist in Germany which produce compost suitable for horticultural, land reclamation and counter-erosion purposes.) Since suitable material for covering landfill sites or for other land reclamation purposes is often in short supply, we feel that with suitable advertising or exchange of information (for example through waste exchanges) there is scope for stimulating greater interest in composted products. We therefore consider that initiatives in this field should be encouraged.

Conclusions

5.32 We agree with the general conclusion of the House of Commons Trade and Industry Committee([15]) that opportunities for recycling and resource recovery from waste materials are not exploited as vigorously in the United Kingdom as they might be. We also agree with the Committee's view that this is due at least in part to the absence of a clear lead from the Government. The Government's decision, which was announced on 15 March 1985 in its response([101]) to the Committee's Report, to designate a particular Minister in the Department of Trade and Industry as having special coordinating responsibility for waste recycling issues seemed a useful though modest administrative measure. There have been subsequent changes in ministerial duties, and it is too early to determine the effectiveness of this arrangement and, more particularly, its adequacy in relation to general environmental policy, for there appears to be an overlap with the responsibilities of the Department of the Environment.

5.33 We consider that the Departments of Trade and Industry and of the Environment should continue to encourage recycling and resource recovery as a means of reducing pollution, including litter. Considered solely with this end in mind, not all forms of recycling merit uncritical support. As we pointed out in Chapter I, one of the chief characteristics of waste is its variability, and this calls into question its reliability as a raw material for certain types of process. Moreover a policy which gives priority to recycling may not necessarily be the best practicable environmental option in all circumstances. The high priority given to recycling in Germany, for instance, is at least partly attributable to social and geographical factors which have made landfill in that country a

---

* A number of small plants in Scotland similarly failed to attain commercial viability.

relatively less attractive (and therefore more expensive) option than in the United Kingdom. Finally, some wastes when disposed of together will react with each other to form less harmful forms of waste, and this may be seen to be a more desirable option than attempting to recover resources from the separate waste streams in question.

5.34 In the case of beverage containers, the initiatives which have been taken, with the notable exception of glass, have not been developed sufficiently to be making a significant contribution to recovery. Nevertheless we consider there are opportunities for further development. We hope that our recommendations in Chapter IV in relation to the EC Third Action Programme and the application of the beverage containers Directive([78]) will serve to stimulate further initiatives by industry and government.

5.35 Whilst we would expect benefits from a more coherent and co-ordinated policy on recycling, particularly to the extent that this results in the removal of institutional obstacles to recycling, we are sceptical about positive intervention by the Government to stimulate the recycling of particular materials. At best the arguments seem to be finely balanced. The candidate most frequently advanced for intervention is waste paper. However the difficulties which have made separate collection of domestic waste paper unattractive (see paragraph 5.9) will not, in our view, be overcome by stimulating the production of low-grade recycled paper for which no demand exists at present. It is much better that recycling should be demand-led; and in this context we see no reason why the Government should not, as has been suggested([2]), help to boost the demand for recycled paper through its own procurement policies, provided that reasonable performance and value for money criteria are met. We note that Government policies do already take these considerations into account([101]). Whether these policies should go further and require recycled materials to form part of the specifications on which tenders are invited by HM Stationery Office will depend on the priority which is attached to reducing the paper content of the waste stream and to other considerations (e.g. import savings). From the pollution point of view, it has to be said that paper is a relatively straightforward waste to deal with and therefore, bearing in mind our terms of reference, we make no recommend-ation on this issue.

5.36 The wide degree of discretion which collection authorities have in setting charges for the collection of commercial waste (see paragraph 8.3) may be a factor which influences the level of recycling. An economically optimum level of recycling of commercial waste materials is most likely to be attained if all collection authorities charge sufficient to recover their full long-run marginal costs of collection. However authorities may choose to subsidise some items in the tariff structure at the expense of others for strategic reasons - for example they may feel it desirable to make only low charges for small loads to discourage fly tipping.

5.37 Although the collection for recycling of bottles, cans and other waste materials may be difficult to justify on grounds of economic efficiency, it helps to create an attitude of mind that when waste is properly controlled and kept to a minimum the environment is less polluted. It is important because it demonstrates that individually we each have a part to play in reducing pollution of the environment.

CHAPTER VI

COLLECTION, STORAGE AND TRANSPORT
OF WASTES

Municipal waste collection, street cleaning and litter

6.1 Though many types of gross pollution have abated over the last few decades([1]), in many parts of Britain litter remains a serious and growing problem. It is no exaggeration to say that many urban areas have a dirty, scruffy appearance. The amount of litter and debris in public places appears to have increased, although some factors that have contributed to this trend may be beneficial in other ways. For example the increased packaging of many goods improves hygiene and often aids efficient marketing; and the replacement of the traditional dustbin by plastic sacks reduces the risk of back injury to refuse collectors and reduces noise from collection.* In a general sense the problems arise because the holder of the waste takes insufficient care or because the waste stream is insecure; even after being discarded with proper care the rubbish escapes into the environment.

6.2 This chapter concentrates on those aspects of waste collection, storage and transport where there is a risk of pollution arising. This pollution is usually in the form of litter, in which we include not only plastic, paper and similar rubbish but also abandoned cars or drums containing chemicals and other materials that drift ashore, etc. The spillage or incorrect handling of wastes during collection and transport can give rise to other forms of pollution. These problems are central to much of the remainder of our report and to our proposal that a duty of care should be placed on the producer and handler.

6.3 The most significant effect of litter is its visual impact and the resulting loss of amenity. A natural or man-made environment disfigured by litter is not only undesirable in itself; it may also act as a deterrent to tourism and business([102]), with a consequent loss of revenue. Certain forms of litter carry other dangers([102]): abandoned cars or white goods† may pose physical hazards to children; drums or smaller containers, with or without the whole of their

---

* On the other hand the need for larger collection vehicles with compactors to cope with the increased volume of packaging waste has increased vehicle noise.
† White goods: domestic hardware such as cookers, refrigerators, freezers and washing machines, traditionally available in white enamel, now increasingly available in many colours.

contents of pesticides([32]) or other chemicals, are potential sources of toxins; whilst general accumulations of litter may be a fire hazard (as was illustrated tragically in the disaster earlier this year at Bradford football ground). Litter is either waste that should enter the municipal waste stream or is material that has escaped from it.

Municipal waste collection

6.4 As explained in Chapter II, 'municipal waste' is a convenient term for domestic wastes, street cleaning wastes and commercial wastes collected by waste collection authorities. A number of different collection systems are used and some are more appropriate to particular local conditions than others. Which system is actually used is influenced by history, financial considerations and local authority employees' conditions of service. The two last factors are, of course, important, but our task is to evaluate the impact of the collection system on environmental pollution.

6.5 Wastes may be collected from the premises or the kerbside using a variety of containers (conventional dustbin, plastic sack, dustbin with attached lid and, usually, wheels) (Plate 1). Sometimes two types may be combined - for instance, plastic sacks used as liners in conventional dustbins. In addition some domestic refuse may be taken by householders for disposal at special sites such as bottle banks, can banks or civic amenity sites: we refer to these methods as centralised collection. In flats or other multi-storey buildings the refuse of individual households is often discharged by chutes into special containers housed inside the buildings. Once the material is in such a container, as with bottle banks, the system is reasonably secure. We have commented on multiple dustbin systems in paragraph 5.10.

6.6 Table 6.1 summarises the main advantages and disadvantages of the different collecting systems for most households. It is based mainly on the evidence submitted by local authority associations and by the Institution of Environmental Health Officers. We note that kerbside collection has been identified by the Audit Commission([104]) as a means of reducing collection costs. However the Audit Commission recognised that this would 'clearly involve a drop in the standard of service to rate payers', and we emphasise its potential for having detrimental effects on the environment. It is an example of the externalisation of costs (See paragraphs 3.11, 6.33 and 8.3).

6.7 There is no doubt that given a high standard of supervision and management most collection systems can operate without causing environmental pollution by adding to the litter problem. For example good practice should ensure that dustbin lids are not removed far in advance of collection vehicles, that plastic bags are handled so that they do not burst or spill, and that any spillages are cleared up by the collection crews. We consider that the practice of leaving plastic sacks at the kerbside is the most prone to produce litter (by spillage - see box on page 67 - and the attraction of other material) (Plate 6). Some authorities clear up spillages by co-ordinating refuse collection and street cleaning, but in many urban, and especially residential, areas parked

TABLE 6.1

**Some advantages (+) and disadvantages (−) of domestic
refuse collection systems**
Characteristics referring to environmental considerations are in bold type.

Characteristic of system	Pick-up point		
	Premises	Kerbside	Central point
Litter creation during transfer; loss of material through spillage, wind action or animals	+	−	+ +
Time taken by refuse collectors	−	+	+ +
Time taken by households	+	−	− −
Opportunities for separation of materials and recycling	−	−	+

Characteristic of system	Container type		
	Dustbin (metal/plastic)	Plastic sack	Special container with attached lid and wheels
Flexibility in relation to changes in quantity of refuse (e.g. over public holidays)	−	+ additional sacks issued	−
Integrity of container − including liability to bursting (owing to sharps, impact or animals)	+	−	+ +
Integrity of container in relation to hot ashes	+ / −	− −	−
Storage area required by container	−	+	− for each container
Ease of moving container − on flat ground − over steps	− −	+ +	+ + − −
Capital costs of containers and special vehicles	+	+	−
Running costs of container	+	−	+
Emptying container into collection vehicle − manual labour required − **spillage /litter creation**	− − −	− − −	+ +
Noise during collection	−	+	−

cars seriously reduce the efficiency of street cleaning. We regret that currently available guidelines from the Institute of Wastes Management for local authorities on 'Contract Refuse Collection' do not stress the need for avoiding litter generation during collection([105]).

**CAUSES OF SPILLAGE FROM PLASTIC SACKS
AT THE KERBSIDE**

General problems (not confined to kerbside collection)
Sacks inadequately closed
Sacks punctured by sharp, very heavy or hot articles*
Spillage from damaged sacks when carried to collection vehicle

Problems specific to kerb side collection
Sacks torn open by animals such as dogs, cats, foxes and gulls
Sacks topple from kerb into roadway and are burst open
   by passing vehicles
Vandalism

* Sacks conforming to the newly published British Standard Specification([106]) are not resistant to rupture from these causes.

6.8 Since the shortcomings of the present arrangements have been indicated to us by those most closely involved (the local authority associations and the Institution of Environmental Health Officers) - and their evidence confirms our own general conclusions - we consider that some existing practices should be improved.

6.9 Accordingly we **recommend** that:

(a)   All waste collection authorities should adopt an explicit policy designed to achieve a secure waste stream, and should provide appropriate training and supervision of their staff.

(b)   Specifications drawn up for tenders for refuse collection services should include conditions to maintain or improve standards of litter prevention and that the Department of the Environment should provide appropriate guidance to waste collection authorities.

(c)   The practice of kerbside collection of plastic bags, being the most prone to produce litter, should be phased out, except where local conditions make it uniquely appropriate, in which case bags of adequate quality should be used.

(d)   Local authorities should adopt wheeled plastic dustbins with attached lids as having environmental and operational advantages, unless particular local circumstances make their use impossible. In making this recommendation we are encouraged by the experience of several local authorities in Britain([107]), by what we saw of their use in the Federal Republic of Germany[87] and from our knowledge of their adoption elsewhere.

Litter bins and street cleaning

6.10 Where litter bins are sited is determined by local authorities*. They are usually placed in shopping areas, near take away food premises and bus stops and in similar sites. They may be emptied daily or more often in busy pedestrianised shopping areas; perhaps as little as weekly in some rural areas. Local authority associations have emphasised to us the need to empty bins before they become full or overflowing both to prevent litter being blown out (Plate 7) and to discourage the dumping of larger items of rubbish, which many people are tempted to do by the sight of an over-full litter bin. We noted a high standard of street cleanliness during our brief visit to Germany. It seems to us that this is due partly to differences in social attitudes, but principally to higher frequency of street cleaning.

6.11 The Department of Transport is currently advising local highway authorities to remove litter bins from lay-bys on trunk roads and replace them by notices telling the public to take their litter home[108] (Plate 8). These may be accompanied by a warning that the penalty for leaving litter can be up to £400. Removal of litter bins from lay-bys is said to have reduced the incidence of rubbish in lay-bys, where over-full bins attracted not only picnic and other litter from motorists but also large items that must have been taken there specially. The question is, where is this litter going now? Is it being taken home and placed in the dustbin, is it being taken to a civic amenity site, is it being scattered along the roads in general, or is it being fly tipped? We have no confidence that the first two of these apply and we have been told by one local official that roadside litter has got worse. Bearing in mind that many motorists use lay-bys for picnicking (whether they are designed for that purpose or not), and the fact that much effort has gone into training the public to use litter bins for picnic rubbish (often with the aid of the slogan 'find a bin and put it in'), it may be a retrograde step to remove bins from these sites. Clearly the present policy represents an immediate economy in a particular authority's budget but we believe it should be seen in a wider context. Accordingly we **recommend** that the Department of Transport should, in conjunction with the Department of the Environment, review the effect of its current policy and, in the light of experience here and abroad, aim to provide or encourage the provision of litter receptacles that can be emptied with sufficient frequency in sites appropriate to the needs of the motoring public.

---

* Responsibilities for street cleaning and litter bins depend on road classification. The Department of Transport has responsibility for motorways and trunk roads, but normally arranges for the county council to act as the Department's agent. The county council is the highway authority for all other roads, except footpaths, bridleways and some unclassified urban roads, for which the district or borough council may take responsibility under section 42 of the Highways Act 1980. The highway authority has responsibility for provision and clearing of litter when it is a matter of road safety; but the district council has responsibility for cleaning roads (including verges) as a matter of public health and amenity.

6.12 It would be appropriate for lay-bys without litter bins to have signs not only advising the public of the possible penalties for leaving litter or other rubbish, but also indicating the alternative locations for disposal such as the local civic amenity site, litter bins in nearby picnic areas, or litter bins on garage forecourts. Provision of the last of these would be subject to agreement between the garage proprietor and the collection authority, but the use of such sites would be in keeping with the growing range of facilities already found there and with the recent trend towards describing them as 'service stations'. In due course consideration of the provision of litter bins might usefully be a requirement of planning applications for service stations. (See our recommendation about siting bottle banks, paragraph 5.15.) Designated picnic areas can have provision for seating and other facilities, and provision of litter bins and their clearance would be required as part of the terms of site permissions, whether the areas are run by local authorities or private organisations.

6.13 One reason why motorists tend not to take litter home is that most family cars do not have a convenient storage receptacle for litter (other than the ashtray). In some countries (e.g. Germany and Australia, and indeed in some areas of Britain during local litter abatement campaigns) special bags are available that can be easily fastened under the glove-box or in a similar position (Plate 9). We **recommend** that the Department of Transport should discuss with the motoring organisations and the Society of Motor Manufacturers and Traders the general provision of such facilities in the UK.

6.14 Litter on railway property and trains is often very conspicuous. British Rail (BR) have told us that litter in stations is recognised as a problem and that there is a general policy of providing litter bins of various capacities (25 litres to 150 litres) on platforms and on station concourses, but implementation of the policy is a matter for area managers or even station masters because of the variations of individual station design. BR are required to keep the track clear under health and safety at work requirements and have a general policy to achieve this, which again is left to area managers to implement. We have been told that on the trains modern Inter City rolling stock does have provision for litter containers in each carriage but that this is not so for some new rolling stock used on provincial services. On suburban or commuter trains provision of litter bins (except in lavatories) is regarded as encroaching on valuable seating space and, in any event, these trains are more readily cleaned by sweeping the floor areas than by emptying litter containers. It seems to us that the effort that has gone into designing litter facilities for long distance travellers should be extended to provincial and suburban travellers, especially as we consider that the lack of litter bins encourages an irresponsible attitude towards litter in the travelling public. We are pleased to note that BR designated 1985 a year for an anti-litter campaign - and hope they will extend their campaigning attitude into 1986 and beyond.

6.15 Some local authorities operate schemes under which local businesses sponsor litter bins (or bottle banks - see paragraph 5.15); they certainly help to encourage civic pride. The aim of these arrangements should be to provide extra litter bins in the area rather than replacing those provided by the local authority. We also believe it appropriate that certain commercial enterprises should be expected to play a special role. We commend those fast-food companies that have undertaken research on the appropriate siting and timing of emptying of litter bins near their outlets[109]. In accordance with the 'polluter pays' principle we **recommend** that local authorities should do all they can to encourage market traders, take away food outlets and other establishments whose activities may contribute to litter to provide and, where appropriate, to service litter bins. If all else fails there may be a case for consideration of increasing the powers of local authorities[110].

Litter abatement schemes

6.16 Most litter abatement schemes operate with advice and support from the Keep Britain Tidy Group (KBTG). The Group receives over 90% of its resources from the Department of the Environment and other public bodies. It has developed the Community Environment Programme, which provides guidance for and can be implemented by local authorities. Litter abatement schemes involve not only the provision and maintenance of adequate litter bins, but also educational campaigns in schools and the use of posters and other advertising to discourage the whole population from dropping litter. Several local authorities have reported that the noticeable reduction in litter achieved with these campaigns tends to be short lived, though others regard success or failure as impossible to assess without conclusive measurements. We note with approval the Cleaner City zone experiment launched by Westminster City Council[110,111] the effectiveness of which many of us have had occasion to observe at first hand. As HRH The Duke of Edinburgh wrote in a message to the Council, 'The state of a city's streets is a measure of the pride and concern of its citizens'.

6.17 A gradual decline after the initial improvement which follows litter abatement campaigns is to be expected. It compares with the results of advertising for product marketing: the most successful schemes are those which balance the diminishing effect of one campaign with the launch of the next. It is only by successive campaigns, keeping the litter abatement theme repeatedly before the public, that a lasting change in public attitudes will be achieved. We believe that the KBTG symbol (known internationally as the Tidyman symbol) should be displayed more prominently on packaging and litter bins, and commend this to the Industry Committee on Packaging and the Environment and other relevant sectors of industry.

Fly tipping

6.18 The illicit dumping, or fly tipping, of domestic or industrial wastes is a problem which throws into sharp relief two of the principles which we have suggested should govern the proper environmental management of wastes - the security of the waste stream and the duty of care which rests with the generators of waste to ensure its proper disposal. Besides its unsightly effects wherever it occurs, fly tipping often brings the risk of harm through physical injury or of damage to health if hazardous wastes have been deposited.

6.19 The fly tipping problem is most acute in the metropolitan areas. The London-wide Initiative on Fly Tipping (LIFT) Working Party([112]) identified some 600,000 tonnes of fly tipped wastes in London, but estimated that the total could exceed 1 million tonnes. Other major cities report similar problems but, while smaller towns and rural areas say their problems are less acute, one rural area, Ogwr around Bridgend, cleared 2,000 tonnes of fly tipped waste in a recent clearing up operation. British Rail estimate that it costs £1.5 million/year to clear litter and fly tipped wastes from railway land.

6.20 The LIFT Report contains a detailed study of the problem in London, identifying the kind and quantity of the wastes that are fly tipped, and also the nature of the depositer. Throughout London wastes are deposited on all kinds of open sites, including car parks, waste ground, verges and alleyways (Plate 10); and in some cases the public highway is used as a dumping ground. Inner London suffers much more severely than the outer boroughs. The wastes concerned are predominantly building wastes originating from construction or demolition sites in the central area; ironically these are wastes that are particularly useful in the management of landfill sites (paragraph 7.16). Domestic wastes predominate in the outer boroughs, with garden wastes, do-it-yourself rubbish, normal domestic refuse and old furniture all being found. In rural areas fly tipped wastes are, again, largely drawn from the construction industry or domestic sources (Plate 11) and may present a major problem to farmers and other occupiers of land particularly in the 'urban fringe'([32]).

6.21 The Report divides the people who fly tip into four categories: the 'organised criminal', the 'commercial', the 'domestic' and the 'traveller'. The organised criminal fly tipper operates to make money through illegal deposition of wastes. Commercial tippers are those who fly tip to avoid the charges or inconvenience of using the proper disposal routes, whether through the waste collection authority or by taking the waste to licensed waste disposal sites. Domestic fly tippers dump rubbish to avoid the personal inconvenience of travelling to civic amenity sites, or waiting for their opening hours, or they fly tip because the normal waste collection services fail to meet their needs and they are ignorant of the special facilities available. Domestic tipping tends to occur at sites where waste has already been dumped. Travellers (i.e. itinerants) have a tendency to dump or abandon rubbish accumulated on camp sites in the course of their activities (e.g. car breaking): this sort of refuse dumping is therefore rather different from the rest of fly tipping and more akin to the abandonment of waste in commercial premises. (See paragraph 6.33).

71

6.22 Although it is unlikely that fly tipping can ever be eradicated totally, we consider that several actions could be taken which would help to reduce the problem considerably. As much domestic fly tipping occurs as a result of ignorance there is evidently scope for more accessible information for the public on, for example, the availability of special collection services for large household items, special domestic wastes (such as chemicals) or garden and do-it-yourself refuse. In addition, more temporary skips in urban areas, and larger numbers of civic amenity sites in convenient locations and with opening hours designed to meet the needs of local communities (Plates 2 and 3), should reduce the temptation for householders to dump their rubbish. In the West Midlands Metropolitan County we have been told that the existing civic amenity sites are located so that every household is within $2\frac{1}{2}$ miles of one; but this is not sufficient to meet demand and the target is to increase the density so that no household is more than $1\frac{1}{2}$ miles from a site.

6.23 Whilst various arrangements are made in different parts of the country for informing the public about special disposal facilities, e.g. through notices issued to parish councils or displayed in public libraries, we consider that the information available to members of the public as individuals is often inadequate. Accordingly we **recommend** that local authorities should provide more information on rubbish disposal, for example by leaflets accompanying rate demands or by frequent notices in local papers, and should indicate the location of the nearest amenity skips and sites on litter bins and in other suitable locations (e.g. in lay-bys, post offices, town halls or on local authority vehicles (Plate 12)). Additionally we **recommend** that civic amenity sites should be open throughout the day, especially at weekends. We received evidence from one waste disposal authority that they regarded the prevention of fly tipping by leaving their sites open but unmanned in the afternoon at weekends as adequate recompense for any unauthorised (and hence free) use during these periods by small builders and other commercial users. We consider that there is much to commend this view, provided that safety is kept in mind.

6.24 The fly tipping of industrial waste has more serious implications for the urban environment. We consider that the registration of waste transporters and the placing of a responsibility on the waste producer (paragraphs 8.29 and 8.21) will provide enforcement officers with effective sanctions against fly tippers. We understand that the origin of industrial waste can often be determined. When our recommendations are implemented, a producer will be liable to prosecution in respect of any of his waste that is found to have been fly tipped, unless he is able to show that he took all proper care and used a registered transporter who he had reason to suppose was competent and responsible. In this event the waste transporter, too, would be liable to prosecution and risk losing his registration. At present a waste producer cannot generally be held responsible for his waste once it has left his hands (unless it is special waste, to which the consignment note procedure applies), and he is therefore not required to have a detailed knowledge of, or to reveal the identity of, any waste transporter he employs.

6.25 In parallel with these general recommendations, there is much that could be done at local level. Local authorities could, for instance, see that vacant sites which they own and which may attract fly tipping are securely fenced or made otherwise inaccessible; local authorities and the police could stimulate public involvement, possibly using devices such as special telephone lines where citizens could report incidents in confidence and, by thus drawing on public good will, improve the chances of successful prosecutions; and collection authorities could try to arrange for rapid removal of any fly tipped wastes, to avoid their acting as an attraction for further accumulations. Differing circumstances will point to differing solutions, which are best decided upon locally.

Abandoned vehicles

6.26 One particular aspect of dumping is the problem of abandoned vehicles. There is general agreement among the local authority associations and the Institution of Environmental Health Officers that existing legislation is adequate but that the procedure for identifying vehicle keepers from licence plates is unnecessarily slow. We therefore **recommend** that appropriately designated local authority staff should have immediate access, comparable to police access, to the Department of Transport's Driver and Vehicle Licensing Centre data for the purposes of dealing with vehicles which appear to have been abandoned.

Medical and health care wastes

6.27 As we described in Chapter II, medical wastes arise from hospitals (National Health Service and private), health centres and clinics, general practioners' surgeries and dental surgeries, and from domestic premises, especially where patients with long term illnesses (e.g. diabetes) administer regular treatments themselves. Wastes with similar characteristics can also arise from veterinary surgeries. Of the several categories of wastes arising from these sources two groups are of special concern to us: the pathological and infectious wastes, and sharps.

6.28 We have not attempted a thorough survey of the collection, segregation and disposal practices for health care wastes, but we have noted the reports of the Working Party on the Disposal of Clinical Wastes in the London area([113,114]) and have received evidence of the practices for disposal of wastes arising from hospitals in the West Midlands, of the results of an informal survey in one city of the waste disposal practices of doctors' surgeries and health centres, and of the disposal practices used in one group of private hospitals. The first two pieces of evidence in particular have caused us considerable concern.

6.29 Although both the Health and Safety Commission (HSC)([55]) and the Department of the Environment([115]) have published guides to the management of medical wastes it is apparent that these are often not precisely followed by hospitals, clinics and surgeries. The evidence from the private hospital group suggests that arrangements for segregation and disposal of wastes are generally well managed, although the use of differently colour coded sacks for the same type of waste in different hospitals does make us wonder if the HSC guidelines are being very closely followed.

6.30 The evidence relating to the NHS hospitals is less satisfactory in that the waste disposal authority reported that their officers had to insist upon proper segregation of wastes, although most hospitals segregated 'to a greater or lesser extent'. Further, the West Midlands survey found that while some hospitals had purpose-built incinerators with excess capacity, others had no disposal facilities, and yet the Regional Health Authority apparently had no waste disposal plan and made little attempt to co-ordinate waste disposal among the different hospitals. We discuss the operation of hospital incinerators in Chapter VII.

6.31 The responses to the informal survey of health centres and doctors' surgeries showed a remarkable degree of variation in waste disposal practices. All those surveyed segregated infectious wastes into colour coded plastic bags, but while most reported that the bags went to hospital or health centre incinerators, one reported that they were put for collection with ordinary wastes, and another that they were 'removed by the cleaners'. Sharps were always segregated into safe boxes and, except for one surgery, incinerated, the exception having its sharps collected with normal waste by agreement with the City Council. Pharmaceuticals were flushed to sewers, collected by the local chemist, or incinerated. In general very little advice was given to patients who had to treat themselves at home, although most diabetics who needed syringes were given safety boxes for them. From this informal survey it was apparent that little positive thought was being given to waste disposal by surgery staff, and little advice was being provided for patients.

6.32 Under the Health and Safety at Work etc. Act 1974 employers have a general responsibility to ensure the health and safety of their employees and others who may be affected by the undertaking, and employees have a similar responsibility for their own actions and their consequences. However, we think that a more positive, and specific, attitude to the disposal of health care wastes should be adopted and we therefore **recommend** that all Regional Health Authorities should prepare and implement waste disposal plans that match the arisings and the disposal facilities in health care establishments. We also **recommend** that publicity should be given by the Department of Health and Social Security and the Scottish Home and Health Department through health authorities to the guidelines and code of practice prepared by the Health and Safety Commission and the Department of the Environment, so that community health care establishments are made aware of good practices which can then be enforced. Similarly we **recommend** that publicity material prepared by the Health Departments should be made available for doctors and nurses in the community to give to patients who may have to dispose of clinical wastes.

Storage of wastes and the duty of care

6.33 Throughout this Report we have been concerned that materials consigned to the waste stream should not be allowed to escape to cause pollution of the environment. In Chapter VII we have tried to assess the comparative security of certain major disposal routes available. Storage of wastes implies temporary accumulation, with postponement of decisions on final use or disposal. When storage is well planned, well managed and is undertaken for a specific purpose, it can be an acceptable interim measure. But storage which occurs by default or as a means of avoiding having to dispose of wastes in an acceptable manner is to be deplored. The worst example of this is the accumulation of wastes on industrial premises, followed by their abandonment (Plate 14), often in the wake of the company ceasing to trade. In most cases the costs of disposal have then to be borne by the local community through the waste disposal authority. There is thus the risk that by storing waste the polluter may avoid paying, because the costs of final disposal become externalised and dissociated from the process which gave rise to the waste in the first place.

6.34 The producer's responsibility for ensuring that wastes are consigned to a proper disposal route - the duty of care which runs as a theme through this Report - applies as much to storage as it does to other aspects of waste handling. The producer must see that transfer and temporary storage of wastes are undertaken by a competent operator, whether the operator is part of his own organisation or a contractor. We appreciate that temporary storage is an inevitable practice in certain circumstances, for instance, where the object is to accumulate an economic quantity of waste for disposal or when the disposal route can accommodate only a limited quantity for destruction at a time. These practices are only acceptable provided, first, they do not lead to indiscriminate accumulations and, secondly, measures for the ultimate disposal of the wastes have been ensured. In the past casual accumulations have been the cause of much of our contaminated land (paragraphs 2.47 - 2.56).

6.35 When wastes are stored there is a need for good record keeping so that the nature and extent of the waste and any associated hazard may be readily identified[198]. Under the Control of Pollution (Special Waste) Regulations 1980, a producer of special waste is required to notify the waste disposal authority when he consigns that waste for disposal. There is no requirement for notification while the waste is stored. We believe that tighter controls are needed over the storage of special wastes. We therefore **recommend** that the Control of Pollution (Special Waste) Regulations should be amended to require waste producers to notify waste disposal authorities of all consignments of special waste to storage.

Transport of wastes

6.36 Throughout this Report we have stressed the need for careful and competent handling of wastes to avoid the risk of damaging the environment. In saying this we recognise that waste differs from raw materials and manufactured products in having little or no perceived value (Chapter I), and by virtue of this characteristic may leave the confines of the secure waste stream to be abandoned at large in the environment (see paragraphs 6.18-6.25). To avoid such indiscriminate abandonment we make recommendations in Chapter VIII for the registration of waste transporters. In doing so we are partly supporting the recommendation of the House of Lords Select Committee on Science and Technology([5]) that a licensing system be introduced, but are suggesting that registration combined with enhanced penalties for infringements of the system should suffice.

6.37 Another of our concerns is that the level of care required in handling any material should be appropriate to the hazards, whether the material is waste or not. In Chapter VIII we propose a mechanism for the registration system for transporters of waste as an addition to the existing legal arrangements governing the transport of hazardous goods in the UK.

Inland transport

6.38 The responsibility of waste producers to consign their wastes to competent transporters and handlers means that the receiving companies must ensure that all their operatives are competent and properly trained. For road transport, drivers must know what action is required to maintain the safety of the environment in the event of accident, as well as knowing how to transfer the waste safely to and from their vehicles in the course of normal disposal. Any codes of practice (or relevant extracts from them) that identify the hazards associated with specific materials, the appropriate labelling required, and the appropriate precautionary measures to offset hazards that are relevant to the transported material must be available to the driver. We consider that any wastes that are hazardous must be assigned to an appropriate category of the relevant hazard code, even though they may be of variable or poorly defined composition, because they contain mixed or diluted constituents. Similar provision must be made for the training of workers involved in handling wastes consigned to transport by rail or inland waterways.

6.39 The transport of spent nuclear fuel by rail has continued to cause concern([1]) and in its Sixth Report the Commission commented on the need for a flask that could withstand a direct blow at the maximum speed of a train([31]). The integrity of the flasks in which the spent fuel is transported was tested in an experimental crash in July 1984. The flask was not breached([116]) and the validity of the test has been widely accepted([117]). However we note a report that very low level contamination has been detected on both flasks and rolling stock used in the routine transport of spent nuclear fuel([118]).

6.40 Whatever the selected mode of transport for wastes, the vehicles used for the task must be appropriately designed to maintain the security of the waste. In this context we commend the new types of barge which have been introduced for transporting London's municipal wastes down the Thames from urban transfer stations to rural landfill sites (Plate 17) and which are designed to maintain the security of the waste stream more effectively. We similarly commend the use of dedicated trains with enclosed containers or covered rail wagons to transport wastes (Plate 18) in bulk to landfills in, for instance, Bedfordshire.These systems are greatly superior to loosely covered (or uncovered) rail trucks, barges or vehicles, which increase the risk of litter becoming dispersed in the environment. Use of rail or water transport reduces the likelihood that people living near transfer stations and landfill sites will suffer from traffic nuisance. This nuisance is one aspect of the loss of amenity which must be taken into account when the location of landfill sites and transfer stations is considered under the planning process. It demonstrates the need for planning officers and waste disposal officers to work closely together at the preliminary stages of any waste disposal development. We discuss this more fully in Chapter IX.

Marine transport

6.41 We are principally concerned here with the problem of material either intentionally or accidentally released from ships at sea which ultimately reaches coastal waters and the shoreline, but we also consider the discharge of sewage from ships, dealing in this chapter with the discharge of sewage generated within the vessel. (The bulk disposal of land-derived sewage at sea is discussed in Chapter VII.)

6.42 It is of particular concern to us to learn from a recent KBTG report[102] that between September 1982 and August 1983 some 254 packages were washed up on to British shores containing, in 131 cases, materials listed in the International Maritime Dangerous Goods (IMDG) Code[119], and, in a further 122, some other substances of at least medium danger. The hazardous materials not listed in the IMDG Code included refined petroleum products, flammable substances, corrosives and poisons. While over half of these items were found on beaches during the winter months, and therefore probably came from accidental losses of deck cargoes in stormy weather, nearly 20% were found during the summer months, when the risk to holidaymakers is obviously greater. Many of the packages containing dangerous goods or suspected dangerous goods were inadequately labelled, lacking either an appropriate hazard symbol or identification of their contents. That these packages should be washed up, often so poorly labelled, demonstrates that the IMDG Code is not being fully and properly implemented. These packages come from ships of many nations.

6.43 We have been informed that there is no statutory requirement for seamen and deck officers to be specifically trained in the handling and stowage of packaged dangerous goods, but we are aware of the UK's active participation in the activities of the International Maritime Organisation and, in particular, in the development of the IMDG Code[119] and its promulgation throughout the shipping industries of the world. As far as British ships are concerned, relevant information and guidance on these matters is provided in Merchant Shipping Notices (M-Notices), now issued by the Department of Transport[120]. Whilst special training is a matter for the shipping industry's discretion, we would expect the health risks of packaged dangerous goods to be part of the industry's general concern for the safety of its vessels and the welfare of its crews. We **recommend** that the British shipping industry should lay renewed stress on the proper handling and security of packaged dangerous goods and that the Department of Transport should review the adequacy of extant Merchant Shipping Notices on this matter.

6.44 Nothing that we have written implies a reduction in the responsibility of waste producers, when consigning packaged wastes for sea transport, to label the containers clearly so as to give precise information on their contents and on any associated hazards. The implementation of Annex III of the International Convention for the Prevention of Pollution from Ships (MARPOL)[121], which sets out regulations for the prevention of pollution by packaged harmful substances, would both affirm and aid the enforcement of this responsibility. We therefore **recommend** that the Government should work towards ratification of Annex III of the MARPOL Convention at the earliest possible date.

6.45 In addition to the packaged dangerous goods, over 2,000 pyrotechnics - distress flares, smoke and flame making devices - were found in the KBTG survey, some of military origin, and almost 200 items of munitions or associated equipment (detonators, floats etc.) were also reported. The pyrotechnics included date-stamped materials, which suggests that, having reached the end of their serviceable life, they had been dumped overboard[122], together with other wastes of more domestic origin. Military pyrotechnics are more likely to have been used in exercises, and in many cases empty containers from which the contents that had been used were found. Munitions present a lethal risk, but most derive from accidental losses, or deliberate dumping at a time when controls were less strict than they have been for the past two decades, and KBTG report that the numbers of munitions recovered annually from beaches has been decreasing for the past few years.

6.46 In addition to operational wastes, such as outdated safety flares, ships dispose of domestic refuse into the sea. If Annex V of the MARPOL Convention[121] were ratified and implemented, disposal of the following categories of refuse overboard would be prohibited or restricted:

    (a)   all plastics (including synthetic ropes and nets and garbage bags);

(b)   dunnage, lining and packaging materials that will float, within 25 nautical miles of the nearest land; and

(c)   food wastes and other garbage, including paper products, glass, rags, metal, bottles and crockery, within 12 nautical miles of the nearest land (except where ground to less than 25 mm, when the distance to land can be as little as 3 nautical miles).

Disposal would also be prohibited within 500 metres of fixed or floating platforms engaged in exploration for or exploitation of the sea bed mineral resources (except food wastes where ground to 25 mm or less). We welcome the statement in the Government's response([123]) to the Commission's Tenth Report that the British shipping industry is recommended to comply voluntarily with the provisions of Annex V of MARPOL, and that there is positive response from shipowners and ferry operators. We also note the Government's comment that ratification of Annex V is being actively discussed in IMO. However such voluntary compliance can only be recommended in this matter for British ships and without international ratification of Annex V there is little or no control on ships from other countries. We therefore **recommend** that the Government should press for ratification of Annex V of MARPOL at the earliest possible date.

6.47 We find it opportune to make reference here to Annex IV of MARPOL, which concerns the discharge of sewage from ships. This annex would prohibit most ships from discharging sewage except:

(a)   comminuted and disinfected sewage at a minimum distance of 4 nautical miles from land;

(b)   sewage not comminuted or disinfected at least 12 nautical miles from land;

(c)   sewage treated on board in approved plant, which does not produce floating solids or discolouration of the surrounding water; and

(d)   in waters under the jurisdiction of a state with less stringent requirements.

These provisions would reduce the risk of sewage from ships contaminating British beaches, and we therefore **recommend** that the Government works towards ratification of Annex IV of MARPOL. (See also paragraph 7.49.)

Import and export of wastes

6.48 The international transport of wastes invariably poses some risks to the security of the waste stream, but provided proper care is taken we consider that the advantages of using a more appropriate disposal facility than the one available locally can justify international trade in waste. From the national point of view there can be no objection to the importation of waste that can be disposed of harmlessly by a method that in no way restricts the capacity of the environment to receive further waste (e.g. destruction by incineration).

However, we consider that wastes that are hazardous should not be exported without the prior informed consent of the receiving country. Within the European Community this is already provided for under the terms of the recent EC Directive on the transfrontier shipment of hazardous waste[124]. We note that within the framework of OECD[125-127] progress has been made towards a wider agreement, likely to be reached during 1987, which would embody the principles that wastes with hazardous characteristics can properly be exported and imported provided that they are accompanied by adequate information, that they are travelling to an environmentally acceptable destination, and that the receiving country has given prior consent.

CHAPTER VII

ULTIMATE DISPOSAL ROUTES FOR WASTES

Introduction

7.1 We now consider the various routes that can be used for the disposal or destruction of wastes and the associated potential risks of pollution. We have already referred to the lack of quantitative information on the waste stream (Chapter II); and the relative importance of the different disposal routes can be assessed only in general terms. (Figure 7.1a-c).

Landfill

7.2 Landfill - the deposition of wastes *en masse* in or on the ground - is currently the most commonly used waste disposal route in Britain, and in most areas it is also the cheapest. Normally the cavity, such as a quarry or sand and gravel pit, is filled to slightly above the original ground level in order to allow for settlement. In a few cases planning approval has been given for landfill sites to have final contours above previous ground levels. Higher finished levels are permitted in several countries, especially West Germany and the Netherlands, where the deposits are known somewhat inappropriately as 'waste mountains'.

7.3 Provided that normal good practices are followed we see no technical reasons why the finished level of a landfill site should not be substantially above the original ground level. Indeed such an arrangement has some advantages, including the more efficient use of land, and if sensitively contoured can be visually attractive. We **recommend** that planning and waste disposal authorities should always consider the possible advantages of permitting deposition to continue to above original ground levels.

7.4 The Department of the Environment's Landfill Practices Review Group, set up in 1982, has prepared a report, of which we have seen a detailed summary([7]). The report itself, when published, will be a comprehensive review of the subject, including legislative controls, site selection and preparation, the landfill operation itself, and subsequent restoration. We consider that the report will achieve its objective of being a sound guide to procedures and practices, and we therefore limit our observations to issues on which we wish to offer additional comment and to make recommendations.

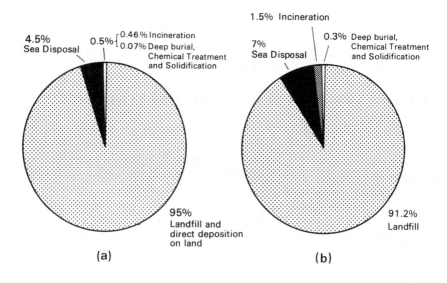

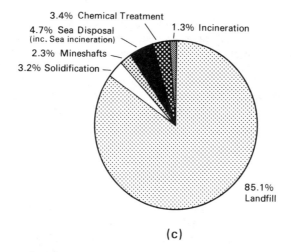

Figure 7.1 Waste disposal routes used in the UK

(a) Total waste arisings including land deposition of wastes not consigned to waste disposal sites: 482.25 million tonnes/year; municipal wastes including medical wastes, controlled industrial (including special) wastes, dredged spoil, sewage, mineral wastes and agricultural wastes.

(b) Municipal including medical wastes, and controlled industrial wastes and sewage sludge only: 148.25 million tonnes/year.

(c) Hazardous wastes in England and Wales only: 4.4 million tonnes/year - drawn from HWI Report([17]).

Leachate generation and control

7.5 Leachate liquors are generated in landfills both as the degradation products of the wastes, whether municipal, industrial or both, and through the percolation of rain, surface or ground water through the mass of waste. These liquors present environmental risks in that they may flow from the landfill site to contaminate ground or surface waters (Plate 22). There are several published accounts of the analyses of leachates[4,128-132]; nevertheless we have a very fragmentary picture of their chemical composition and the precise nature of the chemical and biological processes that give rise to them.

7.6 Landfill sites may be divided into two broad categories according to the overall approach to leachate: non-containment and containment sites. Non-containment sites do not attempt to prevent leachate from percolating to the environment, and the prevention of pollution depends on the attenuation and diluting mechanisms operating both within the waste and in the strata beneath and adjacent to the landfill site. Uncertainty about the attenuation mechanisms[128-132, 134] precludes accurate prediction of the pollution risk.

7.7 In containment sites the aim is to isolate the leachate from the environment either by making use of geological strata of naturally low permeability to prevent leachate percolation, or by lining sites artificially, either with clay or with man-made material. In some cases a combination of synthetic material and clay can be used. By whatever means the containment site prevents leachate from escaping to the environment, it will always need to be capped, on completion of landfilling, by material which is impermeable or of very low permeability, in order to prevent rain or surface water from saturating the wastes. Capping layers for landfill are usually clay, contoured to encourage water to run off. Consideration should be given as to whether subsequent operations, such as tree planting, might breach the capping layer. In many containment sites some provision for extracting the leachate in a controlled manner, for treatment or discharge to a watercourse or sewer, is also required by the site licence. Discharge to a watercourse or sewer is permitted only with the consent of the relevant water authority, who can lay down quality standards for the discharged liquor.

7.8 Landfill liners made of natural soils may be either local materials of low permeability (clays) or imported materials - either clays from other sites or materials such as bentonite, a natural clay found in only a few places, which has the property of swelling when wetted, thus creating an almost impermeable seal. These natural materials must be engineered to provide both adequate cover for the base of the landfill and a sealing layer around the sides of the site to prevent lateral migration of leachate. Clay soils do not entirely prevent leachate percolation, but they have very low permeabilities and high capacities for adsorption of components of the leachate solutions. Until the adsorptive capacity of the liners has been saturated, leachate which does emerge through clay liners will therefore be of considerably lower strength than raw leachate from the waste, and thus less likely to cause severe pollution in groundwater. However it does not appear to be possible to predict the amount and strength of leachate that might be generated, nor over how long a period it will be generated, nor is it possible therefore to predict how thick a clay liner must be to ensure sufficient adsorptive capacity for the period of leachate generation.

7.9 Synthetic landfill liners([135]), usually made from bitumen, butyl rubber or various types of plastics, are normally either of much lower permeability than clay or impermeable and are therefore able to prevent leachate percolation altogether, but in general they have no adsorptive capacity (some organic molecules might tend to be adsorbed but this could impair the qualities of the liner). Synthetic liners are flexible, but are normally protected by clay and sand layers both above and below them to prevent puncturing by rocks or refuse. Drainage facilities for leachate collection can be incorporated in these protective layers. There is little published work on the life and performance of synthetic liners: manufacturers suggest a life of some 25-30 years, but this has not yet been proved in practice. In the United States where, especially for hazardous waste landfills, a common practice is to use two synthetic liners with a permeable layer between them which can house sensors to identify any leachate percolation, monitoring has shown that in several sites leachate does penetrate the upper liner([136]). There is no simple remedy for such leakage apart from ensuring that contaminated water is isolated from the public water supply.

7.10 Collected leachate can be treated on site by either biological or physico-chemical methods([137]). Biological teatments include spraying leachate back on to the landfill, thus allowing evaporation to reduce its volume and encouraging continuing degradation by the biota in the landfill, or alternatively aerobic or anaerobic digestion in specially designed plant. The evidence we have seen leads us to conclude that this is an area where continuing research is necessary to establish efficient and predictable microbiological treatment of leachate. Physico-chemical methods of leachate treatment also often require special plant, and it may thus be most effective to operate them in conjunction with biological treatments. Transfer of leachate to sewer, which may happen only with the water authority's consent, passes the requirement for any further treatment to the water industry and its treatment works.

7.11 It is apparent from paragraphs 7.5 to 7.10 that although much has been learned about leachate generation and control in landfills, much remains to be done. We therefore endorse the continuing programme of research into the generation and control of landfill leachates, and into the attenuation properties of landfill sites (see Chapter XI). This research should lead to better understanding which will contribute to the development of satisfactory standards for leachate control in landfill practice.

7.12 Leachate which is not extracted in a controlled manner but which is allowed to accumulate within the site is a potential risk to the environment, should the site be subsequently disturbed or the sealing properties of the site lining and capping material deteriorate. Sudden release of contained liquors could well have a more deleterious effect on ground or surface water than gradual leakage. We therefore **recommend** that reliance should never be placed on the long-term containment of leachate, which instead should be extracted and processed so that containment failure cannot lead to pollution of an aquifer.

Methane generation, control and exploitation

7.13 Gases are generated by biological degradation processes. In the early stages of decomposition, while aerobic conditions prevail, these are principally carbon dioxide and hydrogen. This phase is usually shortlived (in comparison with the period of waste deposition at the site) and is followed by anaerobic decomposition which produces a mixture of gases known as landfill gas. This contains up to 65% methane and is often contaminated with unpleasant smelling trace gases. Methane can cause damage to vegetation and, in confined locations such as culverts, can present risks of explosion or asphyxiation. Since gases can migrate laterally as well as vertically the risks may not be confined to the landfill site itself.

7.14 The growing number of large landfill sites is increasing the opportunities to exploit methane as an energy resource([138,139]): for instance, London Brick Landfill Ltd are firing a kiln with methane drawn from the Stewarby landfill site (an exhaused brick pit); the Greater London Council and National Smokeless Fuels Ltd (a subsidiary of the National Coal Board) are selling methane from the Aveley landfill site (Plate 23) to Thames Board Ltd to fire factory boilers([140,141]). A study([142]) commissioned by the Energy Technology Support Unit of the Department of Energy suggests that about 20-25 large landfill sites in the UK could be identified as having potential local users for the landfill gas. However the majority of sites at which landfill gas is evolved may never be suitable for energy recovery because uncertainties in yields of gas and the costs of processes([2,39]) may well inhibit this development. It follows that although the efficient collection of methane for combustion and energy recovery should eliminate the risk of pollution, we cannot rely on this as a solution at all sites.

7.15 We consider that the primary objective in controlling methane should be the reduction of pollution, but we would encourage mitigating the cost of control by exploiting the energy content of the methane where this is practicable. We **recommend** that all licences for new landfill sites should require provision for adequate control of methane both during and after the period of deposition of wastes.

Co-disposal

7.16 'Co-disposal' is a term which lacks precision. It is generally used to refer to the deposition of municipal and certain types of industrial waste together in a single landfill site. The use of inert materials from building and other industries for cover or road making in municipal landfill sites is not normally termed co-disposal. The recommended practice is that domestic wastes should have been deposited some time (perhaps 5 years) in advance of the deposition of industrial wastes. This is intended to ensure that the effect of this combined disposal on groundwater, or on the environment in general, is not affected by the inhibition of the degradation processes in domestic wastes which the industrial wastes might cause in freshly deposited domestic wastes.

7.17 In the past many of the industrial wastes now co-disposed might have been landfilled in factory tips([33]), but with the introduction, through the Control of Pollution Act 1974, of waste disposal site licensing, much more industrial waste is now disposed of away from factory premises. Combined disposal of two (or more) wastes in a single waste disposal site offers the opportunity to use the characteristics of the different wastes to offset each other's potential for pollution. The report of the Department of the Environment's co-operative programme of research on the behaviour of hazardous wastes in landfill sites([4]) stated that 'co-disposal of domestic and industrial wastes should be carried out in order to optimise the effects of the attenuating processes'; and considerable stress was laid on selecting appropriate industrial wastes for such operations and ensuring that the adsorptive capacity of the domestic waste was not exceeded. Although there has not been sufficient investigation of co-disposal sites([39,134]), the data available on leachates from them show that they are similiar to leachates from municipal landfills([132]). Co-disposal practice in the UK has been criticised on the grounds that the inclusion of industrial wastes with municipal waste increases the risks of groundwater pollution, especially in non-containment landfill sites.

7.18 We conclude that, for many industrial wastes, properly managed co-disposal is an environmentally acceptable option in containment sites (see paragraph 7.7). However we are concerned that inappropriate materials are sometimes admitted to co-disposal and that there is still some lack of knowledge about the processes involved and their long-term effects on the environment (see also Chapter XI).

7.19 The materials for which we consider landfill inappropriate include acid tars, volatile and flammable organic liquids and drummed wastes. Acid tars are particularly persistent, and do not degrade readily in landfills. We consider incineration of flammable organic liquids is a more acceptable disposal route (see also paragraph 7.29), where the liquids can serve as fuel and the process is less likely to lead to pollution. Drummed wastes are temporarily inaccessible to the degradation processes but when, sooner or later, the drums are ruptured or corrode a very high concentration of the contained waste is exposed. In line with the Hazardous Waste Inspectorate's recommendations, we therefore **recommend** that alternative methods of disposing of acid tars should be encouraged; that for volatile and flammable organic liquids alternative disposal routes such as incineration be used rather than landfill; and that drummed wastes should not normally be landfilled.

Aftercare provisions

7.20 Landfill sites have a permanent presence in the environment and continuing influence on it. Because of the long-term nature of some of the biological degradation processes which work upon the deposited wastes producing leachate and landfill gas, the risk of damage to the environment continues after the period of active deposition. This could stem from rupture of a landfill liner allowing contained leachate to escape and contaminate either ground or surface water, or from the accumulation and migration of methane.

7.21 However, the licence holder for a disposal site is responsible for the safety and security of the site and the landfilled wastes only while the site licence is current (unless he continues to be the landowner after the licence or operating period). Indeed the licence can be surrendered to the waste disposal authority before the landfilling operation is complete, leaving the landowner with responsibility for the safety of the site (Chapter VIII). This short-term tenure of responsibility for the site operator contrasts strongly with the long duration of landfill degradation processes and the associated risks to the environment. As the law stands at present, if a pollution incident occurs after landfill operations have ceased, the costs of dealing with it cannot be claimed from the site operator unless he is the landowner.

7.22 We **recommend** that planning and licensing authorities should include among site licence conditions means for ensuring site aftercare. We discuss the administrative arrangements of site licences more fully in Chapters VIII and IX.

Standards of site management

7.23 The evidence we received caused us to be concerned at the variability in standards of site management and the probability that wastes inappropriate to landfill are being disposed of in this way. The application of the standard procedures for a properly managed site (Plate 20), as recommended by the Landfill Practices Review Group[7], entails certain costs (Table 7.1); in all but exceptionally large sites these will be in excess of £4 per tonne, which is itself low in comparison with the charges faced by industry and local authorities in some other industrial countries (Table 7.2). However, lower figures appear in statistical returns[44], and we have been told of sites accepting waste at little more than £2 per tonne. Such low charges could be a further indication that standards may not be adequate. The Hazardous Waste Inspectorate's First Report[17] confirmed our anxieties and showed that practices at some landfill sites are very unsatisfactory (Plate 21) and likely to cause pollution now or in the future. Proper procedures should be imposed by the site licence conditions, practised by the site management and enforced by the regulatory authorities. (See also our discussion and recommendations for a single pollution inspectorate in Chapter IX). We **recommend** that waste disposal authorities should ensure that they are imposing appropriate conditions on all sites in their areas, whether their own or those of independent operators.

TABLE 7.1

Recent landfill charges in the UK based on good practice([143]), arbitration([144]) and list prices([17]), with comparative overseas data([2,145,146]).

Basis of charge or estimate	*Charge/tonne*
United Kingdom:	
Theoretical calculations based on good practices for a range of site conditions:	
Very large sites (100,000-250,000 tonnes/year)	£ 3.50-£ 6.65
Medium sites (50,000 tonnes/year)	£ 6.90-£ 9.40
Small sites (25,000 tonnes/year)	£ 9.00-£12.30
Recent arbitration award (very large site)	£ 5.50
Quoted list prices - solid waste	£ 2.50 (discounted to £ 1.50)
Overseas costs:	
Germany	£10.00-£11.00
Japan	£15.00-£20.00
Netherlands	£ 3.00-£ 4.00

TABLE 7.2

Typical hazardous waste landfill charges in the UK (1984)([17]) and the US (1985)([147])

Waste type	*List price/tonne (Discount price for large quantities)*
United Kingdom:	
Solid hazardous waste	£ 5.00 (£2.80)
Neutral sludges	£14.00 (£7.00)
Liquid hazardous waste	£18.00 (£8.00)
United States:	
Solid hazardous wastes liquids or drummed wastes	£50.00-£65.00* surcharge added

* At exchange rate of $1.36 to £1.

Burning wastes

7.24 The treatment of wastes by burning is an ancient practice, and bonfires have surely been a means of waste disposal for thousands of years. Well managed incineration can serve several purposes: combustion will destroy some wastes; the volume and weight of waste can be reduced significantly, thus leaving smaller quantities of residual ash for disposal by landfilling; and these residues should be sterile. Incineration can present some risks to the environment: for instance, emissions from incinerator stacks can be high in acidic gases if large quantitites of waste containing chlorine or sulphur compounds are burnt; and dust or particulates can be emitted to the atmosphere. In the following sections we discuss environmental aspects of the combustion of municipal and industrial wastes, incineration at sea, incineration of hospital wastes, and straw burning.

Municipal incinerators

7.25 Incineration of municipal refuse in the UK is the primary treatment for some 10% of total arisings: this is just less than 2 million tonnes/year. Greater proportions of municipal refuse are incinerated elsewhere: for example 46% in Japan and 70% in Switzerland and Denmark. Residues from incineration, representing between 25% and 50% of the original weight (depending on the amount of ferrous scrap removed) but usually only 10%-25% of the original volume, consist of ash and non-combustible material (metals etc.) and normally go to landfill. Incineration clearly reduces the volume of landfill space required, although space is required for the incineration plants. It has been suggested that disused power stations would provide suitable sites for new incinerators in many urban areas[148]. In some installations the opportunity to extract ferrous and non-ferrous metals from the residues as they emerge from the incinerator is taken, but the cost of doing this is not always covered by the income from the sale of the scrap metal. The proportional decrease in the ash content and increase in the plastics and paper content of municipal refuse since the 1930s has raised its calorific value and encouraged some waste disposal authorities to recover and utilise the energy of the refuse, usually as hot water or steam, or as heat sources for housing (district heating schemes) or industry (space heating or process heat). These uses provide income which can be offset against the high capital and running costs of incinerators. We have discussed this aspect already in Chapter V when we dealt with energy from waste.

7.26 Municipal waste incinerators are generally operated with furnace temperatures between 800°C and 1100°C. Exhaust gases are usually quenched to around 300°C and various gas cleaning devices are used to reduce emissions of particulates, chlorides and sulphur oxides. The emissions, and the effect on emissions of altering some process parameters, have been investigated for several incinerators in the UK[149]. These investigations showed that emission rates for particulates, sulphur dioxide and hydrogen chloride were all higher

89

than for municipal incinerators in the United States. The major reason suggested for this difference is the widespread use in the US of wet flue gas scrubbing systems to clean the flue gases. The municipal incinerator that we visited in Düsseldorf was replacing a dry gas cleaning system with wet scrubbing equipment to reduce the particulate emissions. We have been told that one of the main causes of the recent closure of the municipal incinerator in Edinburgh was the high emission rate of particulates.

7.27 The high levels of hydrogen chloride emissions may be a particular cause of concern, for they are much higher than the emissions which would be expected from the combustion of equivalent quantities of fossil fuels. Furthermore, there has been some public concern (paragraphs 1.18-1.20 and the boxes on pages 7-9) about the risks of municipal wastes generating emissions of dioxins (polychlorinated dibenzo-dioxins — PCDD) with hydrogen chloride released from chlorinated plastics (especially PVC) as a precursor for dioxin formation. This concern has been particularly strong in the United States and in the Federal Republic of Germany, but in the UK it has grown in significance recently with the well-publicised controversy surrounding the incinerators operated by Re-Chem International Ltd at Bonnybridge, Scotland (now closed) and Pontypool, Wales. We have not considered it appropriate in this Report to discuss in detail those particular cases, which have in any case been investigated by others([150,151]) and are the subject of continuing study([152]). The overall conclusion to be drawn from the theoretical and practical work on dioxin formation during combustion of municipal refuse (see boxes on pages 91 and 92) is that while there is a small risk that the precursors could exist in the stack gases, this risk of emissions could be reduced to insignificant levels by operating incinerators with furnace temperatures in excess of 1000°C, and ensuring that an adequate air supply is always well mixed with the refuse. We are aware that the nature of municipal refuse, which has variable moisture content, makes it very difficult for municipal incinerators to maintain precise combustion conditions.

7.28 There is a clear need for continuing research in this area, both monitoring actual emissions from UK incinerators and in assessing the operating conditions which are required to preclude significant formation of dioxins. We are encouraged to see that the current DoE funded research programme includes work on the gaseous emissions from the incineration of refuse, and hope that this will be concerned both with direct incineration and with emissions from waste derived fuel (Chapter V). We conclude that there is a strong case for reviewing the technology available internationally for incineration and flue gas cleaning, and the mode of operation of municipal incinerators. We **recommend** that the Department of the Environment should set up an Incineration Practices Review Group, whose report would lead to the preparation of standards for the operation of incineration plants.

PCBs

Where do they come from? How widespread are they?
Commercial production of PCBs in the US started in 1929, but several countries have now ceased manufacture of PCBs (e.g. Japan - 1976; UK - 1978; US - 1979; FRG - 1983; Italy - 1984), however there continues to be production in France and Spain. Those countries which have banned PCB manufacture are also trying to restrict their use and also their further dispersion through the environment. However there is evidence accumulating that PCBs are already widely dispersed through the environment with studies from Sweden[153] and the Mediterranean[154] demonstrating their presence in lacustrine and marine sediments. In Canada the use of PCBs is now regulated under the Environmental Contaminants Act and in 1978 guidelines[155,156] on the management of wastes containing PCBs were published.

How can they be destroyed?
Although there is some evidence[157] that PCBs can both be generated and degraded by biochemical or photochemical processes in the natural environment, intentional destruction by man is normally achieved by incineration. The incineration conditions required to ensure virtually complete destruction include sufficiently high temperature, sufficient residence time and sufficient oxygen.
The US recommended conditions for commercial incinerators
are: 2 seconds residence time at 1200°C, with 3% excess oxygen or
    1.5 seconds residence time at 1600°C, with 2% excess oxygen.
The requirements of the West German Technical Guide Line for Clean Air (T.A.Luft) specify a residence time of 0.3 seconds at temperatures of at least 1200°C.

The incineration of toxic industrial waste

7.29 High temperature incineration, followed when appropriate by removing dust and washing the gaseous products, is a safe and effective way of destroying toxic organic waste*, mainly from the chemical industry. The critical operating requirements are: high temperature, excess of oxygen well mixed with the feed and adequate residence time in the hot zone. The precise conditions will depend on the nature of the materials that are to be burnt and must, of course, be established for any substance or mixture before substantial quantities are incinerated. Preliminary tests at laboratory scale, though not conclusive, will provide a good guide but analyses of flue gas during full-scale trial incineration are also necessary. The composition of the ash should also be checked especially if the feed contains organo-metallics. It follows that the composition of all materials fed to the incinerator should be known and the rate of feed should be carefully controlled. Some wastes which are best treated

---

* Organic chemicals are those in which the molecular skeleton is essentially carbon.

in an incinerator do not themselves have sufficient fuel value and it is therefore desirable that flammable organic liquid wastes should be consigned to incineration, as burning them can help to avoid the wasteful use of supplementary fuels, and to ensure adequate combustion of the low calorific value wastes (see also paragraph 7.19).

DIOXINS AND FURANS

Where do they come from?

The possible sources of dioxin and furans in the environment include[18]:

(i) manufacture and use of chlorophenols, especially in the wood processing/treatment industries;

(ii) the combustion of organic materials including fossil fuels, wood in wood stoves and bonfires, cigarettes and municipal wastes;

(iii) herbicide manufacture and use (specifically 2,4,5-T and 2,4-D) which is a significant source of di-, tri- and tetra CDDs, although these are not thought to be particularly toxic.

The widespread distribution of dioxins in the environment is evidenced by their identification in remote locations[158], which in turn leads to the conclusion that atmospheric transport is a significant distributor and disperser for dioxins, furans and, indeed, PCBs.

Can burning PCBs generate dioxins or furans?

Several groups of workers[159-161] have investigated the chemistry of processes which form dioxins and furans. Dioxin formation has been established in laboratory experiments when high levels of precursors are present usually in oxygen depleted atmospheres, but theoretical studies suggest formation can occur sometimes when both oxygen and chlorine are present with the precursors.

The most effective formation of dioxins and furans in laboratory experiments occurred at temperatures in the range 500° to 600°C; and that higher temperatures (e.g. 840°C) reduced the amounts generated. Dioxins and furans will only be generated when refuse (from which all potential sources cannot be excluded) is burned at too low temperatures, for too short residence times, and with insufficient oxygen.

Destruction of dioxins and furans

Comparison of the conditions required for dioxins and furans destruction and those for PCB destruction shows a marked similarity. Conditions such as operating temperatures (throughout furnace and after burner) in excess of 1000°C, with residence times in excess of 1 second, and with an excess oxygen supply which is well mixed with the waste materials, should if fully implemented achieve minimal emissions of PCBs, dioxins and furans. Poorer standards of operation would result in increased emissions.

7.30 A major concern in the design of incinerators is to incorporate an effective control system with built-in safeguards against foreseeable malfunction or maloperation and, as far as is possible, protection against the consequences of the unforeseeable. We return to this in our discussion of design in Chapter X. The values of the control parameters should be continuously recorded and the records, together with those of the incinerated consignments, should be kept. It has been demonstrated in many operational incinerators that sufficiently severe conditions can be maintained to burn to non-toxic products even the more resistant materials such as PCBs.

7.31 The responsibility for the operation of plant falls principally and legally on its management but the regulatory inspectorates have essential roles through the formulation of standards, through advice and through enforcement([162]). (Our recommendations concerning the inspectorates are in Chapter IX.) The First Report of the Hazardous Waste Inspectorate([17]) states that there are at present 50 incinerators located within waste producing plants, which burn predominantly waste generated within these plants, and 4 operated independently as merchant incinerators burning a variety of wastes, some direct from the chemical industry and some from other sources. A fifth merchant incinerator, operating in Scotland, closed during 1984 and we share the concern of the HWI that there may soon be insufficient and inadequately distributed capacity to burn all chemicals for which incineration is the BPEO, with the consequence that more will be consigned to less appropriate disposal such as landfill.

7.32 We have evidence that chemical companies work closely with the management of independent incinerators to which they consign waste, in order to establish suitable conditions for combustion. We are satisfied that some of these incinerators are capable of safely incinerating difficult materials such as PCBs. Nevertheless, it seems to us that the most appropriate location for any additional incinerators that may be needed to burn toxic chemical waste, including that arising in the hands of users of chemicals, would be within the chemical industry itself. It may be that some of the existing incinerators within the industry could deal with additional arisings. In expressing this opinion we do not in any way criticise the action of those companies outside the chemical industry that perceived an opportunity to provide an incineration service, for which there was undoubtedly a need.

7.33 Broadening the issue a little we feel that for the chemical industry to make itself responsible for the destruction of toxic chemical waste is consistent with the duty of care that we advocate in this Report. Moreover, it is within that industry that the skills necessary to design, construct and operate de-toxifying processes, including incinerators for demanding duties, are best represented. Certainly with its available sites, resources and experience the chemical industry should be able to design, build and operate facilities that meet the necessary standards at least as cheaply as any other organisation. The American 3M Company told us of their progress in moving towards consigning waste for disposal outside their organisation only after detoxification and of the probability that they will participate with local interests in Belgium in a consortium to build and operate an incinerator. Such a cooperative enterprise, if endowed with adequate technical expertise and resources, could well be as effective as a plant wholly controlled by the chemical industry. We visited a waste disposal site of the German chemical company, Bayer AG, at Leverkusen which, we were told, serves to some extent as a public facility. It includes, among other facilities, an incinerator and a biological waste water treatment plant (Plate 24) both built to the highest standards and incorporating the latest state of the art([163]). As is the case at the 3M incinerator in the USA, visitors are welcome and the facility is clearly intended not only to discharge Bayer's responsibility of care but also to let it be seen that this is done. A pharmaceutical company in Hungary is reported([164]) to be building a high temperature incinerator to handle both its own wastes and those of other companies. American chemical companies have established a 'roundtable' ([71,88,165,166]) for exchanging information on waste disposal and environmental practices, and we have commended earlier the general guidance prepared by CEFIC([65]).

7.34 We applaud these trends in the chemical industry towards increasingly shouldering the responsibility of care, not only because we consider that the examples that we have given represent desirable environmental options but also because they could properly allay to some extent the fear and mistrust that is damaging economically important industries([164]). We do not suggest that all toxic waste be consigned for treatment to the chemical industry. Where users of chemicals have the ability to operate de-toxifying processes for their own waste this may be the most desirable option and the appropriate way of discharging their duty of care. We commend these approaches to the chemical industry.

Incineration at sea

7.35 Incineration of liquid wastes, especially chlorinated hydrocarbons, has been practiced in European waters since 1969. At first converted tankers were used but latterly both the vessels and their incinerators have been specially designed for the purpose. The amounts of waste from European countries that was incinerated at sea in 1983 are set out in Table 7.3.

7.36 International control over marine incineration is exercised through the Oslo (1972) and the London (1975) Conventions on Dumping at Sea. The former applies to the North Eastern Atlantic and North Sea and the latter worldwide. The Oslo Convention with its annexes and codes of practice lays down requirements for, *inter alia*, operation of the incinerators and the recording of the critical parameters and requires that land-based alternatives be considered before incineration at sea is undertaken. Under the Oslo Convention, before a ship is permitted to incinerate waste at sea a member state must carry out extensive tests to verify that the equipment on broad is appropriate for its purpose and that all the requirements of the Convention are met. The tests are repeated at intervals of about two years. The Netherlands undertakes the testing of the ship that burns the waste from the UK.

TABLE 7.3

Amounts of waste incinerated at sea in 1983 (in tonnes)([167])

Country of origin of the waste	Total amount incinerated
Austria	25
Belgium	8,218
France	2,425
Federal Republic of Germany	37,800
Italy	2,192
Netherlands	4,361
Norway	6,894
Spain	62
Sweden	4,154
Switzerland	1,096
United Kingdom	2,102
Belgium, France, Italy (wastes delivered by one company)	10,590
FRG, Belgium, Netherlands, Italy, France, Switzerland (wastes delivered by another company)	5,757
Total	86,376

7.37 Wastes incinerated at sea are, for the most part, mixtures of organic liquids containing organochlorine compounds, but excluding PCBs, dioxins and DDT. The advantage over incineration on land is that a scrubbing system to absorb the hydrogen chloride produced is not needed. It is liberated near the surface of the sea where humidity is very high and is rapidly transferred in water droplets into the sea, neutralisation is rapid and the bulk acidity of the sea is not affected because of its high buffering capacity. The need for alkali to neutralise the acid and to dispose of sludge from the neutralisation is also avoided. In consequence incineration at sea is cheaper than incineration on land.

7.38 The results of a number of studies([168]) have shown that, provided the correct conditions are maintained, incineration can be conducted at sea without harm to the oceanic or coastal environment. In the United States the Environmental Protection Agency (EPA) has issued proposed regulations for incineration at sea([169]) and a research strategy([170]) but long term operational

95

permits will not be granted until the regulations are made final which will, presumably, be dependent on the results of the research.

7.39 We conclude that incineration at sea, under the strict conditions prescribed, and provided that the critical incineration parameters are continuously measured nd recorded, and that the records are kept, is an acceptable option for some liquid wastes: whether it is the best option will depend on the particular circumstances of each case. As with all options, the situation will need to be kept under review in the light of continuing technical and economic developments[168,171].

Incineration of hospital wastes

7.40 We have already discussed (paragraphs 6.27-6.32) the generation of medical wastes, the need for segregation of different types of wastes, and the lack of co-ordinated planning and management of the totality of such wastes arising within a given health authority's area. A survey in the West Midlands showed that some hospitals have incinerators with excess capacity while others have no such facility. Unless there is co-operation between hospitals so that incinerators can be run more or less continuously there may be cyclic operating patterns with repeated start-up and shut-down phases. When this occurs, unless large quantities of non-plastic domestic wastes are available, purchased fuel will be required to bring the incinerators up to a satisfactory operating temperature. It might be that groups of hospitals could sensibly pool their waste streams and keep a smaller number of incinerators operating efficiently, and we have recommended (paragraph 6.32) that health authorities should prepare and implement waste disposal plans.

7.41 We have received evidence of a considerable number of complaints from councils that hospital incinerators do not operate satisfactorily, generating copious black smoke and not meeting the provisions of the Clean Air Acts. National Health Service hospitals are exempted from meeting the provision of this Act by virtue of the Crown immunity which we discuss in Chapter VIII.

Straw burning

7.42 Straw burning is a subject that was discussed in the Commission's Tenth Report and a recommendation was made that a legislative ban on straw burning should be introduced to take effect in 5 years' time. This recommendation has not been accepted yet, but new model bye-laws for local authority implementation have been prepared and the NFU Straw and Stubble Burning Code has been revised. The exceptional problems of 1983 have not been repeated, probably as a result of these changes[133]. Nevertheless, during the later summer and autumn of this year (1985), the cereal-growing regions of eastern England continued to experience serious atmospheric pollution from smoke and smuts resulting from straw burning[172]. After poor summer weather, the harvest was compressed into a few weeks, during which time there were acute episodes of smoke pollution in some regions. Widespread smoke dispersion was accompanied by smuts and smell and by a reduction in the hours of sunshine. In some regions, we have been told that the prohibition of burning at weekends did not prove effective in reducing the nuisance because the air had only just begun to clear after Friday's burning before burning began again on Monday.

7.43 It is estimated that some 6 to 7 million tonnes of straw have to be disposed of each year in the UK. The proportion of this that was burned in the open in 1984 is thought to have produced about 18,000 tonnes of black smoke([173]). During a period of several weeks, therefore, atmospheric pollution in cereal-growing regions is generally worse than would be tolerated in industrial regions. In its 1983 report([174]) the Industrial Air Pollution Inspectorate comments on the public indignation caused by straw and stubble burning, and points out that an industrial cause of smoke and smuts of such magnitude would be required to reduce emissions speedily, but straw burning does not fall within the responsibilities of the Inspectorate. We believe that this is an unacceptable and avoidable source of pollution which should be eliminated as soon as possible.

7.44 We are encouraged by the efforts being made to develop new means of straw disposal, including the development of locally-based incinerators to burn straw under controlled conditions for uses such as grain drying, domestic heating and various industrial processes. We hope that more effort will be devoted to finding methods for composting straw and to seeking new uses for straw such as the industrial production of cellulose([175]).

7.45 We applaud these and the many other initiatives taken by individual farmers and by associated industries and research organisations for the solution of the problem. In the western half of the UK, where the greatest livestock density occurs, straw for feeding and bedding is usually in short supply. This is so particularly in wet summers such as 1985. New methods for the compaction of baled straw would permit it to be transported more easily. The use of straw for bedding provides a source of manure and has the additional advantage that the volume of farmyard slurry produced is thereby reduced. This reduces another potentially serious source of pollution. We **recommend** that the development of these and other alternative methods of straw disposal should be further encouraged by financial support from Government for research and development, perhaps in the form of Department of Trade and Industry funding on a joint basis. In addition we **recommend** that the Government should put forward these methods as eligible candidates for European Community grants.

7.46 As was pointed out in the Tenth Report the setting of a timetable for the introduction of a ban on straw burning should serve as an incentive for the development of new equipment and techniques. We therefore reiterate the **recommendation** of the Commission's Tenth Report:

'that the Government should announce the introduction of a legislative ban on straw burning on stubble fields to take effect in five years' time; the legislation should be introduced now and come into effect on the prescribed date without the need for subsequent statutory instruments or commencement orders.'

In the light of the recent extension of the bye-laws to cover the practice of burning leguminous and oil seed rape residues we **recommend** that the legislative ban should be extended to all field crop residues.

Sea dumping

7.47 In this section we are concerned with the risks of pollution of the sea from the deposition of wastes. Such deposition is carried out under either the Oslo Convention 1972 (North East Atlantic and North Sea), or the London Convention 1975 (worldwide) and national legislation such as Dumping at Sea Act 1974*. We note also the proposed EC Directive on the Dumping of Waste at Sea[176], put before the Council in August 1985 and intended to achieve standardised rules for sea dumping in all Member States. The wastes which are dumped at sea may be divided into four groups: sewage sludge (both at sea and from shoreline outfalls); industrial wastes such as brines, liquid wastes and drilling muds; mineral wastes from coal mining and sand and gravel extraction; and radioactive wastes. Table 7.4 gives an indication of the quantitites dumped in some of the different categories over a seven year period.

TABLE 7.4

Quantities of sewage sludge and industrial wastes dumped from the UK in the Oslo Convention Area, 1978-83 (million tonnes)[46,167]

	1978	1979	1980	1981	1982	1983
Sewage sludge	8.08†	9.85	10.55	10.02	8.14	7.30
Industrial waste	1.22	0.70	0.54	0.47	0.30	0.33

† excludes Scotland

7.48 The Commission discussed the environmental aspects of disposing of industrial wastes in the North Sea and Irish Sea, and the coastal deposition of mineral wastes in its Tenth Report, so we have not considered them in detail in this study. In the case of radioactive wastes, deposition at sea of British low and medium level wastes was halted in April 1984[177] pending a scientific review of dumping these wastes[178], but despite the results of this review at a recent meeting of the London Dumping Convention (September 1985) there was a large majority in favour of an indefinite moratorium on all dumping of radioactive waste at sea (see paragraph 12.15). We have already in this report discussed litter and refuse dumped from ships, especially when these reach the coast and generate litter along the shoreline (paragraphs 6.42-6.46). The following sections, therefore, deal with the disposal of sewage sludge at sea - a topic that we distinguish from the discharge of sewage to sea from outfalls at

---

* Soon to be superseded by Part II of the Food and Environment Protection Act 1985, due to come into effect on 1 January 1986.

the shoreline. The Commission considered the latter subject in relation to the quality of bathing beaches in its Tenth Report. Our views have not changed and we reiterate its **recommendation** that full implementation of the recommendations of the Working Party on Sewage Disposal should be achieved to an agreed timetable (see paragraph 6.47).

Sewage sludge

7.49 The UK uses about sixteen offshore sites to dump sewage sludge[167]. All are licensed under the Dumping at Sea Act and the dumping operations are inspected by enforcement officers from the Ministry of Agriculture, Fisheries and Food, the Welsh Office, the Scottish Development Department or the Department of the Environment (Northern Ireland) as appropriate. Although when deposited in bulk sewage can overload the natural decomposition processes and, in water, create an excess oxygen demand[29], the main concern over its polluting effect arises from the concentration of toxic metals within it. These largely derive from accepted industrial discharges to sewers, and the recent trend has been for these concentrations to fall (Figure 7.2), either because of improved methods of pretreating the discharges, or because the decline in relevant industries has reduced the total burden on sewage treatment works. It is to be expected that the introduction of lead-free petrol[179,180] will cause to a further reduction in the burden transmitted to sewers. As techniques are available and others are being developed[181] for reducing the concentrations of heavy metals in industrial effluents, it would be more efficient, overall, to achieve this than for the UK to have to seek other ways of disposing of sewage sludge. If it can be freed of the heavy metal burden from industrial wastes, sewage sludge is a natural organic manure: in appropriate quantities it should have a beneficial effect on the productivity of marine habitats, and there is evidence of this occurring[182,183]. We **recommend** that the water authorities should consult the relevant industries in their areas with a view to increasing the removal of metals from industrial discharges at source and reducing the metal content of sewage. We also **recommend** that in view of the importance to the UK of international acceptance of economic methods of sludge disposal, the Government should consider ways and means of assisting the further reduction of the heavy metals load in sewage sludge.

Deep burial

7.50 Land based deep burial involves either the deposition of liquid or solid wastes into existing underground cavities such as coal mines or salt mines, or the sinking of special shafts for the purpose of deposition of wastes. The principal danger to the environment that this kind of disposal can present is contamination of ground water. The theoretical possibilities of radioactive waste disposal at sea outside territorial waters in deep sea trenches or subduction zones have been suggested, but these have not been extensively explored in the course of this study and we shall not consider them further.

7.51 However, the geology of much of Britain where mineshafts or other voids exist is such as to pose problems of ensuring the integrity of the disposal

**Figure. 7.2   Heavy metal concentrations in sewage sludge dumped at sea
from England and Wales, 1976-83(g/tonne wet weight)**

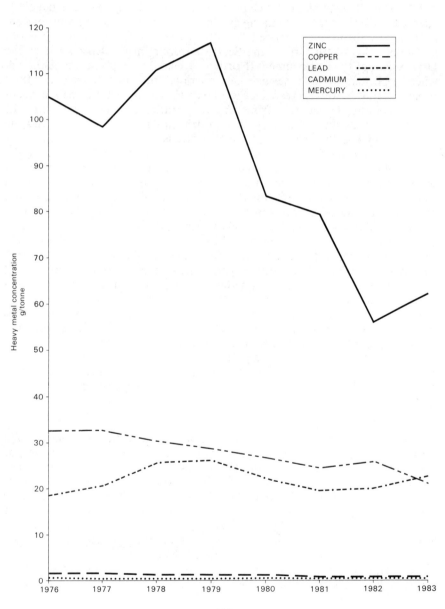

site and its isolation from groundwater or adjacent workings. Some solid wastes such as mineral wastes are stowed underground so that they fill the void, and can improve the stability of the area. Other wastes, such as very toxic materials, might be deposited underground either in concrete vaults or in labelled drums, and the deep salt mines of Central Europe may provide appropriate conditions for this([31,184]). But such deposition is storage rather than disposal (paragraphs 6.33 - 6.35). We conclude that deep burial is appropriate for the disposal of materials that have been immobilised and for which the BPEO is their return to the earth's crust (paragraphs 3.15 - 3.18).

7.52 Deep burial methods are employed for liquid wastes at 20 licensed sites in the United Kingdom([17]) and it is of the greatest importance that thorough records of the quantities and types of waste deposited are maintained. This has particular relevance in future developments of the site. Foundations, especially deep piles, could penetrate the zone of deposition and knowledge of the material deposited underground should be available for consultation by the engineers and others involved. Accordingly we **recommend** that details of wastes disposed of by deep burial should be recorded on the Land Register as a local land charge and that waste disposal authorities should make such recording a condition of the licence (see also Chapter IX).

Chemical and biological treatment of wastes

7.53 We have already discussed the neutralisation of wastes being consigned for landfill and the biological processes which degrade wastes in landfill, creating leachate liquors and landfill gas, and converting the wastes to material like compost (paragraphs 7.5 and 7.13).

7.54 A form of treatment, which is probably more physical than chemical, often goes under the name of 'chemical fixation'([185]). This involves mixing hazardous inorganic materials (such as those containing heavy metals) with cement, resin or pulverised fuel ash, transferring the mixture to a landfill void and allowing it to harden. The 'fixed' materials may not be chemically bonded to the cementing agent; it is more probable that they are physically held within the hardened mass, which renders them less available for incorporation in leachates. We believe these systems are satisfactory, provided that they are properly managed, and that inappropriate materials are not included. But if they are improperly used they can present additional hazards of physical instability, and we ourselves saw an incident where a landslide had occurred after the treated materials ought to have solidified. Another treatment of this type is the encapsulation of materials in vitrified blocks or, in the case of asbestos, its conversion into vitrified form([186]).

7.55 We consider that the immobilisation and re-incorporation in the earth's crust is the BPEO for certain wastes (paragraph 3.17), but further research and development is desirable. We therefore **recommend** that the Department of the Environment should continue to include provision for research into immobilisation of hazardous wastes in its research programme.

7.56 Organic waste which does not contain unduly high concentrations of heavy metals or other toxic components can be transformed into a useful compost, as mentioned in Chapter V. This transformation occurs as the result of the activities of micro-organisms - bacteria, fungi, algae and protozoa - which are generally present in the natural environment and particularly abundant in soils. These micro-organisms in breaking down organic matter utilise the energy released and some of the products of breakdown for their own growth and multiplication, different species having requirements for different kinds of organic substances so that their combined action is able to degrade complex materials. The residue which resists breakdown forms the humus which is the valuable component of compost. Besides breaking down substances which can sustain their growth some micro-organisms can additionally break down organic substances which by themselves cannot sustain growth and may even be toxic to higher organisms. This phenomenon, known as co-metabolism[187], is potentially of great value for waste disposal since it offers the possibility of biological degradation of noxious organic substances as in co-disposal. To operate efficiently it requires conditions which provide for vigorous microbial growth and the presence of strains which are able to co-metabolise the particular organic substances which make the waste otherwise difficult to deal with.

CHAPTER VIII

WASTE MANAGEMENT LAW AND PRACTICE

Introduction

8.1 The framework for responsible waste management is set by the law, and the extent to which those who are ignorant or heedless of this framework can be obliged to have regard to it depends on the adequacy of that law and of the means by which it is enforced. In this chapter, therefore, we discuss the provisions, operation and enforcement of the law on waste management and make our recommendations in these areas. An outline of the relevant statutes has already been given in Chapter II.

Duties of local authorities

Household and commercial waste collection

8.2 The statutory power of local authorities to remove household refuse derives from sections 72-75 of the Public Health Act 1936. These empower local authorities to make byelaws regulating, amongst other things, the method by which the refuse shall be collected, the provision of dustbins by either the local authority or the householder, and the types of material that may be deposited in the dustbin. In theory, the detailed procedures of the Control of Pollution (Special Wastes) Regulations 1980 (see paragraphs 2.9-2.10) apply as much to special wastes arising in the home - for example, wood preservative residues and some other wastes from do-it-yourself activities or building works and some articles containing asbestos - as to those from commercial and industrial activities. In practice, however, collection authorities will prefer to advise residents on how to dispose of such wastes safely and, in some cases, to make special arrangements to accept or collect these wastes, and other noxious materials such as medical wastes and sharps when these arise domestically, separately from normal household refuse. The adequacy of such advice and arrangements falls within the terms of reference of the Hazardous Waste Inspectorate([17]).

8.3 Sections 72-75 of the Public Health Act 1936 also empower, but do not oblige, collection authorities to collect trade refuse and require them, if they do so, to make a reasonable charge for the service. The majority of collection authorities do in fact collect trade waste and most make some charge, although it is difficult to believe that the very wide variation in what is considered reasonable([44]) reflects the actual costs of collection and disposal in different areas. If charges are high relative to the perceived benefit of the service provided there is an increased risk of fly tipping. On the other hand, as we noted in paragraph 5.36, if charges do not fully cover costs, producers of commercial waste will be insufficiently motivated to consider avoiding or recycling some of their material instead of consigning it for disposal.

8.4 Sections 12-14 of the Control of Pollution Act 1974 were enacted to clarify, modernise and replace the earlier provisions on the collection of waste, but have to date been only partially implemented. Their principal effect would be to require district councils to collect commercial waste on request, but the Department of the Environment has said that the opportunity of implementation would be taken to clarify, by regulations under sections 12(3) and 30(4) of the Act, the types of waste that were classified as 'household', 'commercial' and 'industrial'. This could, for example, lead to garden waste and bulky items such as old furniture and white goods being prescribed as items for which authorities were entitled to make a collection charge. The status of clinical wastes should also be clarified - something which is clearly necessary since even the Department of the Environment admits that 'currently the legal position regarding the collection and disposal of clinical wastes is somewhat uncertain' and that, until responsibilities are clarified by implementation of sections 12-14 (and section 1) of the Act, the security of this waste stream 'must rely on sensible arrangements being made locally'([115]).

8.5 Reluctance to implement the new provisions stems from the additional costs that might be imposed on collection authorities not only when they have to collect commercial waste but also when the definition of the household waste they have a duty to collect becomes that given in section 30(3) of the Control of Pollution Act - namely 'waste from a private dwelling or residential home or from premises forming part of a university or school or other educational establishment or forming part of a hospital or nursing home'([188]). We note that such a broad definition embraces some wastes that require special handling (see paragraph 8.2). A survey carried out by DOE in 1982 estimated that full implementation of sections 12-14 might add £17.5 million per annum and £10.4 million over five years to collection authorities' net current and capital expenditure respectively([189]). Most of the increase was seen as arising from the collection of bulky household waste and garden refuse. The survey did not investigate the scope for offsetting increased costs with charges or the extent to which regulations might be used to limit the range of 'household' items that may be put into dustbins. Other commentators([190]) have quoted significantly lower estimates and the Association of Metropolitan Authorities has maintained that all the extra costs could be met from charges([189]).

8.6 Particularly in view of our findings on the poor security of the waste streams arising, for example, from some medical establishments (paragraphs 6.30−6.31), we consider clarification of collection authorities' duties to be a matter of urgency. The Commission's Tenth Report noted the difficulties created by prolonged uncertainty over the implementation of other sections of the Control of Pollution Act, and the same arguments apply here. Accordingly, we **recommend** that implementation of sections 12-14 and the enactment of Regulations under sections 12(3) and 30(4) of the Control of Pollution Act 1974 should be completed without further delay.

Litter

8.7 The principal legislation controlling litter in Great Britain is the Litter Act 1983, which consolidates and extends earlier provisions dating from 1958. Under the 1983 Act, parish and community councils as well as county and district authorities in England and Wales, and island and district councils in Scotland, are designated as litter authorities and empowered to provide and service litter bins and to take other steps to promote litter abatement. We believe the involvement of parish and community councils is important because these bodies are often ideally placed to take a lead in moulding public attitudes and to monitor the results of abatement measures. We see considerable scope for local initiatives to tackle this problem at source and consider that results are more likely to follow, at least in the shorter term, if available resources are used to foster such initiatives rather than to prepare the formal litter plans that would be required if section 4 of the 1983 Act were to be brought into force and acted upon[191]. Arrangements for the disposal of litter should be included in the waste disposal plans prepared under section 2 of the Control of Pollution Act 1974 (see paragraphs 9.8 - 9.9).

8.8 We have already drawn attention (paragraph 6.10) to the importance of emptying litter bins before they become over-full. We therefore particularly note that, under section 5 of the 1983 Act, it is a statutory duty of litter authorities in England and Wales to ensure that 'the regular emptying (of their litter bins) shall be sufficiently frequent to ensure that no such litter bin or its contents shall become a nuisance'. It is for local authorities to set an example to the community as a whole.

8.9 We have concluded in Chapter VI that litter is prevalent in many parts of Britain today. We have observed some flagrant examples ourselves and have noted concern expressed by several of our witnesses and in Parliament[192] on this issue. While we agree with the Government's view that, in the long term, the answer to the litter problem must lie in educating and persuading the public not to drop litter[193], we feel that further action is necessary to secure early improvement. In 1983 there were 1685 convictions under the Litter Acts[192]. This figure strikes us as disproportionately low in relation to the extent of the litter problem. This may be due not only to the limited priority that the police feel they can properly devote to litter abatement but also to the fact that the full processes of prosecution and conviction are involved for what, when taken in isolation, must be considered trivial offences. Moreover, there are said to be technical difficulties in obtaining convictions: for example, several witnesses have pointed out that the wording of the offence is 'to throw down ... and leave' and have suggested that the requirement to show that the offender intended to leave the litter can make the provision of adequate proof difficult.

8.10 We note that in some cities the offence of dropping litter is subject to an on-the-spot fine or a fixed penalty, rather like a parking ticket (see box). The right to challenge the imposition of the penalty in court is reserved, but in most cases the offence is admitted and the enforcement authority collects the appropriate fine. In this way more efficient and effective use can be made of the resources which enforcement authorities are able to devote to litter offences. We believe that so far as possible enforcement should be on a local basis and that it should not be limited to the police. For instance in the urban context traffic wardens, who operate under the aegis of the police and whose job entails patrolling public places, might assist with enforcement.

Examples of fixed penalties for violation of litter laws

Place	*Penalty notices issued by:*	*Fine*
New York	sanitation department officers	$50
Pittsburgh	police and traffic wardens	$38.50
New South Wales	police and authorised local authority officers - no court proceedings if fine paid within 14 days	A$25
Peking	municipal officers	$\frac{1}{2}$-1 Yuan ($17-34)

Source: Press reports etc.([194-196])

8.11 In the light of the above, we **recommend** that the Department of the Environment, the Home Office and others as appropriate should review the enforcement of the law on litter and identify what changes in the law and procedures are needed to improve the efficiency and effectiveness of this enforcement.

Producers of waste - the duty of care

8.12 The producers of all waste generated in the course of business or employment have responsibilities under the Health and Safety at Work etc. Act 1974 to conduct their activities so as to secure the health and safety of their employees, of those with whom they do business and of the public. Duties under that Act and under the regulations and codes of practice that derive from it relate primarily to the protection of people. They were not designed to protect the environment - which is what a policy of providing for the security of the waste stream from production to final disposal is designed to achieve.

8.13 As we have made clear in Chapter III, security of the waste stream stems from the continuity of care exercised by the producer of the waste, the transporter or handler of that waste and those responsible for its ultimate disposal. We refer to these three stages of waste management below. We turn first to the duties of the waste producer.

8.14 Both the evidence we have received and some of the activities we have observed during our visits have convinced us that it is too easy for a producer of waste either deliberately or passively to relieve himself of all responsibility for the ultimate disposal of that waste. For instance, if the operator of an industrial plant uses his own transport and drivers to take waste for disposal at a licensed landfill site, he will be liable if the waste is dumped in an unauthorised place. On the other hand, if he engages a contractor to transport the waste he will, in general, be relieved of responsibility for its proper disposal once the waste has been entrusted to that contractor. If the contractor deposits the waste on land unlawfully a charge under section 3 of the Control of Pollution Act might lie against the producer of the waste, but the burden of proving either connivance between producer and contractor or failure of the producer to take reasonable steps to ensure that the contractor would deposit the waste lawfully frequently renders these provisions unenforceable.

8.15 We consider that no producer of controlled waste should be entitled to rid himself of all responsibility for the waste by simply handing it over to a contractor for disposal. We propose, therefore, that the responsibilities of all producers of controlled waste should be governed by a statutory duty of care for the security of the waste stream and that, to discharge this duty, the producer should have to fulfil specified requirements. For special wastes, these would be the strict requirements of the Control of Pollution (Special Waste) Regulations 1980. For other controlled wastes, the requirements would be fairly limited and simple and would include the selection of a competent and suitable contractor and the provision to him in writing of an unambiguous indication of the nature of the waste and clear instructions for its disposal.

8.16 The joint committee of government, local authority, industrial and environmental representatives that completed its review of the Control of Pollution (Special Waste) Regulations 1980 in April 1985 agreed that 'in response to the present difficulties of enforcing control when waste is passed from one person to another it would be right to embody in the parent (Control of Pollution) Act a general obligation on all waste producers to take all reasonable steps to ensure that the waste they produce is appropriately disposed of in accordance with the provisions of the Act and the Regulations made under them'[6]. The new duty of care which we propose should be imposed upon waste producers implements that recommendation.

8.17 This duty of care and our later recommendation for the registration of transporters of waste (paragraph 8.29) are together intended to provide a simple set of rules which will enable the producer of waste to discharge his responsibilities either himself or, if he chooses to employ a third party to undertake the work, by facilitating the selection of a suitable contractor. Our recommendations are also designed to assist those responsible for monitoring the security of the waste stream by providing an unbroken chain of responsibility and accountability between those who produce, transport and dispose of waste.

8.18 We believe that the duty of care imposed on the waste producer should be non-delegable. There are many, long-standing precedents which establish duties which cannot be delegated at all or only subject to the exercise of proper care. An example in the environmental field is the case of *Robinson v. Beaconsfield RDC*, in which the Court of Appeal held that the local authority retained a share of liability when a contractor it employed to dispose of sewage failed to do so properly[197]. We are not, however, proposing that the duty of care should extend so as to impose on the waste producer a 'cradle to grave' responsibility for the safe management of his waste. Such a responsibility is imposed in respect of certain wastes in Belgium, where the producer is liable for any damage howsoever caused by his waste, and in the United States waste producers have sometimes been held liable for shortcomings in the transport and disposal of wastes[66]. We consider that it would be unduly onerous to impose on the waste producer absolute criminal liability for the wrongful acts of a contractor. We propose, therefore, that the producer should be entitled in his defence to show that he had acted reasonably by fulfilling the conditions indicated above.

8.19 In the case of producers of domestic and many commercial wastes, the duty of care will be discharged by the collection authority collecting the waste and passing it to the disposal authority (when different) for disposal. There will, however, be instances where the domestic producer is required to take more positive action to discharge his duty of care - for example, when the waste includes hazardous components such as sharps or other medical wastes (see paragraph 8.2). For practical reasons the obligation to make special collection arrangements for these wastes must lie with the collection authority, but this does not absolve the domestic producer of his obligation to advise the collection authority of the hazards or of his duty to use the services it provides. Producers of commercial wastes who employ contractors to collect and dispose of their wastes, and any domestic producers who do not use their collection authority's services for wastes requiring separate handling, should observe in full the procedures we have described above for the majority of controlled wastes.

8.20 The circumstances in which controlled wastes are produced, the hazards they present and their potential to pollute the environment vary widely. It is, therefore, desirable that there should be guidelines to establish the detailed procedures which should be followed in different circumstances. Regulations made under the primary legislation would be difficult to formulate and to adapt to changing circumstances. It seems preferable and more practical for the details to be contained in a statutory Code of Practice, which can be more specific and more readily revised from time to time. Failure to comply with the provisions of the Code would not itself be an offence, but would be available as evidence to support the charge that the waste producer had failed to discharge his duty of care.

8.21 Accordingly, we **recommend** that the Control of Pollution Act 1974 should be amended to provide:

- that producers of controlled wastes have a duty of care to take all reasonable steps, having regard to the hazards presented by their wastes, to ensure that their wastes are subsequently managed and disposed of without harm to the environment;

- that the steps that it is reasonable for the waste producer to take in different circumstances to discharge his duty of care shall be contained in a Code of Practice issued by the Secretary of State;

- that producers of commercial, industrial and certain domestic wastes who engage contractors to transport their wastes remain liable for the proper disposal of those wastes unless they use a contractor registered as a waste transporter in accordance with our later recommendation and provide him in writing with an unambiguous indication of the nature of the wastes and clear instructions for their disposal.

Information requirements

8.22 Some of the local authority members of the joint review committee (see paragraph 8.16) felt that enhancing the duties of waste producers on the lines we have recommended would not, by itself, sufficiently improve enforcement authorities' knowledge of and control over hazardous waste arising in their areas. They therefore favoured the introduction of a scheme of registration or licensing of producers of hazardous wastes, a principal aim of which would be to make enforcement authorities better informed[6]. The House of Lords Select Committee on Science and Technology took a similar view when it recommended that all producers of hazardous wastes should have to register with their waste disposal authority, identify the person responsible for hazardous waste disposal, and make detailed quarterly returns of disposals[5]. It has also been argued[38] that registration of waste producers is necessary for full implementation in the United Kingdom of the EC Directive on toxic and dangerous waste[37], which requires records to be kept of the production and storage as well as the disposal of such waste while the Control of Pollution (Special Waste) Regulations 1980 at present require records only of waste consigned from a producer's premises and of its deposition on land.

8.23 In its comments on the joint review committee's report, the Select Committee has stressed that waste disposal authorities should have ready access to information about the production of all hazardous waste, not just special waste, in their areas[199]. Section 1 of the Control of Pollution Act 1974, giving disposal authorities a duty to ensure the adequacy of arrangements for the disposal of all controlled waste in their areas, would likewise increase waste disposal authorities' need for information about waste. Although this section has not been brought into force because of its financial implications for disposal authorities, the Government has accepted that it should be brought into force as soon as practicable[200]. Even without the duty of section 1, waste disposal authorities need adequate information for the purposes of preparing waste disposal plans under section 2 of the Act. While section 93 of the Act empowers authorities to require the provision of information by waste producers, it does not help them to identify such producers in the first place.

8.24 We also have considered the question of registration or licensing of waste producers, principally as a means of improving the flow of information to waste disposal authorities. We have concluded that the need for a formal registration or licensing scheme is at present not proven. We do not rule out such a scheme for the future but feel that alternative less onerous means of satisfying disposal authorities' information requirements should first be examined more closely. Accordingly, like the joint review committee, we **recommend** that the Department of the Environment should set up a working party to review the information needs of waste disposal authorities and the adequacy of the existing sources of information available to them. Such a review would be particularly timely since it would coincide with the period during which the Metropolitan District and London Borough Councils will be gaining experience of their new responsibilities as waste disposal authorities, including their responsibilities for preparing waste disposal plans, following abolition of the Metropolitan County and Greater London Councils on 1 April 1986.

Transporters of waste - registration

8.25 It is central to our recommendations for improving the security of the waste stream that there should be an unbroken chain of responsibility and accountability for waste from its production to its disposal and that there should be a clear set of rules to enable those involved at each stage to discharge their duty of care with confidence. We therefore believe that it is imperative that a system for identifying and monitoring the competence of waste transporters is established, for without such a system, a vital link in this chain of responsibility will be missing. By waste transporters we mean all those in the business of transporting waste whether this is their principal activity or ancillary to handling waste for treatment or other purposes. We discuss below existing controls on the operation of heavy goods vehicles and later (paragraph 8.33) suggest an extension of these to lighter vehicles carrying waste.

8.26 Waste transporters are already subject to a range of statutory controls that apply to all businesses and to the operation of vehicles. Most of the legislation applying to vehicles is intended to ensure their safe operation irrespective of the nature of the goods carried. However, several broad categories of waste are already amongst the items covered by the Dangerous Substances (Conveyance by Road in Road Tankers and Tank Containers) Regulations 1981. These and comparable Regulations being prepared for the carriage of packaged goods by road derive from Schedule 3 of the Health and Safety at Work etc. Act 1974. It is disturbing to find that one third of the tankers checked in a recent survey by the Health and Safety Executive were in breach of the 1981 Regulations[201]. We welcome the Executive's proposals for reducing this figure significantly by encouraging consignors to carry out periodic audits of hauliers to ensure that tankers are properly maintained and drivers adequately trained. This illustrates precisely the manner in which we consider the waste producer should conduct his affairs in discharging his duty of care.

8.27 Operators of goods vehicles over 3.5 tonnes gross weight (heavy goods vehicles) are also subject to the system of operator licensing established by the Transport Act 1968. The principal features of this system, under which the general competence and reputation of goods vehicle operators are periodically assessed, are set out in the box overleaf. It will be seen that whilst convictions under environmental legislation can be taken into account by the licensing authority there is no obligation on it to do so. It will also be seen that operators who transport only their own goods are not obliged to use the services of a qualified transport manager. This has enabled some waste contractors to claim a 'restricted' licence on the grounds that they acquired ownership of the waste they collected, though the Department of Transport has proposed that this practice should be stopped([6]).

8.28 The possibility of adapting the operator licensing system in order to compel the licensing authorities to consider applicants' convictions under environmental legislation was considered by the joint review committee as one means of strengthening controls over transporters of waste([6]). Local authorities enjoy a statutory right to lodge objections to the grant or variation of operators' licences and those authorities that were also waste disposal authorities would be well placed to keep licensing authorities informed about operators' waste management activities. However, the local authority representatives on the joint review committee felt that such measures would not be a significant extra deterrent of illegal dumping. Furthermore, the House of Lords Select Committee on Science and Technology felt that the existing operator licensing system was not suited to the task of regulating waste transporters since it does not apply to vehicles below 3.5 tonnes gross weight([199]). The Committee preferred a separate, national system of licensing for all waste transporters.

8.29 Notwithstanding these difficulties and the disparate views of various commentators, we consider that operator licensing merits further consideration as the basis for the system of registration or licensing of waste transporters that we consider is an essential link in securing the waste stream. First, we accept that at present it would be quite unrealistic and impractical, on both financial and organisational grounds, to establish yet another system of licensing, specifically for waste transporters, and a bureaucracy to operate it. Secondly, our deliberations have perhaps taken a different and rather broader view of the role to be played by licensing in that the system we propose has to be seen as part of the implementation of the waste producers' non-delegable duty of care and not solely as a means of vetting waste transporters. This will be particularly important in tackling such problems as fly tipping. Accordingly, we **recommend** that the existing system of licensing for the operators of heavy goods vehicles should be supplemented by a system of registration for

FEATURES OF THE LICENSING SYSTEM FOR HEAVY GOODS VEHICLE OPERATORS

Statutory authority : Transport Act 1968 and Regulations made thereunder

Licensing authority : statutorily independent judicial authority

System administered and enforced by : the Department of Transport's Traffic Area Offices

Vehicles covered : goods vehicles and trailers over 3.5 tonnes gross weight, with exceptions for local authority and other vehicles of specialised types

Applications : must be advertised; the police, local authorities and some Trade Unions and Trade Associations may object if they believe any licence requirement is not met; local residents may object on environmental grounds only

Appeals : to the Transport Tribunal

Licensing requirements

(a) *For operators carrying goods for hire or reward* — standard licence

Fitness to hold a licence - the licensing authority is obliged to have regard to any convictions for a list of offences relating to the use of vehicles.

Good repute - the licensing authority may also have regard to 'such other information he may have as to [the applicant's] previous conduct appearing to relate to his fitness to hold a licence' - i.e. environmental offences *may* be taken into account.

Professional competence - deemed to be satisfied by operators established in the haulage business before 1974, but subsequent entrants must demonstrate competence by becoming or employing a qualified transport manager. Such a manager may be qualified through membership of specified professional institutions or by passing a written examination the syllabus for which includes the basic legal requirements for the transport of hazardous and dangerous loads ([202]).

Financial standing - the licensing authority must be satisfied that the applicant has sufficient resources to run his business and to maintain his vehicles adequately.

Operating centre - the licensing authority must have regard to the environmental suitability (e.g. parking space available) of the operating centre when determining new applications.

(b) *For operators carrying only their own goods* - restricted licence

Applicants have to show they are fit to hold a licence, have adequate financial resources to keep their vehicles serviceable and have a suitable operating centre; they do not have to establish good repute or professional competence (but see paragraph 8.27).

the operators of all vehicles, irrespective of weight, carrying controlled wastes for hire or reward. In the following paragraphs we examine how such a system would work and how some of the difficulties foreseen by others might be overcome. We refer throughout to a system of registration though we recognise that, by including sanctions, it also has elements of a system of licensing.

8.30 The contributions that registration of waste transporters can make to improving the security of the waste stream are:

- helping the waste producer select a competent contractor;

- applying and, in due course, enforcing standards as to the manner and means by which wastes are transported;

- ensuring that adequate information about the identity and movement of wastes is available to those who handle and dispose of it, and to the enforcement authorities.

8.31 We have considered the means by which a system of registration might be introduced, including the possibility of vetting applicants prior to the first grant of a registration certificate. We have concluded that this would prove a costly and probably ineffective exercise since, at the outset of the system, there would be no firm criteria or comprehensive record of offences against which to judge each applicant's fitness. The holding of a valid operator's licence would be a prerequisite for registration as a waste transporter. We suggest, therefore, that in the first instance anyone holding an operator's licence and wishing to transport controlled waste for hire or reward should have his application for registration granted automatically unless it can be shown that he has persistently committed environmental offences. The registration would run with the licence and on application for renewal of the latter - or sooner, should the licensing authority so require - there would be an opportunity for an assessment of the operator's record, performance, training and other factors to establish whether his registration, as well as his operator's licence, should be renewed. Progressively, therefore, the competent operators will be separated from the 'cowboys' and, because of the responsibility imposed on the waste producer to select a competent contractor in order to discharge his duty of care, we believe there will also be a commercial bias against less reputable transporters.

8.32 In recommending that registration of waste transporters should be an adjunct of operator licensing, and thus the responsibility of the licensing authorities and the Department of Transport's Traffic Area Offices, we have had to establish whether a registration scheme grafted on to an established system could adequately fulfil the requirements that would be expected of a separate, tailor-made registration scheme if this were a realistic proposition. There are several reasons why we concluded it could:

- the majority of contractors who specialise in transporting waste already operate fleets of vehicles and could readily indicate, when registering, which of the vehicles specified on their operator's licence were to be used for carrying waste;

113

- licensing authorities and the staff of the Department of Transport's Traffic Area Offices already have considerable expertise in assessing the professionalism and competence of fleet operators and the Department's Vehicle and Traffic Examiners are similarly skilled in enforcing the law relating to the operation of vehicles;

- it would be possible to add the provisions of the registration scheme for waste transporters, for example on documentation and description of wastes carried, to those that the Department's Examiners already check during roadside inspections; additionally, since all vehicles carrying waste will be obliged to display a prominent distinguishing sign (see paragraph 8.35), it will be simple for such vehicles to be identified and flagged down for roadside inspection;

- a system of registration and enforcement necessarily entails the withdrawal of registration from operators who persistently offend against waste disposal legislation and, accordingly, a mechanism for appeals is essential; an appeal from the decisions of licensing authorities already lies to the Transport Tribunal.

8.33 We recognise that a major difficulty in grafting registration on to the operator licensing system is that vehicles below 3.5 tonnes gross weight are at present excluded from licensing. Since many vehicles below this weight are known to have been involved in fly tipping[112], it would be unthinkable for such vehicles to be excluded from the requirement to register. We consider, therefore, that if vehicles under 3.5 tonnes gross weight are used for the carriage of controlled waste for hire or reward their operators should comply with the same conditions as the operators of heavy goods vehicles used for this purpose and that such vehicles should consequently be brought within the scope of operator licensing. We do not, however, envisage that the requirements for more stringent annual testing and driver licensing that apply to heavy goods vehicles should apply to lighter vehicles when used for the carriage of waste.

8.34 We see no reason why local authority vehicles involved in commercial transactions for the transport of waste and which are at present exempt from operator licensing should be excluded from the requirement to register. Arguably the operators of such vehicles should be setting the standards for the whole industry. Moreover, if such vehicles were excluded waste producers might be in some doubt about whether they were adequately discharging their duty of care when using the collection authority's services.

8.35 An important function of registration will be to identify those permitted to carry waste for hire or reward. We therefore **recommend** that each vehicle covered by a registration should display a conspicuous sign which immediately identifies that vehicle as such. This sign should be as visible and as readily identifiable as, for instance, 'Haz-Chem' or 'L' plates and should show an expiry date so that waste producers can readily check whether the registration is current.

8.36 In addition to these arrangements the third arm of our proposals (paragraph 8.30) is the need to establish an audit trail to enable the regulatory authorities to monitor the security of the waste stream and to assist the producer of waste in proving that his duty of care has been discharged. This will mean that paperwork associated with the movement of waste will have to be established where it does not already exist. There are many precedents for this: for instance, no item of value is moved in the course of business without an invoice or delivery note; deliveries made under the Petroleum Spirit (Conveyance by Road) Regulations 1957 have to be recorded on prescribed certificates; the operation of heavy goods vehicles has to be logged by use of a tachograph; and in the United States hazardous wastes must invariably be accompanied by a detailed manifest (Plate 19).

8.37 Since stringent documentation requirements for movements of special waste are included in the Control of Pollution (Special Waste) Regulations 1980, the main effect of our proposals will be to require adequate documentation for movements of other controlled wastes. This documentation can be quite simple. Thus, the consignment note accompanying such waste should specify who is consigning the waste, to whom it is being consigned and the nature of the waste itself. The note would, therefore, be much simpler than that prescribed for special waste or the example illustrated in Plate 19. The consignment note would be receipted by the registered transporter or, where the producer uses his own transport, by the disposer or ultimate recipient of the waste. The producer would retain a copy as proof of discharge of his duty of care and copies would travel with the waste for retention in the records of the transporter and the disposal site operator, where they would be available for inspection by the enforcement authorities. Full details of these procedures, including guidance on the important question of describing the waste accurately, would be included in the Code of Practice which we recommended should underpin the producer's duty of care (paragraph 8.21).

Disposers of waste
Landfill
8.38 Both the House of Lords Select Committee on Science and Technology([5]) and the joint review committee([6]) examined in detail the provision and enforcement of the existing law on the landfill disposal of wastes and the Landfill Practices Review Group([7]) has set out its views on the standards and best practices that should apply to landfill. Many of our witnesses have also drawn attention to deficiencies in the drafting and enforceability of the relevant statutes. Their general concerns are summarised by West Midlands County Council:

> 'The purpose and intention of the Control of Pollution Act 1974 and the Regulations made thereunder are quite clear. However, they are, in the County's view, a very poor example of legal draftsmanship. Put quite bluntly, it is often possible by applying

the strict rules of legal interpretation to either wholly or at least partially defeat the object of the legislation.'

8.39 Particular concern has been expressed to us about:

- the poor enforceability of many of the conditions attached to waste disposal site licences;

- the inability of waste disposal authorities to refuse site licences to operators known to be unsatisfactory;

- the unduly lengthy process for appeals against licence conditions;

- the need for site licence conditions to cover matters of restoration and aftercare;

- the ease with which licence holders can renounce their licences and consequent responsibilities for a landfill site;

- the great disparity of standards and practices required by waste disposal authorities in different areas.

The last of these problems was discussed in detail in the first report of the Hazardous Waste Inspectorate[17] and we have referred elsewhere (paragraph 7.23) to the need for greater consistency in landfill standards and for greater recognition of the level of landfill charges below which poor practice must be suspected. We discuss below each of the other deficiences listed above.

8.40 *Enforceability of conditions*: Concern about the enforceability of site licence conditions stems from the fact that the offence created by section 3 of the Control of Pollution Act 1974 is failure 'to deposit controlled waste ... in accordance with the conditions, if any, specified in the licence'. It has, therefore, been held that the actual deposition of waste is a necessary component of the offence. However, only four of the 37 model conditions suggested in DoE's Waste Management Paper on site licensing[203] are concerned with the deposition of waste. The majority relate to the proper management of the site as a whole and cover such matters as fencing, monitoring and the keeping of records. Breach of such a licence condition is, therefore, an offence only in so far as it renders any concurrent deposition of waste illegal. If it were made an offence in its own right, waste disposal authorities would have the means to enforce licence conditions intended to secure good landfill practice. At present the only option available to them is to threaten to revoke the licence, which may in fact be the outcome preferred by an operator who is not fulfilling the conditions of his site licence (see also paragraph 8.45).

8.41 *Refusal of site licences*: As the law stands at present, waste disposal authorities must grant site licence applications if planning permission exists for the use of the site for waste disposal and if water resources and public health are not threatened. This means that they cannot refuse a licence even to applicants whom they know to be unsuitable, perhaps as a consequence of enforcement action at another site, provided they satisfy these conditions. The introduction of some concept of good repute or professional competence, comparable to that used in operator licensing, would enable waste disposal authorities to take account of the qualifications and previous conduct of applicants when determining site licence applications.

8.42 *Appeals* : Applicants dissatisfied with a waste disposal authority's decision on their site licence application have a right of appeal to the Secretary of State. In the case of new applications that are declined or granted subject to conditions unacceptable to the applicant, the application is held in abeyance until the appeal is determined. However, waste disposal authorities are also entitled to impose additional conditions on an existing licence, perhaps as a consequence of new information becoming available about a site. In such circumstances, and when the disposal authority proposes to revoke a licence, the lodging of an appeal suspends the disposal authority's proposals until the appeal is determined unless the authority can show that there is a serious risk to water resources or public health. There is, however, no prescribed time limit by which applicants have to lodge the particulars of their appeal. Unscrupulous licence holders can therefore manipulate the procedure for appeals to their advantage, even to the extent of accelerating tipping regardless of the environmental consequences, in the face of impending revocation or tightening of the site licence. The prescription of a rigid time limit for appeals, with the waste disposal authority's proposals deemed to be granted in default, would prevent further such manipulation in future. It would, of course, be incumbent on the Secretary of State to expedite the determination of valid appeals.

8.43 *Restoration and aftercare conditions*: The need for waste disposal authorities to be able to impose site licence conditions that relate to periods in addition to those during which waste is actually deposited at a site was considered in detail by the joint review committee. The most usual such conditions would cover matters of site restoration and aftercare, including monitoring. It is possible for some limited requirements for site restoration to be imposed by planning authorities, for example when granting planning permission for minerals extraction, and the Department of the Environment told us that it is now usual for such conditions to be imposed. Until recently, however, planning authorities were unable to review the conditions attached to permissions for minerals extraction (which may be active for several decades), to take account of developments in technology and best recommended practices, without risking claims for substantial compensation.

8.44 This position was changed recently by Regulations([204]) which set thresholds below which planning authorities are not liable to pay compensation if they feel it necessary to tighten conditions already attached to permission for minerals extraction. While we welcome this development, we also feel that it is very important for the life cycle of a landfill site to be planned and managed as a single entity. The success of each phase depends on that of the previous one. Thus, while the planning process is the correct mechanism for determining whether landfill is an appropriate or acceptable use of land and for imposing conditions which will determine what further uses that land is capable of once landfilling has ceased, it is preferable for detailed conditions relating to the proper operation and aftercare of the site while it is still a landfill to be contained within the single framework of the site licence. While the licence is in force the waste disposal authority can seek to raise standards, by imposing new or amended conditions, in the light of technical developments and experience during the lifetime of the site (see also paragraph 8.42).

8.45 *Arrangements for surrender of licences*: Site licence conditions on restoration, aftercare or other matters will, however, be of little practical effect if a licence holder is able to renounce his licence at any time merely by informing the waste disposal authority of his intention to do so, as he is currently entitled to do under section 8 of the Control of Pollution Act 1974. In such circumstances some responsibility for the prevention of pollution from the site may revert to the owner of the land concerned, but such responsibility may be unwelcome and in practice the landowner may not be in a position to take over management of the site, at least in the short term. We therefore feel that a licence holder's ability to renounce his licence should be constrained by the need to ensure continuity in the safe management of the site. We discuss in Chapter IX various other means of ensuring that waste disposal sites do not become sources of environmental or financial liability in the future.

8.46 We consider that all the deficiences discussed above can and should be remedied. Accordingly, we **recommend** that the Control of Pollution Act 1974 should be amended:

- to make clear that a breach of waste disposal site licence conditions is an offence in its own right, unrelated to any deposition of waste;

- to empower waste disposal authorities to have regard to the qualifications and previous conduct of applicants when determining site licence applications;

- to provide that, unless otherwise agreed by the parties concerned, an appellant against a decision of a waste disposal authority in respect of a disposal site licence shall have three months in which to present his case to the Secretary of State, failing which the authority's decision shall take effect;

- to make clear that waste disposal authorities are entitled to impose site licence conditions that relate to periods additional to those during which waste is being deposited at a site;

- to provide that the holder of a waste disposal licence shall be permitted to surrender that licence only if the waste disposal authority or, on appeal, the Secretary of State is satisfied that adequate arrangements have been made for the continued safe management or aftercare of the site.

Incineration

8.47 Statutory control over the operation of chemical incineration works registered under the provisions of the Alkali etc. Works Regulation Act 1906 and the Health and Safety at Work etc. Act 1974 is exercised by the Industrial Air Pollution Inspectorate in England and Wales and by HM Industrial Pollution Inspectorate in Scotland. These incineration works are required to operate according to the best practicable means as set out in published Inspectorate notes([205]). These cover such matters as the design and operation of plant, receipt and handling of materials, flue gas treatment and monitoring. We discussed the technical details of some of these requirements earlier (see paragraphs 7.29–7.32). Although some of our witnesses have been concerned at the adequacy of the resources available to the Inspectorate, we have received no evidence that the basic law or mechanism for its enforcement in this area is inadequate. However, in view of the importance which we attach to the continued availability of chemical incineration facilities in the United Kingdom, we urge the Inspectorate to pay particular attention to technical developments in this field, including those which may arise from the surveys and research now in progress (see paragraph 11.13), and to ensure that these are reflected in its future statements of what constitute the best practicable means for the design and operation of chemical incinerators.

8.48 Control over municipal and most other commercial incinerators is exercised by local authority environmental health departments in accordance with the provisions of the Clean Air Acts and again we have received no evidence to suggest that, in the majority of cases, this control mechanism in inadequate. However, we have received considerable evidence that the scope of this control mechanism is inadequate in that it does not effectively extend to a major class of incinerators - namely those operated by health authorities, a significant proportion of which would fail to meet the standards required by the Acts. Although case law([206]) has established that section 22 of the Clean Air Act 1956, which entitles local authorities to report and requires the Secretary of State to investigate instances of air pollution from Government and Crown premises, applies to NHS premises, in practice this section appears to be little used. We appreciate the rationale underlying the concept of Crown immunity and see no practical alternative to the notion that activities for which Ministers are directly responsible should aim to satisfy the spirit of the law from which they are in reality exempt. However, we consider it to be a historical anomaly that the National Health Service, which operates under the general guidance but not the day-to-day control of a Minister of the Crown, should have any lesser restriction on its entitlement to pollute or contaminate the environment than comparable bodies in the same field, such as private hospitals or clinics, or with analogous links to Ministers, such as the National Radiological Protection Board, British Nuclear Fuels plc and the Research Councils.

8.49 The disquiet which has recently been expressed by the Institution of Environmental Health Officers([207]) and others about a potentially more serious problem (although outside our terms of reference) - the allegedly poor standards of hygiene in many hospital kitchens - and a recent report on the incidence of insects and other pests in hospitals([208]) only serve to reinforce our view. Accordingly, we **recommend** that Crown immunity should cease to apply to the National Health Service and that incineration and other waste disposal facilities operated by or on behalf of the NHS should, in consequence, be subject to exactly the same controls and standards as similar facilities operated by other organisations.

Penalties and pillories

8.50 Even the best law counts for nothing if it is not adequately enforced or if the penalties for breaking it are derisory. Indeed, several of our witnesses have said that many problems in the field of waste management persist at least as much because of insufficient vigour in application of the existing law as from any deficiencies in the statutes themselves. We comment in Chapter IX on the role played by the different statutory authorities. We discuss here the penalties appropriate for those convicted of offences under waste management legislation.

8.51 The principal concern put to us on this issue is that fines which are small in relation to the extra profit made (or cost avoided) by the offender by virtue of his offence are no real penalty and, far from deterring further offences, may actually encourage them. A further concern is that the costs which fall on public agencies such as waste disposal authorities and water authorities for cleaning up illegal deposits of waste can in some cases be very substantial (as, indeed, can the costs of bringing a prosecution) and that, unless such agencies see that offenders are adequately deterred by fines, they can become increasingly reluctant to mount investigations and prosecutions following pollution incidents.

8.52 The range of offences to which our attention has been drawn in this matter includes the deliberate discharge of liquid waste into a stream, illegal disposal of toxic waste on a municipal tip and by dumping at sea, and fly tipping of building rubble and other potentially more hazardous materials. The common feature is that the costs (if any) incurred in disposing of the waste illegally, even including any subsequent fines, are considerably less than the costs, including in some cases significant transport costs, of proper disposal.

8.53 The Lord Chancellor has expressed firm views on this subject in speeches to magistrates:

> 'Whilst I am on fines I would like to express, again subjectively, that whilst magistrates' courts on the whole sentence adequately, especially where The Magistrates' Association recommends a penalty, there is a whole range of cases, usually profit-related, e.g. the overloading of vehicles or keeping them in an unsafe condition, or offences relating to public health, where fines are frequently ridiculously small. When fines are used as a means of disposal they must be high enough to establish that illegal behaviour can be seen not to pay.'([209])

'I was speaking out, as I have done on numerous occasions, at the often derisory financial penalties handed down at petty sessions for statutory offences affecting public health, the safety of employees or the public, or pollution. In some cases the statutory maximum may be inadequate and, if so, that is not your fault. But on the assumption that the maxima are given to you to use I recommend a certain vigour in using them. Take, for instance, the offence known as "fly-tipping", that is the unlawful disposal of waste material. It may be that the maximum penalty is £1,000* or six months. But I am told by my advisers that if you fine an offender even as much as £250, the financial benefit of the offence is likely to outweigh the penalty by as much as fifty times. It is worth studying these things, as otherwise you will find the offender, even when he is found out, laughing all the way from the court to the bank. I am sure you would wish to avoid that if you can.'[210]

8.54 The Magistrates' Association was unable to say whether the Lord Chancellor's remarks had resulted in any change in sentencing for the offences mentioned. The Association did, however, point out that waste management prosecutions were likely to arise only occasionally before any particular Bench and that magistrates may therefore be unfamiliar with the relevant legislation and the gravity of the offence as seen by those responsible for enforcing the legislation. The Association felt that, in such circumstances, the most effective way of ensuring that adequate penalties were imposed was for the prosecution to put the court in possession of all the relevant facts, including an appreciation of the profit which the defendant may have derived from disregarding the law and of the extent to which the offence was committed innocently, deliberately or by mere ineptitude. 'If the case is inadequately presented, it is almost inevitable that the court will err on the side more favourable to the defendant'[211]. However, to supplement the efforts of prosecuting solicitors in presenting their cases, we **recommend** that the Lord Chancellor should arrange for formal advice to be given to magistrates of the serious and possibly long-term damage to the environment that can be caused by improper handling and disposal of waste and of the need to sentence offenders accordingly.

8.55 In Table 8.1 we list the maximum sentences available for a selection of waste management offences and in the box on page 123 we give some examples of the results of prosecutions reported in local newspapers. In the box on page 124 we show the results of a selection of prosecutions in the United States over approximately the same period. Even though the cases quoted have not been selected systematically, the contrasts in the scale of penalties are striking, though we note that in nearly all cases the penalties constitute only a fraction of the maximum available. We also note that prosecutions in both countries are directed at individuals as well as companies.

---

* In May 1984 the maximum fine was increased to £2,000.

8.56 Publicity can also be an important weapon of enforcement, and there are ways and means by which pollution control authorities can turn it to their advantage without, of course, in any way interfering with the process of justice. The opprobrium of being convicted can have just as severe an impact as the imposition of a substantial fine on an individual's attitude to the environment and to his responsibilities for safeguarding it. Where a company is involved in an alleged offence, proceedings are more likely to attract attention in the press if they are brought against directors as individuals as well as against the company, particularly if high fines are imposed.

TABLE 8.1

Maximum penalties for some offences involving waste

offence	on summary conviction- Magistrates Court	on conviction on indictment- Crown Court
CONTROL OF POLLUTION ACT 1974		
s3(1) - deposit of controlled waste on land without site licence or in breach of licence conditions	£2000 fine	2 years imprisonment and/or unlimited fine
s3(3) - as above, but where an 'environmental hazard' exists; also applies to wastes other than controlled	6 months imprisonment and/or £2000 fine	5 years imprisonment and/or unlimited fine
s5 - giving false information in licence application	£2000 fine	2 years imprisonment and/or unlimited fine
s16 - failure to comply with notice from WDA requiring removal of waste deposited in breach of s3	£2000 fine plus £50 fine daily for non-compliance	not indictable
s17 : Control of Pollution (Special Waste) Regulations 1980, reg. 16 - failure to comply with direction of Secretary of State under reg. 15 to accept and dispose of special waste at named site	£400 fine	not indictable
- failure to comply with requirements of regulations other than reg. 15	£1000 fine	2 years imprisonment and/or unlimited fine
REFUSE DISPOSAL (AMENITY) ACT 1978		
s2 - abandoning anything without lawful authority in the open air or on a highway	£100 fine; £200 fine on subsequent offence; and/or 3 months imprisonment	not indictable
LITTER ACT 1983		
s1(3) - leaving litter in a public place	£400 fine	not indictable

Examples of successful prosecutions for waste disposal offences in the United Kingdom		
The Offence	*The Defendant*	*Result*
Deposition of 20-30 gallons of waste industrial oil on company's land.	Waste disposal company	£50 fine + £50 costs
Failure to complete consignment note for 12 drums of concentrated hydrochloric acid.	Health Authority	£50 fine + £50 costs
6 offences of permitting controlled waste (household rubbish, demolition material, slurry/paint tins/asbestos) to be deposited on unlicensed site and 3 offences of depositing same.	Owner of site	£900 fine + £50 costs
3 offences of causing unauthorised deposit of controlled wastes at licensed site (asbestos sludge over a period of 4 years) and	Building firm (originator)	£10,000 fine
3 offences of depositing same.	Haulage contractor	£5,000 fine
Source: Macrory and Withers([212])		

Examples of successful prosecutions for waste disposal offences in the United States		
The Offence	*The Defendant*	*Result*
Waste transporter dumped 600 gallons of liquid wastes containing xylene, ethanol, toluene and other solvents into a stream bed.	Haulage company	$25,000 fine + $6,000 damages.
A motor vehicle repair company paid an employee to dispose of 16 55-gallon drums of paint thinner waste. The drums were dumped at roadside locations.	Company	$15,000 fine.
	Company chairman	$15,000 fine + 3 year suspended prison sentence.
	Employee	$250 fine + 3 year suspended prison sentence + 2 years' probation.
A weed control company dumped 60 55-gallon drums of tar, paint wastes, and industrial solvents which rusted and leaked into the ravine used as a dumping site.	Company	$1000 fine.
A metal fabrication and processing plant discharged 4,000 gallons of toxic wastes containing chromium and corrosive chemicals into the sewer system.	Company	$75,000 fine + $250,000 damages + required to advertise offence in the Wall Street Journal, at cost of $34,410.
	Company vice-president	1,000 hours community service + 1 year probation.

Note: Maximum fine for these offences is at least $25,000, ranging up to $1,650,000 in one case, with maximum prison sentences from 0 to 70 years depending on the offence or group of offences the defendant is charged with.

Source: United States General Accounting Office([213])

CHAPTER IX

WASTE MANAGEMENT PLANNING AND ADMINISTRATION

Introduction

9.1 Effective waste management requires the integrated planning of apparently disparate activities that take place on a wide range of scales - from the emptying of domestic dustbins to the selection of regional landfill sites and the international movement of wastes for treatment. Operational responsibility for some activities can be local, but planning needs to be undertaken on a large scale if the best practicable environmental options are to be identified and adopted. Linkages are extensive and the consequences of changes in waste streams can be far reaching.

9.2 Economies of scale and developing technology, for example in landfill practices and incineration, favour increasingly large-scale plant and sites, with large catchment areas to ensure efficient use of capacity. This in turn requires increasingly professional management, with need for access to sophisticated research, analysis and other facilities. Local authorities need to match industry's expertise both as disposers of waste themselves and in their planning, supervisory and enforcement roles.

Development Control

9.3 Whatever national and regional waste management plans are made, their implementation is through decisions on individual applications for planning permission, without which site licences cannot be issued. The development control system therefore has a part to play in securing effective waste management; indeed, it has been suggested that the planning discipline fostered by the United Kingdom's long established development control system has helped to avoid most of the irresponsible dumping of wastes that has left a troublesome legacy in some other countries. We have, however, already indicated (paragraph 8.44) that it is not an adequate mechanism for detailed regulation of the operation and aftercare of a landfill site.

9.4 However, satisfactory arrangements for the management and disposal of waste from an industrial plant should be an integral part of the plant's design and should be required before planning permission is given. Arrangements should not be accepted as satisfactory unless all reasonable steps are taken to avoid, reduce in volume and detoxify the expected waste on site. A

125

hazard and operability or similar study (see paragraph 10.8) should be part of the design of any process and the EC Directive on Environmental Impact Assessment([214]) require assessment of the waste management aspects of major new projects.

9.5 Landfill is and will remain the major disposal route for most wastes in the UK and so planning decisions to allow sites to be used for landfill should be taken with particular care. Planning permissions for mineral extraction now cover arrangements not only for the disposal of mineral wastes but also for site restoration, though the rate of restoration may in some cases be limited by shortages of suitable waste and other fill material. Restoration was not always considered so important nor were the techniques of restoration so well developed: a survey undertaken by mineral planning authorities for the Department of the Environment in 1982 showed that restoration conditions either were unsatisfactory or did not exist for about 32% of the 100,000 hectares of permitted surface mineral workings in England and for about 59% of the 18,300 hectares permitted for the surface disposal of mineral wastes. The conditions for satisfactory reclamation of 11,000 hectares of surface mineral workings depended on the use of waste imported as fill from elsewhere([215]).

9.6 Mineral extraction generates the majority of voids used for landfill and it is, therefore, particularly important that the cycle of mineral extraction, waste disposal and site restoration should be seen as a single entity. Evidence from DoE Land Wastes and Minerals Divisions illustrates that there is in some areas a considerable disparity between the availability of suitable voids and demands for landfill capacity. The fact that the Greater London Council finds it necessary to send waste considerable distances - for example, by rail to Bedfordshire and by barge to Essex - for disposal illustrates the scarcity of landfill capacity close to London. Pressure on existing landfill capacity close to all major urban areas will inevitably increase, particularly if public opposition increasingly prevents new sites that are technically suitable for landfill being used for this purpose.

9.7 We conclude, therefore, that landfill capacity is already a scarce resource in some parts of the country and will become increasingly so in others. It should, therefore, be conserved by being used only for the disposal of wastes for which it clearly constitutes the best practicable environmental option. The recommendations we have made on avoiding waste and reducing the waste stream will, therefore, need to be applied with particular vigour in these areas.

Waste management plans

9.8 Section 2 of the Control of Pollution Act 1974 requires Waste Disposal Authorities to prepare and revise plans for the disposal of controlled wastes in their areas. The section was brought into force in 1978 but only 16 out of 46 Waste Disposal Authorities in England have yet taken their first Plans through to completion, though a further 12 are at an advanced stage of preparation. In Wales the Secretary of State has been promised all 37 plans from district councils by the end of 1985 and in Scotland most district and island councils have plans that are either completed or at an advanced stage of preparation[200]. The Local Government Planning and Land Act 1980 removed the power of the Secretary of State to set a timetable for completion of Plans. The Secretary of State does not have to confirm waste disposal plans, but he may determine disputes between authorities about proposed disposal of waste from one area in another.

9.9 The House of Lords Select Committee on Science and Technology[5] considered that 'in present circumstances the sum of unsynchronised and largely independent planning by 165 waste disposal authorities can hardly be expected to produce a coherent whole'. The impending abolition of the GLC and Metropolitan County Councils and the evolution of new arrangements for waste disposal in metropolitan areas will not only add to the total number of waste disposal authorities but will also render some existing plans and drafts out of date. Despite the drawbacks seen by the Select Committee and reiterated by some of our witnesses, the need for each waste disposal authority to compile a plan at least acts as an incentive for the authority to review present practices and invite public scrutiny. We therefore **recommend** that all non-metropolitan waste disposal authorities should complete their waste disposal plans forthwith, that new or revised plans covering waste disposal in Metropolitan areas and Greater London should be completed by 31 March 1987, and that all plans should be regularly updated.

Local authorities' responsibilities for waste management

9.10 Since reorganisation of local government in 1974, waste management and disposal has been a statutory responsibility of County Councils (including the Greater London Council) in England. In Wales it is the responsibility of District Councils, and in Scotland of District and Island Councils. The operation of these responsibilities at different levels of local government in different parts of the UK for over a decade has provided an opportunity to assess whether there is any correlation between the quality of service that a waste disposal authority can provide and the status and size of that authority. The evidence available suggests that there is such a correlation. For example, several of our witnesses have pointed to the greater range of expertise available in larger authorities and to problems, such as inadequate forward planning for the provision of landfill capacity, arising essentially from parochial attitudes and pressures in smaller ones. The Prince of Wales' Committee noted that a third of the waste disposal authorities in Wales had fewer than three technical waste disposal staff and could identify only one hydrogeologist working on the assessment of landfill sites anywhere in the Principality. In contrast, we and many of our witnesses have been impressed by the expertise of the teams of staff that have been established at county level and by the range of sophisticated laboratory facilities at their disposal. We met members of the teams and inspected some of the facilities in London and the West Midlands during our study. As the Hazardous Waste Inspectorate has observed([17]), the presence of such teams and facilities has enabled the disposal authorities concerned to be effective regulatory bodies (see paragraph 10.3).

9.11 The allocation of responsibilities for waste management in metropolitan areas was a major point of debate during passage of the Local Government Act 1985, giving effect to the Government's proposals in the White Paper 'Streamlining the Cities'([216]), as amplified for waste disposal in a consultation document issued by DOE in November 1983([217]). Such was our concern lest the manner in which the Government's proposals were implemented should undermine local government's abilities to protect the environment in metropolitan areas that we wrote to the Secretary of State in June 1984 and February 1985 to seek reassurance. Our letters and the replies from the Secretary of State are reproduced in Appendix 4. An interim report by the House of Lords Select Committee on Science and Technology([218]) on the provision of scientific services in local government drew further attention to the importance of maintaining intact the centres of expertise developed on such matters as environmental protection. The House of Lords amended the Bill, to provide for the establishment of statutory waste disposal authorities for Greater London and the Metropolitan County areas([219]), but the Commons restored the provision in an amended form, giving the Secretary of State a duty to set up statutory authorities in the absence of satisfactory agreement between the district authorities concerned([220]). We note that, if he has to use these powers, he is required by section 10(2) of the Local Government Act 1985 to have 'particular regard to the need for satisfactory arrangements in respect of hazardous waste'.

9.12 Under section 10(1) of the 1985 Act, Metropolitan District and London Borough Councils have until 15 November 1985 to make arrangements which the Secretary of State considers satisfactory for discharging the responsibilties for waste regulation and disposal which they will inherit on 1 April 1986. As we sign this Report it seems probable that proposals made by the district councils in Tyne and Wear, South Yorkshire, West Yorkshire and West Midlands and by at least two groups of London Boroughs will be acceptable to the Secretary of State but that he will decide to use his powers to prescribe arrangements in Greater Manchester and Merseyside and for most areas of Greater London. In addition, it seems likely that the Secretary of State will need to establish a single authority for all regulatory purposes for the whole of Greater London([221]).

9.13 The Select Committee on Science and Technology([5]) recommended that in Wales and Scotland waste disposal and planning responsibilities should be transferred from District to County Councils and that throughout the UK waste disposal authorities should be formally grouped on a regional basis to co-ordinate waste disposal plans and the provision of facilities and scientific services. In reply, the Government pointed out that three regional and district council groupings had been set up in central Scotland, with more informal groupings elsewhere in Scotland, and that three regional groupings of district councils, water authorities and the private sector had been set up in Wales. In general, though, the Government preferred to rely on informal regional consultations and to build on existing groups for this purpose, with central guidance being given by the Hazardous Waste Inspectorate and other Divisions of the Department of the Environment([200]).

9.14 Nevertheless, following the Select Committee's Report, the Government did decide to review the decision, which dated from reorganisation of local government in England and Wales in 1974, to leave responsibility for waste disposal in Wales with the District authorities. The original basis for that decision had been that it would be wasteful to provide separate administrative organisations to deal with refuse collection and disposal in sparsely populated areas. The Welsh Office review revealed scope for improved performance and in February 1984 the Secretary of State for Wales announced that, unless the district councils managed to work together to plan and develop waste management strategies on a wider basis, the possiblity of transferring responsibility to the County Councils would again be considered([222]). The position is to be formally reviewed at the end of 1985 and a decision taken at the end of 1986.

9.15 Thus, the adequacy of arrangements for waste regulation and disposal in Wales, in the metropolitan areas of England and in Greater London will continue to be under particularly close scrutiny in 1986. It would be unrealistic to propose yet a further reorganisation of responsibilities, on a regional basis, before the outcome of the further review in Wales and the consequences of the Local Government Act 1985 for waste management in metropolitan areas of England have been properly assessed. However, like the Select Committee on Science and Technology([5]), we see several advantages in the organisation of waste management on a regional basis. It would avoid undue parochialism (see also paragraph 12.25), enable authorities to be of sufficient size to employ a full range of technical specialists and, by bringing together all aspects of waste management affecting a large area, would facilitate identification and adoption of the best practicable environmental options for waste disposal. We note that the Water Act 1973 created water authorities whose areas are based on river basins and water catchment areas. Waste management can also be considered in terms of catchment areas and the control and supervision of material flows. Accordingly, we **recommend** that, if doubt persists about the adequacy of arrangements for waste regulation and disposal in any part of the United Kingdom, the Government should give further consideration to the scope for reorganising these arrangements on a regional basis.

Avoiding future problems

9.16 We have discussed in the previous two chapters the technical aspects of the management and aftercare of landfill sites (paragraphs 7.2-7.22) and have recommended that waste disposal authorities should be able to make explicit provision for aftercare in site licences, and that site operators should be allowed to relinquish their responsibilities provided that they can satisfy waste disposal authorities that satisfactory arrangements have been made for continued management and aftercare of their sites (paragraphs 8.43-8.45). One such arrangement would be for an operator to transfer responsibility for site management to a third party - perhaps the landowner, or more likely a private company or the waste disposal authority.

9.17 Problems may remain, however, with former landfill sites that change hands, perhaps after the period of active aftercare and management and with sites whose operators or owners lack the financial resources to undertake remedial measures in the event of some failure that results in pollution. There may also be a need for better safeguards against sites being redeveloped in unsuitable ways in the future. These problems may affect both sites which have been used specifically for waste disposal and those which may have been contaminated by industrial activity (see Chapter II). We discuss them under two headings.

Maintaining records of land contamination

9.18 The first aspect is the keeping of proper records. We have emphasised this in other contexts (see, for example, paragraph 8.37) and what we are concerned about here is that there should as far as possible be permanent records of sites which contain wastes or are otherwise contaminated, including details of the particular substances in them, so that unsuitable future development can be avoided. For instance, a disused landfill site may be capable of perfectly satisfactory redevelopment provided that the clay capping is not disturbed (see paragraph 7.7).

9.19 The existing system of landfill site licensing, particularly if coupled with enforcement of best standards as recommended by the Landfill Practices Review Group (see paragraph 7.4) and in this Report, should be adequate to prevent unsuitable future development of currently licensed sites. However, current controls may be less effective in preventing contamination of industrial sites. In principle the site licensing provisions (and the special waste regulations) apply as rigorously to on-site waste disposal as to off-site operations, but there is likely to be less day-to-day supervision by the waste disposal authority and the future safety of the site is therefore all the more dependent on the industrialist exercising proper care.

9.20 Because of these potential problems, a number of witnesses have suggested that the law should be changed so that any known contamination or potential contamination of land should be registered as a local land charge. We noted earlier (paragraph 2.54) that it was important for local authorities to collate information about contaminated land during the preparation of local plans and structure plan alterations and to have regard to this information when considering applications for development under planning legislation. We consider that this information should be readily available to the public and, in particular, to prospective purchasers of land. Whilst we have not been able, on the evidence before us, to determine what would be the most appropriate mechanism for making such information available, we nevertheless

recommend that the Government should review the present system of land registration with a view to establishing whether it would be desirable and feasible for the fact that land is contaminated to be registered as a local land charge.

Insurance of waste disposal operations

9.21 The recommendation we have made on the surrender of site licences (paragraph 8.46) will go some way to meet the problem of the operator who simply walks away from his responsibilities. But what if the operator lacks the resources to comply? Dissatisfaction with the prospect of the taxpayer or ratepayer having to foot the bill has led many to suggest that waste disposal site operators should carry compulsory 'environmental impairment' insurance. For instance, the House of Lords Select Committee on Science and Technology[5] commented:

> 'Bonds from site operators to insure against environmental
> damage, especially after site closure, are strongly encouraged.'

9.22 It would require primary legislation for insurance to be a universal requirement (the Secretary of State having had no powers, since the enactment of the Local Government Planning and Land Act 1980, to make regulations laying down conditions that must be imposed in site licences); nor is it possible under current Department of the Environment policy for waste disposal authorities to require insurance at their discretion. Even though section 6(2) of the Control of Pollution Act 1974 says that 'a disposal licence may include such conditions as the disposal authority which issues it sees fit to specify in the licence', the Secretary of State's policy, in determining appeals under section 10 of the Act against site licence conditions, has been to regard the imposition of conditions requiring a bond, or insurance cover securing due compliance with other conditions, as being outside the scope of section 6(2)[223]. We understand that this policy is currently under review.

9.23 There are several forms insurance could take:

(a)   compulsory environmental impairment insurance, individual operators being free to seek the best terms they are able to secure on the insurance market;

(b)   performance bonds lodged with the waste disposal authority; these would normally take the form of a guarantee by an insurance company or other financial institution, for which the operator would pay interest or premiums; or

(c)   mutual insurance schemes - for example, a managed sinking fund operated through a mutual company in which all operators are shareholders.

9.24 Experience in the United States suggests that the prospects for the first of these categories are poor[224]. The Environmental Protection Agency insists that hazardous waste handlers must have insurance cover for both 'sudden and accidental pollution' (this would cover disasters as at the Bhopal chemical plant) and 'environmental impairment liability' (i.e. arising from gradual pollution such as seepage into groundwater); alternatively they must be able to demonstrate that they have sufficient financial strength to handle claims on their own([225]). It is now virtually impossible for US companies to obtain cover on reasonable terms. This may have something to do with the very broad way in which US Courts tend to interpret the concept of negligence and fault; it may be also be connected with the prevelance of litigation by citizens' groups.

9.25 The current attitude of the European insurance industry, although cautious, appears not yet to have hardened on the lines of its US counterpart. We know of one landfill operator in England who has obtained insurance on favourable terms because he has been able to demonstrate a high level of professionalism, backed by monitoring by an independent consultant. An important feature of his policy is that it provides cover for public and products liability on a no-fault basis in the event of an enforcement notice served by the waste disposal authority or other statutory body.

9.26 It would seem that performance bonds are in general difficult to obtain. In its response to the recommendation (cited above) of the House of Lords Select Committee on Science and Technology, the Government stated:

'The Department of the Environment have conducted some preliminary investigations into the possibilities of a bonding scheme but there appear to be substantial practical difficulties. Consultations carried out hitherto with the insurance industry would suggest that there is little prospect of performance bonds being issued to cover the liability of site operators for environmental damage and that this would be better covered by some form of environmental impairment insurance or by a sinking fund. The Department are currently reconsidering the possibilities.'([200])

9.27 The experience with mutual insurance schemes appears more promising. For example, there are parallels in the fund established by the Association of British Travel Agents to relieve stranded holidaymakers and in the mutual insurance schemes of the shipping industry against major oil pollution disasters([11]). The advantage of a mutual fund is that it can remain in existence even though not all of the original contributors may still be in business. There may however be problems where there are great disparities in the standards observed by members of a scheme. It is therefore essential that premiums should be sufficiently discriminatory to recognise that good management means low risk. The cost of cover should be directly related to the individual insured's track record, as an incentive to raise standards of performance and to deter 'cowboys'. Otherwise the unscrupulous might carry out temporary cosmetic work but leave behind a long-term pollution trail for the fund to resolve at some future date.

9.28 We believe that, despite these difficulties, it is important to pursue the matter of insurance. We therefore welcome the fact that the Department of the Environment is doing this as part of the follow-up to the work of the Landfill Practices Review Group, even though we regret that the discussion of the subject which the Group's full report was expected to contain is now being omitted. We have been informed that the Department intends to incorporate some information on the issue in a revised version of Waste Management Paper No.4 (on site licensing), but we suspect that it may need rather more vigourous pursuit. Whilst we make no recommendation as to whether environmental impairment insurance should be compulsory for all waste disposal site operators, we consider that it is unsatisfactory that waste disposal authorities are not at present able to stipulate it as a condition of site licences. We **recommend** that, if the Department of the Environment's review of its application of section 6(2) of the Control of Pollution Act 1974 suggests that the sub-section does not permit the imposition of insurance or bonding requirements as conditions of waste disposal site licences, the sub-section should be amended to make clear that such requirements can be so imposed. We also **recommend** that model insurance and bonding requirements should be developed and embodied in appropriate codes of practice.

9.29 The possible use of insurance or analogous arrangements has been suggested in two other contexts:

(a)   to cover the costs of disposing of hazardous materials from abandoned or derelict industrial premises, particularly in the event of business failure or bankruptcy;

(b)   to cover the costs of decontaminating and reclaiming contaminated land.

9.30 In the first context, a number of witnesses have emphasised to us the problem of businesses which fail, leaving stocks of waste or other materials to be cleared up (Plate 14), usually at public expense. Waste disposal authorities already have powers to prevent the accumulation of waste on process sites, and if used with determination they ought to be adequate for preventing potential problems of site abandonment. In the event of a company's insolvency, it may be that the cost of rendering safe a site left in a hazardous state has to fall on the local authority, at least in the first instance, in the interests of removing the hazard as soon as possible. Short of some universal compulsory insurance requirement, there are probably no effective economic incentives to deter companies from abandoning materials in these circumstances; and even making the local authority's costs a prior claim on any assets of the company in liquidation - while possibly an answer to the 'who pays?' question in some circumstances - is unlikely to deter the directors when their legal responsibilities are about to be cast off and would appear inequitable to the company's other creditors. Whilst we recognise the frustration which local authorities feel when faced with this situation, we see no case for a fundamental change in the arrangements which already apply.

9.31 In the second context, that is to say in the situation where pollution has already occurred, we regard the 'Superfund' type of approach (see paragraph 2.52), where a whole industry bears the costs of making good the shortcomings of its former members, as largely cosmetic. There may be a case in either equity or economic efficiency for passing clean-up costs of that kind on to the present customers of the polluting industry rather than to the general taxpayer, on the ground that these costs should properly have fallen on past customers; but we do not consider the case to be a strong one. We therefore do not support the concept of an environmental fund, financed through levies on industry, to meet a retrospective liability for past practices. For the future we prefer to rely on the maintenance of standards which satisfy the duty of care.

Compensation and incentives for the community

9.32 In general in the United Kingdom it is not possible for people to obtain compensation for environmental risks or nuisances arising from the activities of 'bad neighbours', apart from the limited relief available through the rating valuation system and compensation for injurious affection by public works under Part I of the Land Compensation Act 1973 (which does not cover waste disposal authority activities). We note however that in France operators of nuclear power stations and developers of disposal facilities for radioactive wastes put great emphasis on the benefits, such as improved social services and recreation facilities, for the local community that are likely to accompany the location of major facilities in their areas([226]). It appears that this has contributed to a markedly lower level of resistance to these installations in some parts of France than in Britain and Germany (although other factors may be involved too). Studies in the United States of public opposition to the siting of hazardous waste facilities have supported the hypothesis that individuals are prepared to negotiate financial compensation for accepting specified environmental risks([227]). In addition to monetary compensation (reductions in property taxes for local residents, or the imposition of special taxes on the waste facility operators), inducements might take the form of risk reductions such as increased monitoring frequency and increased supervision of those who do the monitoring. There are also studies in progress in Britain on public attitudes to the payment of compensation to individuals and the community([228]). We **recommend** that the Government should examine the appropriateness and feasibility of adapting UK law and administrative procedures to provide for some form of discretionary compensation or inducement to individuals or communities affected by waste handling and disposal sites, such that the costs fall ultimately on those who generate the waste.

9.33 It is sometimes suggested that a local community may have to bear extra costs because a facility which serves a wider area (regional or national) happens to be located in its midst. For example, during a recent adjournment debate on the Re-Chem incinerator at Pontypool, South Wales, the Parliamentary Under-Secretary of State for Wales (Mr Wyn Roberts) stated:

'Torfaen Borough Council has a large responsibility in relation to the complex subject of waste disposal. It has responsibilities as the licensing authority for the incinerator plant ... and it is responsible for seeing that its licensing conditions are met.

'The Council has asked for extra resources to undertake a programme of environmental monitoring, but it is part of a local authority's responsibility to undertake whatever monitoring it judges to be necessary.'([152])

9.34 Without going into the merits of the particular case, we consider that the situation revealed by this exchange is unacceptable, and inconsistent with the 'polluter pays' principle. This is a case of a small local authority with responsibilities as a waste disposal authority which are unique in Wales: only a handful of authorities in England (all of them much larger) have comparable responsibilities in relation to hazardous waste incinerators. We doubt whether the present rate support grant system can ever be made sufficiently flexible to allow special provision to be made in circumstances where an individual local authority has to provide in effect a national service, and we therefore consider that a different method of funding is called for.

9.35 We agree with the comment by the House of Lords Select Committee on Science and Technology([5]) that 'it is unjustifiable that ratepayers have to pay for the control and monitoring of hazardous waste disposal'. We note that the Government has accepted in principle([200]) the Committee's recommendation that, in order to avoid this problem, charges should be introduced for applications for site licences and, on a recurring basis, for the licences themselves. This proposal (which requires primary legislation) would enable waste disposal authorities to set charges at whatever level was necessary to recoup the costs of monitoring. These charges would then be reflected in the prices charged to customers of landfill and other disposal sites.

9.36 Some specialist facilities may, however, require to be monitored more intensively than would normally be considered necessary, possibly because of sensitive locations. We note that certain major health service facilities are directly funded by DHSS rather than through health authorities; and bearing in mind that the costs of the Industrial Air Pollution Inspectorate and the Hazardous Waste Inspectorate are met by the taxpayer, we believe that analogous provision should be made where waste disposal authorities have to undertake exceptional tasks. Where exceptional monitoring is required, we consider that this should normally be the responsibility of the unified pollution inspectorate which we discuss later (see paragraphs 9.42–9.47). However, it could be appropriate (as the Commission recommended in the Fifth Report) for the staff of local authority environmental health departments to act on behalf of the inspectorate under an agency arrangement. By this means there would be no financial disincentive for a community to accept the location of a facility in its area, particularly one which draws its custom from a wider area than that for which the local authority is responsible. We therefore **recommend** that the Government should introduce arrangements that would allow for the monitoring of specialist facilities which are the responsibility of a national pollution control inspectorate to be undertaken by local authorities on an agency basis.

The role of central government
Departmental staffing and organisation

9.37 We discussed earlier the role and status of local government involvement in waste regulation and disposal. Central government oversees that role by providing the law and authorising the funds with which it operates. We have, therefore, also given considerable thought to the role that central government in general, and the Department of the Environment in particular, should play in waste management planning. We have been helped in our study by the many excellent guides produced by the Department, through a series of working groups, and agree that the provision of such advice is a role that the Department should continue to develop. The existence of clear and authoritative guidance can do much to encourage uniform standards and practices and can assist enforcement agencies in their duty.

9.38 Even if the Department's role continues to be only advisory (apart, of course, from the Secretary of State's role in determining appeals), it will need sufficient staff to ensure that its advice is kept up to date and well publicised. Although we appreciate that the staff concerned have recently been under abnormal pressure - for example, advising on the Government's response to the report of the House of Lords Select Committee on Science and Technology[5], servicing the review of the Special Waste Regulations and preparing for and dealing with the waste management aspects of the Local Government Act 1985 - we are not convinced that the number of specialists currently employed is sufficient to maintain satisfactory progress in this area. At the Department's headquarters there is, for example, just one specialist on land contamination and the number of technical staff in the whole of the Division responsible for policy on management of non-radioactive wastes, including the Hazardous Waste Inspectorate, is 14. The Department's management information system for Ministers (MINIS) reveals that a number of targets, for example for revision of Waste Management Papers, are not being met[229]. Accordingly, we **recommend** that the complement of technical staff in the Department of the Environment's Land Waste and Toxic Substances Divisions should be reinforced.

9.39 We noted earlier (paragraph 9.6) the importance of concerted planning of the cycle of mineral extraction, waste disposal and site restoration. Achievement of this depends on regular contact, within both local and central government, between those with the primary responsibility for each stage of the cycle. The Department of the Environment told us that, as a result of an internal exercise known as the 'Wastelands Forum', which operated in 1983 and 1984 to co-ordinate Departmental policies for bringing vacant and derelict land back into productive use, needs for improving the inter-relationship between minerals extraction and waste disposal and the coverage of land use implications of waste disposal matters in structure and local plans were identified as issues for future action. We find it disturbing that it should take a special exercise to identify such important needs, though we note that all relevant Divisions contributed to the work of the Landfill Practices Review Group (see paragraph 7.4). Accordingly, we **recommend** that the Department of the Environment should strengthen, on a permanent basis, its arrangements for liaison between the Divisions responsible for policy on minerals extraction, waste management and land reclamation and should ensure that local authorities are likewise advised of the importance of co-ordinating their responsibilities in these areas.

The Hazardous Waste Inspectorate

9.40 Several of our witnesses and other commentators have proposed that the remit of the Hazardous Waste Inspectorate should be extended and that the Inspectorate, and the Department of the Environment generally, should play more than a largely advisory role in protecting the environment. The Inspectorate, whose establishment was first recommended by the House of Lords Select Committee on Science and Technology[5], has rapidly established itself as a forceful organisation whose advice is not to be lightly disregarded. It has interpreted its remit widely and has taken the 'hazardous' wastes in its title to refer to more than special wastes designated under section 17 of the Control of Pollution Act. We commend this and suggest that, particularly in view of our earlier comment (paragraph 2.23) that, rather than attempt to define 'hazardous waste', the aim should be to ensure that all controlled waste is handled in an appropriate manner, this position should be formally acknowledged. We therefore **recommend** that the remit of the Hazardous Waste Inspectorate should be formally designated as concerning all controlled waste.

9.41 At present the Inspectorate has no statutory existence and no powers of enforcement above those available to the rest of the Department of the Environment - which, in the field of waste management, are slight. It cannot, for example, compel waste disposal authorities or contractors to follow particular practices, and it cannot bring prosecutions. For the most part, responsibility for any enforcement action necessary against waste producers, transporters and disposers properly rests with waste disposal authorities (and, following our recommendation on registration of transporters, would also rest with the Department of Transport). However, there is at present no agency with any statutory control over the way in which waste disposal authorities operate their own facilities or supervise those operated by others. In most cases we hope that advice from the Inspectorate would be sufficient to ensure improvements, but there may be instances where this is not so and where public confidence in the operation of waste disposal authorities would be strengthened if there were some agency with the ability to compel them to meet environmentally acceptable standards. Accordingly, we **recommend** that the Hazardous Waste Inspectorate should be made a statutory body with powers of enforcement over the actions of waste disposal authorities. We also **recommend** that the Inspectorate should remain firmly as part of the Department of the Environment.

A unified Pollution Inspectorate

9.42 Our recommendation for making the Hazardous Waste Inspectorate a statutory body within the Department of the Environment prompts us to consider the relationship of this Inspectorate with comparable bodies, notably the Industrial Air Pollution Inspectorate (formerly the Alkali Inspectorate), that already exist. The Commission's Fifth Report, on which work was started in 1974 largely because of the then impending transfer of the Alkali Inspectorate from DOE to the Health and Safety Executive under the terms of the Health and Safety at Work etc. Act 1974, looked in detail at the role of such Inspectorates and the significance of their placing within government machinery.

9.43 The decision to make the Alkali Inspectorate part of HSE arose from the 1972 Report of the Committee on Safety and Health at Work, which was chaired by Lord Robens. The Committee believed that 'where the internal and external problems arise simultaneously from the same technical source, it is not sensible to divide the control arrangements'[230]. Thus the Factory Inspectorate and the Alkali Inspectorate were placed under the same management. The Committee distinguished this type of problem 'from more discontinuous matters such as arrangements for the safe disposal of liquid and solid industrial wastes, where the problems arising are of a different character'.

9.44 The Fifth Report, however, concluded that it was an over-simplification to argue that common control arrangements should apply since this ignored the great differences in the nature and scope of the two Inspectorates' interests. The Factory Inspectorate was (and still is) principally concerned with the protection of workers and of the public near the workplace, while the Alkali Inspectorate was concerned solely with air pollution and its effects on the population as a whole and on the wider environment. The distinction is the same as the one we drew earlier (paragraph 8.12) between responsibilities derived from the Health and Safety at Work etc. Act 1974 and the duty of care for the environment that is a theme of this Report.

9.45 We see no reason to dissent from the views of the Fifth Report, as further discussed in the Sixth Report and again endorsed in the Tenth Report, recommending that the Alkali Inspectorate should be returned to the Department of the Environment as the nucleus of an Inspectorate capable of ensuring an integrated approach to difficult pollution problems. Indeed, the arguments for such action are now stronger than they were in 1976 when the Fifth Report was published. As the Tenth Report noted, there has been considerable progress in tackling the grosser, traditional forms of pollution - which might be thought of as pollution of a single sector of the environment, such as the atmosphere - and concern has been growing about more subtle and complex forms of pollution with a bearing on several environmental sectors simultaneously. We therefore see a strong case for grouping together all the national inspectorates with responsibilities for environmental protection in order to ensure that they are best placed to co-ordinate their activities and to undertake the complex and demanding tasks of implementing the concept of BPEO. The Government has accepted this concept and emphasised the need for waste management policies to stand the test of the BPEO principle[123].

9.46 The Fifth Report referred to the recommended unified Inspectorate as Her Majesty's Pollution Inspectorate (HMPI). The initial organisation of such an inspectorate could be achieved essentially by grouping together staff already engaged in the relevant fields, and therefore there need be no major implications for public expenditure and manpower. We believe that the creation of such an inspectorate is essential. It would through advice, example and enforcement enhance the status and professionalism of pollution control and waste management in this country; it would be an appropriate response to the high standards of environmental protection which the public rightly expects; and placed in the Department of the Environment it would help to underpin the leading role which we would like to see the United Kingdom playing in international environmental affairs.

9.47 Accordingly, we **recommend** that the Industrial Air Pollution Inspectorate should be returned to the Department of the Environment and should there form the nucleus of a unified Pollution Inspectorate embracing also the Hazardous Waste Inspectorate, the Radiochemical Inspectorate, and those concerned with the protection of fresh and sea water.

CHAPTER X

PROFESSIONALISM: DESIGN, STANDARDS AND TRAINING

Introduction

10.1 In this Report we have developed the concept of a duty of care, which would be binding on all who have to deal with waste. We have identified specific areas where it applies and have indicated some of the practical means by which it may be fulfilled. Of these, one of the most important is for all those involved in waste management to aspire to high standards of professionalism.

10.2 By professionalism we mean the skilled and conscientious performance of tasks of all types concerned with managing wastes. Professional competence at all levels and all stages underpins the safety of any operation. If competence is suspect there can be no confidence in the reliability of the system.

10.3 That such professionalism is frequently lacking in waste management is clear from the evidence we have received and from the First Report of the Hazardous Waste Inspectorate([17]). This disclosed dramatic differences in operational standards between waste disposal sites, ranging from those conducted in accordance with current best practice to those where there was widespread ignorance of, and disregard for, the best available technical guidance. The HWI drew the conclusion, with which we concur, that bad practice was by no means uncommon. The HWI also noted that few waste disposal authorities, for various reasons, sought to manage hazardous wastes but rather operated 'in a responsive mode'. The Inspectorate noted that the GLC and the Metropolitan County Councils were generally better equipped and staffed and had had some success in curbing the activities of disreputable elements.

10.4 Several reasons for this state of affairs may be identified. One is financial: not all waste disposal authorities are prepared to allocate adequate resources to waste disposal and enforcement. Another is indifference to, or lack of awareness of, obligations with respect to waste disposal and control. Uncertainty about the future organisation of some authorities is a third factor.

10.5 However, the real cause is probably neither lack of resources nor indifference, but the fact that there is little or no incentive to achieve professionalism. In particular there is no compulsion to undertake specific training in waste management, whatever the area of responsibility - producer, site operator or control officer.

10.6 We suggest that professionalism in waste management has three important aspects. The first of these is design, to ensure that at all the stages of the production, packaging and consumption of goods and services pollution from waste is minimised. The second is the setting and observance of standards both to establish the goals to which design should work and to ensure that in everyday practice these goals are met. The third aspect is training, that is the process of acquiring both formally and through experience on the job a thorough knowledge about waste, its characteristics, the ways of disposing of it, and the effects of its disposal on the environment. In the industrial context it means, in particular, acquiring an understanding of the nature of waste as a function of the production process.

Design

10.7 Pollution prevention rarely pays better than when built in at the design stage of a project. Agreed standards of procedure for operation and for dealing with emergencies are an important element in design and, as we discuss below, we believe that the British Standards Institution should make a contribution.

10.8 Design is a complex task which goes well outside the scope of this Report, but there is one aspect of particular importance in avoiding pollution to which we wish to draw attention. At the completion of a design most chemical companies regard it as essential to carry out a Hazard and Operability (HAZOP) study or some similar procedure. (For the sake of brevity we will use HAZOP to indicate all such procedures.) HAZOP[231-235] not only subjects the proposed design to a critical analysis under the assumed conditions of operation, but tests it against other possibilities that go beyond normal expectation and past experience. In this way such a procedure will expose as complete a set as is possible of the potential hazards, including those of remote possibility. Explicit decisions can then be taken as to which hazards are unacceptable and what steps must be taken to eliminate or reduce them.

10.9 That HAZOP contributes not only to safe operation but also to cost reduction through improved design is, we believe, well recognised in the chemical industry, despite expressions from some of concern on the grounds of cost effectiveness[232]. Whilst we know that some experienced professionals feel that checking the design of a plant of a kind that is already in operation is generally straightforward and is unlikely to warrant a very formalised approach, we would point out that even a slight change in design and a move to a new site will alter the operating conditions and context so that a new assessment is necessary. Indeed there is extensive evidence showing that minor modifications to plant often contribute to accidents by vitiating original built-in protection - so much so that many companies now insist on a HAZOP review (which can, of course, usually be very much shorter than the original study) before any modification to a plant is undertaken.

10.10 We were concerned therefore to learn that the Chemical Industries Association, though satisfied that its members took care to check the competence of those to whom they consigned waste, did not enquire whether their operations had been subject to HAZOP or a similar procedure. We believe that the extent to which these types of procedures are current practice among responsible companies must lead to the conclusion that a potentially hazardous process that has not been subjected to a HAZOP or related investigation cannot be accepted as properly designed.

10.11 We consider that the practice of HAZOP should be widely used in the waste industry, particularly when hazardous waste is being moved or treated, or when co-disposal (see paragraphs 7.16-7.19) is being practised. The extent and form of the procedure will be determined by the complexity of the operation. We **recommend** that an appropriate hazard and operability or similar study should be undertaken as a standard part of the design procedure for all installations handling, processing and disposing of wastes which might present significant hazards.

Standards

10.12 In order to guide those whose responsibilities are for the design and operation of waste handling and waste treatment equipment, it is important that there are accepted national standards that can be followed (see paragraph 3.14). At present there are some British Standards for certain classes of incinerators and for limited aspects of waste management (see box). These standards deal with certain general aspects of equipment and operation, but do not address, for example, the detailed design of furnace chambers, the required temperatures and residence times for complete combustion, the equipment to control emissions, or specific operating procedures. There are no British Standards for landfill design and operation, none for large incinerators or incinerators for hazardous waste, and there are no codes of practice for most waste handling and management functions.

10.13 We believe that the preparation of new engineering standards would encourage good practice in the waste industry and provide a sound basis for staff training. We **recommend** that the British Standards Institution should review equipment and procedures for the management and disposal of wastes and the treatment of contaminated land, including existing standards, with a view to developing new standards and codes of practice in this field.

10.14 The implementation of high professional standards in the waste industry depends, in part, on the attitude of professional institutions to the industry. In addition to the Institute of Wastes Management, the chartered institutes in engineering, chemistry and environmental health have important

---

CURRENT BRITISH STANDARDS
RELEVANT TO WASTE MANAGEMENT

BS 3107: 1973
Small incinerators

BS 3316: 1973
Large incinerators for the destruction of hospital waste

BS 3456: Section 2.30: 1971
The testing and approval of household electrical appliances
- food waste disposal units

BS 3813: 1964
Incinerators for waste from trade and residential premises
Part 1: capacities between 50 lb/h and 1000 lb/h

BS 5832: 1980
Compacted waste containers for lift-off vehicles

BS 5906: 1980
Code of practice for storage and on-site treatment of solid waste from
buildings

---

roles. The organisation of conferences and symposia and the encouragement of technical papers in institution journals can help to enhance the status of waste technology and to promote the development and maintenance of high engineering standards. We hope that these bodies will continue and, where possible, intensify their professional interests in waste management, handling, treatment and disposal.

Training

10.15 We believe that formal training has an important role to play in developing professionalism in waste management. The recognition of this in the field of pollution control generally is not new. As long ago as February 1971 the Royal Commission commented, in its First Report([237]):

'Modern industry gives rise to novel and sometimes highly technical problems of pollution control. While many of these can be solved within industry, there remain some which will fall upon local authorities and River Authorities. We doubt whether some staff engaged in these services, especially those attached to small local authorities, have the scientific and technological training, or the contact with experts, which would enable them to make informed decisions on unforeseen problems. All this leads us to think that a review of the qualifications and training, and access to scientific and technological information, of those who control pollution might lead to measures which would encourage these services and improve them.'

10.16 In the event the study which the Commission intended to carry out was postponed, mainly because of local government reorganisation, but some interim conclusions, reinforcing the Commission's preliminary views, were included in the Fourth Report([238]). Since then the relevance of environmental training in industry has been stressed in relation to the World Conservation Strategy([239]).

10.17 It is appropriate therefore that the Commission of the European Communities has been funding a programme of some 27 separate studies in Member States of various aspects of training needs for environmental specialists. Among the several contributions from the UK is a report by the Imperial College Centre for Environmental Technology on training for pollution control in industry([240]), the conclusions of which (see box) we fully endorse in the waste management context.

10.18 A report to the EC Commission on the whole programme, by the UK consulting firm ECOTEC, was published recently([241]). Although its conclusions are too numerous and detailed to summarise here, we are pleased to note the widespread endorsement, from all over the Community, of the close link between maintaining the momentum of environmental improvement and high standards of training and professionalism.

10.19 Nevertheless, the view has been expressed to us([242]) that the current level of provision for education and training in waste management in the United Kingdom is inadequate if professionalism in the industry is to be improved. We agree. The problem is one of lack of demand. Both industry and local authorities have, for one reason or another, failed to support the courses that have been offered and we understand that one waste disposal authority recently eliminated its training budget. In our view, what is needed is adequate training in all aspects of waste management at all levels.

10.20 At the graduate level, waste management is multi-disciplinary. We suggest that typically an individual should initially qualify in civil, mechanical or chemical engineering, chemistry or environmental health or some other relevant discipline and follow this with secondary training in waste management and pollution control. The objective should be to produce individuals with an appropriate balance of breadth and depth of understanding. We note that there are a number of one year masters, diploma and similar courses in pollution control, public health engineering and environmental technology offered by universities (including the Open University) and polytechnics. These courses usually include a relatively small component on waste management.

10.21 At the same time we see a need for main-stream vocational training to place greater emphasis on the concept of waste as a product requiring the same degree of expertise to control its disposal as is required for other parts of the production process. This could be very helpful in heightening a sense of responsibility in industry for the security of the waste stream and in underpinning the duty of care.

**TRAINING REQUIREMENTS FOR POLLUTION CONTROL
IN INDUSTRY**

*Conclusions of a study for the European Commission
by Imperial College Centre for Environmental Technology*

1. Qualifications in a traditional subject such as chemistry or engineering are in general viewed by industry as the preferred training for work in pollution control, possibly followed by further environmental training, either through educational courses or by post entry training.

2. Further in house training would appear to be the most acceptable way of increasing environmental training in industrial pollution control. Short courses are also used for some levels of staff in certain companies.

3. There is a general recognition that increased environmental awareness among industrial employees would be beneficial, and a significant proportion of companies feel that further environmental training would be of benefit.

4. There is considerable feeling, particularly among the smaller companies, that information and advice on pollution, and pollution control, could be improved.

5. Increased employment of staff on pollution control in some industrial sectors is envisaged in the event that pollution controls increase.

6. Since there would seem to be a demand for increased information and advice, and increased post entry training, this has employment implications for the control authorities, government establishments and other institutions who can supply such needs.

7. There are often differences between the needs of the larger and smaller companies in the areas of pollution control training, and in the provision of advice and information.

Source: Imperial College[240]

10.22 There is also a specific need for the training of environmental health officers in the management of contaminated land, since it is usually these officers who have to provide advice to planning colleagues (see paragraph 2.55) and to developers on the identification and assessment of land which may be contaminated.

10.23 In-service training is as important in the waste management field as it is in others. For those in either the private or the public sector who have responsibilities for supervising or managing waste disposal there are several extended part-time courses, some of which lead to qualifications adequate for corporate membership of the Institute of Wastes Management. In addition there are a number of short courses (1-5 days) on specialised aspects of waste management offered by local authorities, educational institutions and the National Association of Waste Disposal Contractors.

10.24 We also note that the National Association of Waste Disposal Contractors is one of several co-sponsors of a tanker driver training course that provides the training necessary for drivers to maintain the currency of their hazardous goods certificates: 3 days' training are required every five years. Since the advent of the regulation requiring this training demand has increased to the extent that 9 courses are scheduled for 1985 along with 18 one day refresher courses.

10.25 Several organisations have in the past run courses or seminars on waste management (mainly hazardous), but now no longer do so. Among those are the Environmental Protection Unit of AERE Harwell, whose programme of short courses ran for a number of years until 1979. We consider it is a matter for considerable concern that centres of expertise such as this should have curtailed their activities in this way.

10.26 The lack of demand for training is a reflection of the lack of a requirement for standards. Standards may of course be adopted voluntarily but ultimately they may be established by law. Where specific qualifications are required, the demand for training can rise significantly, as it has done in the case of the course for tanker drivers. Therefore we **recommend** that the Department of the Environment in consultation with local authority associations, industry and other relevant organisations should seek to establish national standards of competence and qualifications for all those involved in the management of waste. These consultations should take account of, and where appropriate should contribute to, developments in this area within the European Community[241].

(Hazardous Waste Inspectorate)

Plate 13   Unsatisfactory disposal of waste agro-chemicals and containers. (paragraph 2.42).

(West Midlands County Council)

Plate 14   An abandoned store of industrial materials. (6.33).

(a)   (b)

(Tyne and Wear Metropolitan County Council)

(c)   (d)

Plate 15   The Byker waste derived fuel plant: (a) processes crude refuse; (b) separates out incombustible material; and (c) makes pellets from the combustible fraction, which can then be stored (d). (5.21).

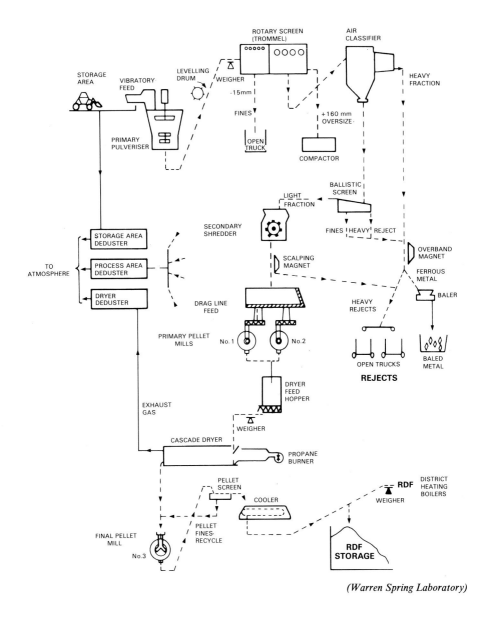

(Warren Spring Laboratory)

Plate 16   A schematic diagram of the waste processing plant at Byker, Tyne and Wear, producing pelletised waste derived fuel. (5.21).

(Greater London Council)

Plate 17   Old barges with loose covers used to transport domestic wastes to landfill are now being replaced with specially designed fixed cover barges. (6.40).

(Greater Manchester Council)

Plate 18   Trains with containers or covered rail wagons are used to transport domestic wastes to remote landfill sites. (6.40).

MINNESOTA POLLUTION CONTROL AGENCY
DIVISION OF SOLID AND HAZARDOUS WASTE
1935 WEST COUNTY ROAD B-2
ROSEVILLE, MN 55113-2785
ATTN: HWIMS

3M In case of Emergency or Spill, Immediately call 3M (612) 733-6100

For MPCA use only

Please print or type.   (Form designed for use on elite (12 pitch) typewriter.)   Instructions on back of form

UNIFORM HAZARDOUS WASTE MANIFEST	1. Generator's US EPA ID No. TXD001806868	Manifest Document No. 23555	2. Page 1 of 1	Information in shaded area not required by Federal Law. Minnesota rules require items H. and I.

3. Generator's Name and Mailing Address
3M
P. O. Box 1669
Brownwood, Tx 76804 (Vaughn Costa, Brownwood,01/054)

BROW

A. State Manifest Document Number
MN 0023555

4. Generator's Phone (915) 646-3551

B. State Generator's ID   30536

5. Transporter 1 Company Name
Montgomery Tank Lines

6. US EPA ID Number TXD490011137

C. State Transporter's ID 40486
D. Transporter's Phone 800 323 0397

7. Transporter 2 Company Name

8. US EPA ID Number

E. State Transporter's ID 31643
F. Transporter's Phone

9. Designated Facility Name and Site Address
3M Chemolite, Bldg. 47
Hwy 61 and County Rd 19
Cottage Grove, Minn 55016

10. U.S EPA ID Number
MND006172969

G. State Facility's ID ZOO
H. Facility's Phone 612-458-2141

	11. US DOT Description (Including Proper Shipping Name, Hazard Class, and ID Number)	12. Containers No.	Type	13. Total Quantity	14. Unit Wt Vol	I. Waste No.
HM						
a.	X RQ (Xylene), Waste Flammable Liquid, NOS *Flammable Liquid, UN 1993 (Xylene, Methyl Ethyl Ketone)	1	TT	4 2 7 2 0	P	D001 TX980800
b.						
c.						
d.						

J. Additional Descriptions for Materials Listed Above
a.   b.
c.   d.

K. Handling Codes for Wastes Listed Above

15. Special Handling Instructions and Additional Information   PLACARDS REQUIRED: FLAMMABLE 1933
TRAILER NO. 69101

16. GENERATOR'S CERTIFICATION: I hereby declare that the contents of this consignment are fully and accurately described above by proper shipping name and are classified, packed, marked, and labeled, and are in all respects in proper condition for transport by highway according to applicable international and national governmental regulations, and Minnesota rules.

Printed/Typed Name	Signature	Date Month Day Year
Vaughn Costa	Vaughn M. Costa	8 30 85

17. Transporter 1 Acknowledgement of Receipt of Materials

Printed/Typed Name	Signature	Date Month Day Year
James H. Reynolds	James H Reynolds	8 30 85

18. Transporter 2 Acknowledgement of Receipt of Materials

Printed/Typed Name	Signature	Date Month Day Year

19. Discrepancy Indication Space

20. Facility Owner or Operator: Certification of receipt of hazardous materials covered by this manifest except as noted in Item 19.

Printed/Typed Name	Signature	Date Month Day Year
Ernie Taylor	Ernie Taylor	

Minnesota Form PQ-00371-01(10 84)

COPY 2: TSDF MAIL TO MPCA STATE

(3M Company)

Plate 19   An example, from the USA, of a waste consignment note. (8.36).

(RCEP)

Plate 20   A well managed landfill site where small cells lead to short advancing fronts of newly tipped waste and allow easy daily cover to be placed. (7.23).

(Hazardous Waste Inspectorate)

Plate 21   A poorly managed site with larger tipping areas, inadequately covered deposits and birds presenting a potential nuisance. (7.23).

(Hazardous Waste Inspectorate)

Plate 22   Leachate liquors are generated in landfills and can contaminate ground and surface
waters. (7.5).

(Department of Energy)

Plate 23   A schematic diagram of the GLC Aveley landfill site at which methane is collected
from the wastes and distributed to fuel a factory's boilers. (7.14).

(a)   (RCEP)

(b)   (RCEP)

Plate 24   Industrial waste: (a) incineration facilities (note the colour coded waste drums
          awaiting combustion) and (b) biological waste water treatment at Bayer AG,
          Leverkusen, Germany. (7.33).

CHAPTER XI

RESEARCH AND DEVELOPMENT

Introduction

11.1 During our study it has become clear to us that a key element in ensuring the success of any strategy for waste is the provision and dissemination of scientific, technical and other advice to those with day-to-day responsibilities for planning and managing waste disposal. The contribution that improved scientific and management training can make to this process has been discussed in Chapter X. In this chapter we draw together our views on the contribution that further research and development might be expected to make in the next decade or so to improved understanding of the behaviour of wastes, to developments in waste management practices, and to new or enhanced opportunities for the recovery of materials or energy from waste.

11.2 The preparation of engineering standards, which we discussed in the previous chapter, requires those concerned to agree about the design methods and practices which are to be embodied in these standards. In some areas of waste treatment and disposal, such agreement may not be possible yet. For example, the design of equipment to remove gas from landfill sites appears to require further development; leachate collection and re-circulation systems are not well developed; knowledge of the properties and lifetimes of lining materials for landfill sites is not complete; operational procedures for co-disposal at landfill sites appear to vary from one site to another. The drafting of new engineering standards in these and other areas should run in parallel to further research and development in waste handling, treatment and disposal.

Organisation of research and development

11.3 Some of the responsibility for research and development on waste handling and disposal rests with the waste disposal industry, which (like any other industry) has an interest in ensuring that its operations are efficient and that new commercial opportunities are identified and exploited. However in accordance with the duty of care, the industries which give rise to wastes in the first place also have a heavy, if not an overriding, responsibility to make proper provision, from the design stage onwards, for the management of wastes arising from their processes and products. Application of the 'polluter pays' principle implies that, so far as possible, waste generators should ultimately bear the costs of the research and development necessary to meet

147

statutory environmental standards. We feel that this is particularly important in the case of difficult industrial wastes, of which the principal generator is the chemical industry. At the same time, since standards are set by pollution control authorities and by government they too have a duty to undertake research and development to the extent necessary to enable them to determine appropriate standards, to demonstrate that these standards are practicable, to give adequate advice and to support enforcement action when standards are not met. Government can also legitimately seek to protect the environment, to the extent that this is achieved by reductions in the waste stream (see Chapters IV and V), by sponsoring research and development on techniques of waste separation and materials recovery which, if successful, should lead to the introduction of processes than can compete commercially with waste disposal in some circumstances.

11.4 As indicated in paragraphs 6.24-6.29 of the Tenth Report, the interests and expertise of the pollution control authorities in protecting the environment and of the waste disposal industry and pollution abatement equipment manufacturers in searching for new commercial opportunities can be complementary. A Government Minister has said recently that British industry must use its capacity to innovate if it is to win a share of the new markets offered by environmental protection[243]. Besides permitting professional standards to be raised, research and development can thus have an important spin-off in strengthening these industries' competitive position in world markets. It therefore seems right to us that the cost of R&D in waste engineering should be shared between the public sector and private industry. For instance, we welcome the co-operation which already exists, and which has been increasing, between local authorities and industry to undertake research and development to exploit mutually beneficial opportunities. Examples of such joint ventures which have been brought to our attention include the development of methane recovery techniques and equipment at the Aveley landfill site by the Greater London Council and a National Coal Board subsidiary (paragraph 7.14); research sponsored by Greater Manchester Council at the Universities of Manchester and Salford to develop a process for extracting oil from cellulose-containing wastes (paragraph 5.29); and plans by Rockware Reclamation to extend to other wastes its arrangements with the 120 local authorities from which it already buys and collects glass bottles for recycling[244,245]. Nevertheless we see drawbacks in a policy which places too much reliance on local initiatives. There is a danger that efforts may be wasted on re-inventing the wheel if there are not proper mechanisms for disseminating the results of R&D and for ensuring that, where it is likely to yield more than local benefits, it receives appropriate funding and support from the centre. Obviously no hard and fast rules for this can be laid down, but we consider that the Department of the Environment - which, because of its functions in relation to local government, has a special responsibility to promote efficient waste management in the municipal sector - should keep under regular review the balance between centrally funded R&D and local initiatives which have potential applications nationally.

11.5 We also perceive, at the national level, a need for an increased level of industrial waste management R&D on a joint basis. We **recommend** that joint funding for engineering research and development in the waste industry should be encouraged and that this should become an area for priority funding by the Department of Trade and Industry. The financial support of R&D should include financial support for the British Standards Institution where this is needed to allow the preparation of new standards which could otherwise not proceed because of lack of money for essential supporting studies.

Waste arisings

11.6 In Chapter II we discussed the data available on the arisings of different types of waste. The reliability and compatability of such data are central to effective planning of waste disposal activities, both for waste disposal authorities and for individual waste producers, and we were disturbed at the extent of uncertainties, inconsistencies and gaps in existing information. The results of research undertaken by the University College of Wales and Clwyd County Council, and submitted to us by the Prince of Wales' Committee, strikingly illustrate the inadequacies of published data on waste disposal in Wales and suggest a number of reasons and remedies. The Hazardous Waste Inspectorate has also listed major reasons why published estimates of hazardous waste arisings should be treated with caution([17]).

11.7 There is, therefore, a need for central advice on the collection of statistics about waste to ensure consistency and compatability and to enable trends to be more readily and reliably identified. The transfer of waste management responsibilities from Metropolitan County to District Councils in April 1986, and the consequent increase in nominally inter-authority movements of waste, underline the need for such compatability of data; and the need for waste disposal authorities in metropolitan areas, where most waste arises, to revise and complete their Waste Disposal Plans under section 2 of the Control of Pollution Act 1974 (see paragraph 9.9) provides a convenient opportunity to phase in a standard system for recording waste arisings in and transfers between such areas. Implementation of the recommendations we have made in paragraphs 2.33, 2.36 and 2.37 will make this possible.

Landfill

11.8 Given the present and likely future predominance of landfill for the disposal of wastes in the United Kingdom, it is particularly important that the continued acceptability of the practice is underpinned by a thorough understanding of the physical, chemical and biological behaviour of wastes in landfill sites and of the long-term performance of sites in isolating or attenuating the effects of the wastes on the surrounding environment. The former includes an understanding of the mechanisms by which methane is generated from waste, so that its production can be stimulated or suppressed as required, and of those by which toxic wastes are degraded in a landfill site, so that the safe boundaries of co-disposal, hitherto determined largely by empirical tests on leachate, can be firmly established in a more analytical way.

The latter includes the long-term reliability and integrity of both natural and synthetic landfill liners, the use of which is likely to increase as more sites suitable only for the containment form of landfill have to be pressed into service, and an understanding of the processes by which leachate from a non-containment site interacts with and is attenuated by both the waste itself and the surrounding strata. Other important aspects of landfill technology include the control of odours, the treatment of leachate removed from containment sites, and site restoration and aftercare.

11.9 The Department of the Environment's programme of research on landfill practices includes studies of all the subjects mentioned above and results to date have been generally encouraging. For example, studies by the Food Research Association on methanogenic activity have enabled certain methanogens present in landfills to be identified, and the results are being used in other laboratory studies at Harwell. Field studies on the pumping, collection and flaring of landfill gas are also being undertaken. The results are also of use to the Department of Energy, which is sponsoring complementary studies on the recovery and development of landfill gas as an alternative energy source. During our study we saw the work on methane recovery being undertaken at the Greater London Council's landfill site at Aveley in Essex, where the need to deal with a problem of odours arising near residential development was turned to practical and commercial advantage to supply heat to the nearby factory of Thames Board Ltd. Although that installation appeared to operate quite satisfactorily, we noted that much of the equipment used (for example, land drains) was simply imported from other technologies. We hope that the research which is continuing on the production and use of landfill gas will lead to the development of equipment and techniques optimised specifically for this purpose and that full account will be taken of relevant expertise, for example in the use of relatively low grade fuels, in other sectors of industry.

11.10 Departmental research on co-disposal has included experiments where layers of cyanide and phenolic wastes were deposited in household refuse[4]. After five years' exposure to rainfall and anaerobic decomposition the waste was exhumed and analysed, when it was found that, after allowing for the small quantities collected in leachate, more than 95 per cent of the original toxic ingredients had disappeared, mainly by biological conversion to relatively harmless species. We believe it is important to give continued high priority to a wider range of studies of this kind, particularly in order to reduce the uncertainties about the degradative mechanisms involved and to deflect any pressure there may be from other EC Member States to restrict or prohibit a practice which is endorsed as environmentally acceptable in the United Kingdom.

11.11 Research on co-disposal should also contribute to improved knowledge of the fundamental processes that take place in landfill sites and complement other research sponsored by the Department of the Environment on means to accelerate such processes and so advance the time when a landfill can be considered stable and inert and available for other uses. The microbial breakdown of organic matter is a complex process involving a wide variety of different organisms and the intermeshing of numerous different biochemical processes. Optimum conditions for general composting can be established empirically for given sorts of materials but the transformation could undoubtedly be made more efficient if special strains of micro-organisms were used instead of those provided by chance. If microbial breakdown is to be used effectively to dispose of refractory or toxic organic materials then detailed knowledge of the processes involved and employment of particular strains will be essential. The phenomenon of co-metabolism referred to in paragraph 7.56 is being actively investigated in a few laboratories([187]) but deserves much more attention. The application of genetical engineering to produce strains of organisms to deal with particular substances and development of biotechnological methods to exploit their properties to best advantage could lead to safe and ecologically acceptable processes for disposal of many of the noxious organic waste products of industry([246,247]). We are pleased that DoE has some projects on microbial breakdown in its research programme. We regard this whole area as having considerable potential and **recommend** that support of work in this field should be continued and where possible expanded.

Incineration

11.12 The technology of incineration is well established and we see no need on environmental grounds for further research or development on the means of achieving any specified operating conditions, though clearly equipment operators and manufacturers will wish to incorporate the latest developments in, for example, energy efficiency, safe handling of materials and control technology when replacing old plant. Research has also established some details of the relationship between the type of waste being incinerated, the operating conditions and the composition of the emissions that can be expected from the primary and any secondary combustion chambers and, after any treatment, to the atmosphere. Continuing research sponsored by the Department of the Environment at Warren Spring Laboratory on gaseous emissions from the incineration of both unsegregated waste and waste derived fuel should shed further light on this relationship. We particularly emphasise the importance of analysing the gaseous emissions from WDF under different conditions of combustion so that potential users of the fuel can be made aware of the technical requirements that equipment intended to burn WDF will have to satisfy.

11.13 Monitoring of the effects, if any, of waste incinerators and other waste management operations on the surrounding environment is, of course, also a useful check on the efficacy of the operations themselves. We therefore welcome the Department of the Environment's proposal to commission a survey of the incidence of dioxins and furans in soils as fall-out from waste management operations. We stress that it is important that this survey should cover contamination around landfill sites as well as incineration plants and should be supported by adequate measurements of background concentrations of these substances in areas remote from known industrial sources of potential contamination. We have already recommended (paragraph 1.20) that there should be the fullest possible support for related research in the European Community context.

Waste collection and recycling

11.14 In view of our comments in Chapter VI on the importance of minimising the generation of litter during the collection of domestic wastes, we welcome the Department of the Environment's proposal to commission an evaluation of the use of storage and wheeled bin systems in refuse collection.

11.15 The research and development work on the experimental waste sorting plants in South Yorkshire and in Tyne and Wear, and the construction in the West Midlands and Manchester of plants incorporating the lessons of the experiments, were described in Chapter V. When the latter plants are fully operational it will be primarily for other local authorities and waste management companies to assess, largely on commercial grounds but also with regard to any environmental benefits, whether the techniques demonstrated can be applied elsewhere. We note that, meanwhile, the Department of the Environment proposes to continue its sponsorship of work at Warren Spring Laboratory on the technical evaluation of mechanical separation systems and also to involve local authorities and the private sector in research on advanced methods of waste sorting.

Treatment of waste

11.16 In Chapter VII we discussed various chemical and biological methods for treating wastes in preparation for their disposal. To a large extent it is the responsibility of the waste producers and the business of waste management contractors to devise treatment methods that will render wastes acceptable to the regulatory authorities for disposal. However, the authorities must be in a position to appraise new techniques and to give advice in difficult cases. In these categories we would include such matters as the treatment and disposal of asbestos wastes and acid tars and the techniques used for immobilising wastes to render them less available for incorporation in landfill leachates. Since there is some uncertainty about the fundamental science of such techniques (paragraph 7.54), we **recommend** further research on waste fixation techniques to improve scientific understanding and control of the processes involved and to enable waste disposal authorities to devise effective tests for the acceptance of the solidified wastes in landfill.

Contaminated land

11.17 As we explained in Chapter I, we have not examined this subject in detail. We see a need for continued research to support the activities of the Interdepartmental Committee on the Redevelopment of Contaminated Land (see paragraph 2.49), and we endorse the priorities which the Department of the Environment has identified. These are: to develop improved means of assessing the significance of organic and inorganic contaminants; to establish the concentrations at which particular actions should be taken; and to develop more cost-effective methods for treating and reclaiming contaminated sites. There is an interaction between research activity in this field and that in the field of emissions from waste incinerators, and we attach particular importance to an early resolution of the uncertainty which surrounds the origins and effects of dioxins and furans present in the soil.

Conclusions

11.18 Comparing the priorities for future research that we have identified with the research currently sponsored by the Department of the Environment and others reveals no major gaps and in that respect we endorse existing research programmes and plans as being generally satisfactory, subject to our detailed comments above. However, there are various developments on the horizon - including, for example, the improvements in hazardous waste disposal practices recommended by the Hazardous Waste Inspectorate and the impending designation of Metropolitan District Councils as waste disposal authorities - that will make it particularly important for the Department of the Environment to consolidate its ability to advise on the general principles of good waste management. It will also be important, as application of the concept of BPEO develops, for the Department to inject a greater degree of economic analysis into the R&D programme. Apart from a proposed study (yet to be commissioned, at an estimated cost of £30,000) of the use of economic instruments in pollution control, the Department does not appear to be sponsoring any economic research of relevance to waste management.

11.19 At present DoE's research effort in the fields of solid and toxic waste management and materials reclamation from waste is running at about £1.4 million (1984/85) and is planned to increase to just under £2 million (1985/86) with the additional work on dioxins and furans (paragraph 11.13). Under arrangements instituted in 1984 the Commission now provides the Secretary of State with informal advice on the content and overall balance of the Department's research programmes within the field of environmental pollution, and we shall have an opportunity next year to give further consideration to the adequacy of waste management research in relation to other programmes. In the meantime (as we have already indicated to the Department) we regard the present level of DoE sponsored research as insufficient, and consider that implementation of the recommendations which we make elsewhere in this Report will necessarily involve some expansion of the programme.

CHAPTER XII

OVERVIEW

Introduction

12.1 In this chapter we give an overview of our conclusions and general recommendations on the subject of this Report - pollution by wastes - and comment further on a question which we believe is of critical importance: what is needed to reassure the public that risks are being kept to an acceptable level and that best possible practices for the handling of waste are being observed?

12.2 Wastes arise from many activities and processes in society, but they differ from other materials by virtue of some or all of the following characteristics:

(a)   All waste is destined to be consigned to the environment.

(b)   Wastes have little or no value, or even negative value, to the holder.

(c)   There is often uncertainty as to their exact composition.

(d)   Their composition often varies, because whilst the planned products of a process must conform to precise specifications and standards, it is the waste stream that reflects the variability of inputs to the process (raw materials, operating conditions, etc.)

12.3 Because wastes have these characteristics, it is not possible to rely simply on customer-led improvements in standards of waste handling and disposal. This Report has therefore been concerned with the arrangements which, in these circumstances, would be most appropriate for bringing about improvements and maintaining adequate standards. For these the fundamental requirement is that the *security of the waste stream* must be safeguarded: once material has been consigned to the stream, there should be no leakage - which along with inadequate disposal is one of the main causes of pollution. From this it follows that the person who holds or handles waste at any stage - whether it be a beverage can or several tonnes of special waste - has a *duty of care*, to ensure that the waste does not cause pollution by incorrect handling or disposal.

Responsibilities and standards

12.4 The costs of preventing pollution by wastes should, in principle, fall on the waste producers. However, the greater degree of separation between the

154

final disposal of waste and the original process which gave rise to it, the more likely it is that the incidence of costs will in practice be distorted. Storage of wastes is one example of how this may happen: if those initially responsible for the site later abandon it, the cost of disposal may be a burden on the community (paragraphs 3.11, 6.6 and 6.33). The development of standards (Chapter X) is one way of reducing this kind of problem.

12.5 Enforcement of proper standards reinforces the role of education and exhortation. In the short term, if the public is to enjoy a proper level of protection, some injection of public funds is inevitable, but in the long term the benefits will be considerable. A more secure waste stream, a reduction in pollution, and a greater internalisation of costs are all likely to lead to savings elsewhere in the public sector. However, enforcement of the law and standards (as in other areas of human activity) cannot succeed unless it is accompanied by changes in attitude. The force of example is at least as powerful as the threat of penalties. Practices improve when people can identify themselves with those who are seen to be responsible and professionally competent.

12.6 As a means of greatly improving the security of the waste stream and to achieve all the benefits which flow from it, we have recommended the imposition on the waste producer of a formal duty of care, under which he would be legally responsible for his waste unless he could show that he had handed this responsibility over to someone who he had reason to suppose was willing and able to dispose of it correctly. Similarly we have recommended that all commercial handlers of waste should be registered and thereby be given an incentive to maintain the security of the waste stream in their charge. Producers will thus have a means of identifying responsible handlers and enforcement authorities will have a means of bringing irresponsible handlers to book. These recommendations will establish an unbroken chain of responsibility and accountability between producers, transporters and disposers of wastes.

12.7 We are satisfied that practical methods exist for maintaining the security of the waste stream during the collection and transporting of wastes. Unfortunately these methods are not always followed. In particular we note that certain recent trends in municipal refuse collection (Chapter VI) have led to increased pollution in the form of litter - largely, we feel, because of the use of inappropriate financial yardsticks based on crude savings in direct collection costs, which do not take into account wider environmental effects. Another example is the unacceptable quantities of materials lost, thrown overboard or discharged from vessels at sea owing to the continuing failure by the United Kingdom and other governments to implement appropriate international standards devised as long ago as 1973 (paragraphs 6.42-6.46).

Environmental impacts of wastes

12.8 Subject to the further research which we have recommended in Chapter XI, we are satisfied that technically sound methods already exist or are likely to be attainable for the disposal of all currently known forms of waste, with the possible exception of high-level radioactive wastes. However it is essential that enforcement procedures ensure that the best practicable environmental option is followed in each case and not some environmentally unsound route, which appears cheaper because it externalises some of the costs. This will not only safeguard the environment from direct pollution but also underpin the commercial viability of efficient companies that meet the required standards: a firm which observes high standards will be at risk so long as its competitors' waste streams remain insecure and inadequately controlled.

12.9 Wastes should never be discharged at such a rate or in such forms or quantities as to overload the natural processes in the environment that degrade and disperse many man-made pollutants. It is important to identify the critical element in the waste. For example, as was argued in paragraph 4.68 of the Tenth Report, there is no evidence that any damage results from the discharge of properly comminuted sewage through long sea outfalls. By contrast, sewage sludge that contains significant quantities of heavy metals from industrial wastes or from rain water running off road surfaces may present problems (Chapter VII). We believe it is important to give greater impetus to the trend which has seen reducing levels of heavy metals entering the sewerage system, so that eventually the output from sewage works should consist of little more than a natural organic material, which can be disposed of safely to land or to the seabed.

12.10 If the creation of waste can be avoided in the first place (Chapter IV) or valuable uses found for what would otherwise be treated as waste (Chapter V), the size of the waste stream will be reduced or its characteristics altered. In this way the final impact of waste on the environment can be modified. The setting and enforcement of appropriate standards for waste handling and disposal, and the proper allocation of disposal costs, can be important factors in encouraging technological developments in these fields. Additional forms of intervention, for instance to create or stabilise the market for some materials, may be desirable too.

12.11 The waste stream may also be affected by shifts (some of them spontaneous) in public opinion - for instance in the willingness of the public to assist recycling by sorting and taking waste materials to central collection points (e.g. bottle banks). Whilst there may well be hidden costs in these activities[2] (see paragraph 5.9 for example), we believe it is right that they should be encouraged, in so far as they help to reduce the quantity of waste for ultimate disposal and to create an attitude of mind that individually we each have a part to play in reducing pollution of the environment. Similarly we welcome, as a general principle, other measures that can be taken, at relatively low cost, to encourage recycling and reclamation, such as the setting up of waste exchanges (paragraphs 5.4-5.7). These measures help to demonstrate to the public that every effort is being made by those in positions of responsibility to reduce the size of the waste stream.

12.12 The importance of limiting the waste stream is underlined by the fact that some forms of waste disposal use up environmental capacity, either permanently or for extended periods. This is particularly true of landfill. By contrast, other forms, such as properly conducted incineration, are able to continue in the same location indefinitely, because they do not overload the environment. However, the prospective establishment of any new waste handling operation, whatever its long-term impact, is likely to be regarded with some suspicion, if not hostility, in the immediate neighbourhood and further afield. The experience of recent years suggests that planning inquiries relating to waste disposal sites are likely to remain contentious. For all these reasons, we believe it is unwise for the United Kingdom to rely (as has tended to be the practice in the past) on the supply of future landfill sites in most areas being for practical purposes unlimited. We believe therefore that the conservation of landfill capacity where it is needed is a matter to which Government policy should now be directed.

12.13 With most waste handling and disposal sites - unless their use is confined to completely inert materials - the duty of care continues well after the deposition of wastes. 'Out of sight' must therefore not become 'out of mind'. Most waste materials have the potential to damage the environment around them. They must be handled securely and, once deposited, standards of site management must ensure that they are decomposed or degraded to harmless substances or immobilised (as in the case of heavy metals). To reinforce these standards, we have recommended in Chapter IX that consideration is given to other measures, such as performance bonds and compulsory insurance, which would mitigate the problems associated with the management and aftercare of waste disposal sites.

Not in my back yard

12.14 The general acceptability of waste handling and disposal practices is a matter of public interest. In Chapter I we referred to the problem of 'NIMBY' and how it tends to be aggravated by lack of clear information about environmental hazards and by lack of confidence in the regulatory authorities. We feel that the influence of both these factors is well illustrated by various chapters in the history of the nuclear installations at Sellafield (Windscale) and by numerous individual examples reported on by the Hazardous Waste Inspectorate([17]). As Lord Gregson has said, 'the heart of successful waste disposal is public confidence and acceptance'([248]).

12.15 We see NIMBY as a potentially serious obstacle to sensible waste management. In some areas the level of public opposition is apparently so overwhelming that governments and regulatory authorities are tempted to take the easy way out. We could mention many examples of where this has happened - the recent decision by the London Dumping Convention insofar as it applies to the sea dumping of low level radioactive waste (see paragraph 7.48); the pressures from some European countries for a ban on the sea disposal of treated sewage sludge (paragraph 2.45); and the decisions in one *Land* of the Federal Republic of Germany to export municipal incinerator residues (because of alleged dioxin contamination) and to store indefinitely old transformers and other materials contaminated with PCBs. In our view it is unwise to seek to remove people's worries through such temporary and essentially cosmetic measures: indeed, some of these, leading as they do to the storage of wastes (paragraphs 6.33-6.35), may pose significant risks and generate long-term environmental problems. Rather we believe that the concerns that underlie NIMBY must be faced and public acceptability sought.

12.16 We consider that the process of seeking public acceptability of waste handling and disposal facilities has four necessary components:

> Information for the public
> Involvement of the community
> Incentives for the community
> Implementation of high standards and their enforcement.

Information for the public

12.17 A major section of the Tenth Report was devoted to a discussion of the need to avoid unnecessary secrecy over environmental data, and we are pleased to note the positive action which Government has taken in following up the Report's recommendations. While the practical implications are being worked out, we would continue to urge industry and pollution control authorities to be open with information, not to be secretive. We believe that when major new disposal sites are being looked for, there should be public exposure of the principles involved, and when an actual site is selected the specific case for it should be expounded: too often a local community gains the impression that 'something nasty' has been sprung on them. Moreover, when sites are operating it is most important that no attempt should be made to cover up mistakes. If anything, public confidence is enhanced by a timely admission that things have gone wrong if it can be accompanied by positive demonstration that remedial action to prevent a recurrence has been put into immediate effect. As we indicated in Chapter I, there are particular difficulties surrounding the provision and interpretation for the public of data from epidemiological studies of the possible harmful effects of unusual substances which are found at trace levels in the environment. We discuss that problem further in paragraphs 12.23-12.24 below.

Involvement of the community

12.18 Much emphasis has been placed, in evidence to us, on the value of the public inquiry system as a vehicle for public debate on waste management policy and for the presentation of data on safety studies and risk assessment. The point has been made that NIMBY, in the adversarial conditions of an inquiry, has a positive part to play in compelling developers and regulatory authorities to disclose the costs and benefits of their proposals for public scrutiny. We agree that public inquiries provide an important safeguard to the public in this respect. But we believe that much of the information that is provided in response to objectors' pressure would be more effectively and economically made available at an earlier stage and in a less heated atmosphere. In this connection we think that local authorities have a part to play in ensuring that the planning process is as open as possible.

12.19 The Fifth and Tenth Reports recommended that there should be greater use by local authorities of their powers under the Control of Pollution Act 1974 to set up air pollution liaison committees, whilst noting with approval the steps which many industrial companies have taken voluntarily to establish links with the local community on environmental matters generally, often with the encouragement of the Industrial Air Pollution Inspectorate or local authorities. We believe that constructive two-way dialogue can do a great deal of good in building up an atmosphere of trust. It requires, however, a patient and sensitive approach to win the confidence of those sections of the community who are apt to dismiss all efforts by industry to be open and friendly with its neighbours as insincere.

Incentives for the community

12.20 We discussed in Chapter IX the scope for offering some form of discretionary compensation or inducement to individuals or communities affected by waste handling and disposal sites, and have recommended that the Government examines the appropriateness and feasibility of adapting UK law and administrative procedures to this end. We also discussed in Chapter IX the position of a local community which under present arrangements may have to bear extra costs because a facility which serves a wider area (regional or national) happens to be located in its midst. We have suggested that the correct solution would be for the proposed unified pollution inspectorate to assume responsibility for any exceptional monitoring requirements, with possible use of the local authority's environmental health staff on an agency basis (and therefore reimbursed out of central funds). In this way there need be no financial disincentive for a community to accept a regional or national facility in its area.

Implementation of high standards and their enforcement

12.21 We have emphasised throughout this Report the importance of developing and implementing proper professional standards at all levels for the management and disposal of wastes. Public confidence is greatly enhanced by the knowledge (and ability to verify) that effective standards exist and are being consistently and objectively enforced by the regulatory authorities. We recognise that many companies have an excellent record of self-policing, but we regard this as part of their general duty of care and we believe that the public needs the assurance of an independent audit of compliance with the law and recommended codes of practice. We see this as one of the most important tasks for the Hazardous Wastes Inspectorate and the enlarged successor body which we discuss in Chapter IX and in paragraph 12.26 below.

Perception of Risks

12.22 Public perception of risk may bear little relation to the degree of risk when expressed as a mathematical probability, since it depends on a variety of factors other than scientific assessment([1,249,250]). 'It depends upon the information people have received, what information they have chosen to believe, the social experiences and values to which they have been exposed, and their entire world views, ... the dynamics of interest groups, the legitimacy of institutions, the vagaries of the political process, and the historical moment at which it is all happening'([251]).

12.23 The NIMBY problem is particularly difficult to deal with when there is scientific uncertainty about the toxicity of substances present at very low levels in the environment. The problem is exacerbated when a number of cases of an unusual illness appear to occur in a cluster in the neighbourhood of factories or other installations handling the substances in question. We believe that there is a need for the systematic investigation of phenomena of this type.

12.24 For example, several investigations need to be gone through before a hypothesis that there is an association between a reportedly abnormally high incidence of a particular disease and an installation handling or emitting a particular substance can confidently be rejected([252-254]). Investigations on the lines of those described in the box are an essential element in advancing the state of knowledge necessary for the proper management of the installations, and we consider that regulatory authorities should be ready to share the results of investigations with the public in an open-minded way*.

The dangers of parochialism

12.25 NIMBY is a localised expression of opinion. We have therefore expressed our disquiet, in correspondence with the Secretary of State (Appendix 4) and in Chapter IX, at the prospect of dismemberment of waste disposal responsibilities in the very areas of England where there is a greatest need for decisions about best practicable environmental options to be taken on a large scale. We believe that rational decisions on the siting of a particular facility are best made within a broader geographical context, whilst at the same time following the principles we have elaborated in Chapter IX on incentives and compensation for the local community.

A national policy for waste

12.26 As we have argued in Chapter IX, there is a need within government for expert advice on strategic waste management decisions which need to be taken on a national or regional scale; for a capability to evaluate best practicable environmental options on a consistent basis; and for an organisation through which national standards of good waste management practice can be developed, promulgated and enforced. Although we find the approach of the newly established Hazardous Waste Inspectorate encouraging, it has had to operate with very slender resources and without statutory powers.

---

* We have noted an evidently successful example of such an approach in Denver, Colorado([255]).

INVESTIGATIONS WHICH NEED TO BE CARRIED OUT WHEN AN ASSOCIATION IS CLAIMED BETWEEN APPARENT CLUSTERS OF DISEASE AND INSTALLATIONS HANDLING OR EMITTING PARTICULAR SUBSTANCES

1. The reported clustering of the disease around the installation must be verified with regard to both diagnostic precision and statistical significance (bearing in mind that clusters can arise by chance).

2. The level of the substance under suspicion in the surrounding area must be studied. If there is evidence that its concentration is higher than background levels, and if there is biological plausibility for the association, then further investigation is called for. Frequently the level will be in the region of toxicological and analytical uncertainty and the knowledge of background levels may be inadequate.

   The most that is likely to be established at this stage is a correlation, not a causal connection. To explore this further other investigations are needed.

3. Information on the disease in other areas is necessary to determine whether similar clusters occur away from the installation and away from concentrations of the substance under suspicion. Any similar installation to that under suspicion should also be investigated.

4. Data on background levels of the substance under suspicion need to be established by taking measurements both in areas where there appear to be clusters of the disease but with no installation present and in areas where both installation and disease clusters are absent.

5. Using the methods of analytical epidemiology, an additional approach is to try to assess the level of exposure to the substance under suspicion of individual members of the disease cluster compared with that of similar persons in the same locality not suffering from the disease. If members of the cluster are found to have had higher levels of exposure, this would be a cause for concern.

6. Similar procedures would need to be followed in investigating all alternative putative causes of the disease.

Moreover we believe that its remit is too narrowly defined; and even if the task of the Inspectorate were to be enlarged (as we believe it should be) to cover all controlled wastes, we feel that it would be more effective if it were to form part of a unified pollution inspectorate, on the lines of that advocated (and designated HMPI) in the Commission's Fifth Report. As an essential first step we have recommended that the Industrial Air Pollution Inspectorate (IAPI) should be transferred from the Health and Safety Executive to its original home in the Department of the Environment; at the same time we have recommended that the Hazardous Waste Inspectorate should be given statutory status and enforcement powers, and that it should, with IAPI, form the nucleus of a new pollution inspectorate within DoE, to which should be added other functions relating to water pollution and radioactive wastes. The annual reports of this inspectorate would provide an important regular review of the state of pollution control.

Enhancing the status of waste management

12.27 A major reason why waste management practices often fail to command public confidence is the visibly low status of waste management, and of those engaged in it, in many companies and local authorities. That is a reason why we attach considerable importance to waste management training at all levels and to a wider requirement for persons in authority to hold appropriate professional and technical qualifications (Chapter X). The creation of the proposed inspectorate is also of critical importance. It would through advice, example and enforcement enhance the status and professionalism of pollution control and waste management in this country; it would be an appropriate response to the high standards of environmental protection which the public rightly expects; and placed in the Department of the Environment it would help to underpin the leading role which we would like to see the United Kingdom playing in international environmental affairs.

12.28 In most industrialised countries higher standards of waste management are being demanded. This is having the effect of forcing technological development and of increasing the international market in waste management equipment and expertise (paragraph 11.4). This country has the quality and variety of scientific and technical skills which best practice requires. The improvement in standards that will follow from the acceptance of our recommendations will ensure that the United Kingdom participates in this international trend with both environmental and commercial benefits: waste management must not remain the Cinderella of government and industry.

CHAPTER XIII

CONCLUSIONS AND RECOMMENDATIONS

In this Chapter we bring together our formal recommendations and those conclusions which, although not cast in the form of recommendations, we believe to be particularly important for the determination of future policy and therefore ones on which the Government may wish to comment in its response to our Report. Formal recommendations are marked with asterisks.

*13.1 The Government should seek to ensure that the European Community gives the fullest possible support to studies of the possible long-term effects of contamination of human populations by dioxins, arising out of the Seveso incident, and to the proper dissemination of the results of the research. (1.20).

13.2 In the waste management context we reiterate the comment in the Tenth Report that the United Kingdom should play a more positive role in the development of European Community environmental policy. (2.14).

13.3 We endorse the existing distinction in UK legislation between special wastes and other controlled wastes and consider that (apart from the special measures needed for controlling the former) it is better to ensure that all controlled wastes are handled in a careful and environmentally appropriate manner than to attempt to define 'hazardous wastes'. (2.23).

*13.4 The Government, in consultation with representatives of the local authority associations, industry and others as appropriate, should devise a coherent scheme for the recording of information on arisings, movements and disposals of controlled municipal and industrial wastes and of mine and quarry wastes and should encourage the adoption of such a scheme throughout the country. (2.33; 2.36; 2.37).

*13.5 All structures required for the storage or control of slurry, silage and other farm wastes should be made subject to the Building Regulations. (2.39).

*13.6 As previously recommended in the Seventh Report, consultation with the water authority should be a requirement, rather than merely advisory, for all applicants for grants for agricultural waste treatment and disposal systems under the EC Farm Structures Regulations. (2.40).

163

13.7 Notwithstanding the Government's comments in its response to the Seventh Report, we believe that there is still a case for bringing the off-site disposal of agro-chemical wastes fully within the scope of Part I of the Control of Pollution act, and we note that the joint review committee on the Control of Pollution (Special Waste) Regulations 1980 agreed that the application of the Regulations to farm wastes which met the 'dangerous to life' criteria merited further consideration. (2.42).

13.8 Provided that contaminated sites are identified at an early stage in the planning process and, in accordance with current advice from the Department of the Environment, taken into account during the preparation of local plans and structure plan alterations, existing powers appear to be sufficient for dealing with contaminated land. Better co-ordination is needed, however, within local authorities. (2.54).

*13.9 The Department of the Environment, the Welsh Office and the Scottish Development Department, after consultation with relevant parties, should issue planning circulars containing comprehensive advice for local authorities, other statutory bodies and developers on the redevelopment of contaminated land or land which may be suspected to be contaminated. Local planning authorities should ensure that environmental health officers are consulted on all relevant planning applications. (2.55).

13.10 In parallel with duty of care which employers have in relation to the health and safety of their employees and others, producers and handlers of waste have a duty in relation to the general care of the environment. (3.4-3.5).

13.11 We commend the guidelines on industrial waste management published by the European Council of Chemical Manufacturers' Federations as ground rules for sound waste management. (3.6).

13.12 The Government has a clear duty to ease the transition to higher standards and to ensure that there is continued compliance with them. It is therefore right that, without implying any diminution of the powers of local waste disposal authorities, the Government should make a direct input to the setting and enforcement of standards to nationally acceptable levels. (3.20).

13.13 We commend the approach of the EC Third Action Programme on the Environment in providing support for the reduction of pollution at source and the development of clean technologies. (4.5).

13.14 It is essential that the potential environmental impact of a new product and its packaging should be assessed and taken into account during the product's design. (4.6-4.7).

13.15 A reduction in the number of cans entering the waste stream would make a significant difference to the amount of litter generated, and a change to all aluminium drinks cans would make recycling practicable. (4.10; 5.16).

*13.16 The Department of the Environment should continue to support and put into practice the objectives of the EC Third Action Programme on the Environment in relation to waste management and in particular those concerning the encouragement of low or non-waste technologies. (4.12).

*13.17 The Department of Trade and Industry should seek the active co-operation of the Department of the Environment and of industry itself in finding appropriate ways of implementing Article 4 of the Directive on Containers of Liquids for Human Consumption. (4.12).

*13.18 The Government should engage in discussions with appropriate bodies with a view to encouraging the exchange of information about industrial wastes. (5.7).

13.19 We do not consider that the adoption of segregated collection schemes for domestic waste in the UK would significantly reduce pollution. (5.10).

13.20 We commend co-operative initiatives between waste disposal authorities and the private sector in relation to bottle banks, can and PET recovery, and similar activities, as a sensible and economical method of reducing the waste stream, including litter, and believe they should be encouraged. (5.15-5.17).

*13.21 Local authorities, in their capacity as planning authorities, should consider requiring the provision of bottle banks in large retail and other appropriate development schemes and, as waste collection or disposal authorities, should investigate the scope for increased provision of bottle banks at existing suitable sites. (5.15).

*13.22 Until more is known about emissions from combustion of waste derived fuel, it should be burnt only in units where good control can achieve high temperatures, with good oxygen mixing and with sufficient residence times. (5.24; 11.12).

13.23 There may be a continued risk of air pollution arising from the burning of waste oils with inappropriate equipment or of pollution from oils dumped on land. (5.27).

13.24 We consider that further development of technologies for the recovery of energy from used tyres and the conversion of waste to oil should be encouraged. (5.28-5.30).

13.25 We consider that initiatives in the field of waste composting should be encouraged. (5.31).

13.26 We consider that the Departments of Trade and Industry and of the Environment should continue to encourage recycling and resource recovery as a means of reducing pollution, including litter. The fact that opportunities are not exploited as vigorously in the UK as they might be is due at least in part to the absence of a clear lead from the Government. (5.32-5.33).

13.27 A stable market for waste paper and board is the touchstone for an efficient recovery system. We see no reason why the Government should not help to boost the demand for recycled paper through its own procurement policies provided that reasonable performance and value for money criteria are met. (5.9; 5.35).

*13.28 All waste collection authorities should adopt an explicit policy designed to achieve a secure waste stream, and should provide appropriate training and supervision of their staff. (6.9a).

*13.29 Specifications drawn up for tenders for refuse collection services should include conditions to maintain or improve standards of litter prevention. The Department of the Environment should provide appropriate guidance to waste collection authorities. (6.9b).

*13.30 The practice of kerbside collection of plastic bags, being the most prone to produce litter, should be phased out, except where local conditions make it uniquely appropriate, in which case bags of adequate quality should be used. (6.9c).

*13.31 Local authorities should adopt wheeled plastic dustbins with attached lids as having environmental and operational advantages, unless particular local circumstances make their use impossible. (6.9d).

*13.32 The Department of Transport, in conjunction with the Department of the Environment, should review the effect of its current policy on the provision of roadside litter bins and, in the light of experience in the UK and abroad, should aim to provide or encourage the provision of litter receptacles that can be emptied with sufficient frequency in sites appropriate to the needs of the motoring public. (6.11).

13.33 Consideration of the provision of litter bins might usefully be a requirement of planning applications for service stations. (6.12).

*13.34 The Department of Transport should discuss with the motoring organisations and the Society of Motor Manufacturers and Traders the general provision of litter containers in cars in the UK. (6.13).

13.35 The lack of litter bins on public transport encourages an irresponsible attitude towards litter in the travelling public. The provision of litter facilities for long distance rail travellers should be extended to provincial and suburban rail services. (6.14).

*13.36 Local authorities should do all they can to encourage market traders, take away food outlets and other establishments whose activities may contribute to litter to provide and, where appropriate, to service litter bins. (6.15).

13.37 We believe that the 'Tidyman' symbol should be displayed more prominently on packaging and litter bins, and commend this to the Industry Committee on Packaging and the Environment and other relevant sectors of industry. (6.17).

*13.38 Local authorities should provide more information on rubbish disposal, for example by leaflets accompanying rate demands or by frequent notices in local papers, and should indicate the location of the nearest amenity skips and sites on litter bins and in other suitable locations. (6.23).

*13.39 Civic amenity sites should be open throughout the day, especially at weekends. (6.23).

13.40 We draw attention to a number of ways in which local initiatives could help to reduce the fly tipping problem. (6.25).

*13.41 Appropriately designated local authority staff should have immediate access, comparable to police access, to the Department of Transport's Driver and Vehicle Licensing Centre data for the purposes of dealing with vehicles which appear to have been abandoned. (6.26).

*13.42 All Regional Health Authorities should prepare and implement waste disposal plans that match the arisings and the disposal facilities in health care establishments. (6.32).

*13.43 Publicity should be given by the Department of Health and Social Security and the Scottish Home and Health Department through health authorities to the guidelines and code of practice prepared by Health and Safety Commission and the Department of the Environment on the disposal of clinical wastes so that community health care establishments are made aware of good practices which can then be enforced. (6.32).

*13.44 Publicity material prepared by the Health Departments should be made available for doctors and nurses in the community to give to patients who may have to dispose of clinical wastes. (6.32).

*13.45 The Control of Pollution (Special Waste) Regulations 1980 should be amended to require waste producers to notify waste disposal authorities of all consignments of special waste to storage. (6.35).

13.46 Any wastes that are hazardous must be assigned to an appropriate category of the relevant hazard code and appropriate safety information and training must be provided for all operatives involved in the transport of wastes by road, rail or inland waterway. (6.38).

13.47 We commend the introduction of purpose-designed river barges, rail wagons and containers for transporting municipal wastes from urban transfer stations to rural landfill sites. (6.40).

*13.48 The British shipping industry should lay renewed stress on the proper handling and security of packaged dangerous goods and the Department of Transport should review the adequacy of extant Merchant Shipping Notices on this matter. (6.43).

*13.49 The Government should work towards ratification of Annex III and Annex V of the MARPOL Convention at the earliest possible date and towards ratification of Annex IV of the Convention. (6.44; 6.46; 6.47).

13.50 The advantages of using a more appropriate disposal facility than the one available locally can justify international trade in waste, but wastes that are hazardous should not be exported without the prior informed consent of the receiving country. (6.48).

*13.51 Planning and waste disposal authorities should always consider the possible advantages of permitting deposition at landfill sites to continue to above original ground levels. (7.3).

*13.52 Reliance should never be placed on the long-term containment of leachate, which instead should be extracted and processed so that containment failure cannot lead to pollution of an aquifer. (7.12).

*13.53 All licences for new landfill sites should require provision for adequate control of methane both during and after the period of deposition of wastes. (7.15).

13.54 For many industrial wastes, properly managed co-disposal is an environmentally acceptable option in containment sites. However we are concerned that inappropriate materials are sometimes admitted to co-disposal and that there is still some lack of knowledge about the processes involved and their long-term effects on the environment. (7.18).

*13.55 Alternative methods of disposing of acid tars should be encouraged; for volatile and flammable organic liquids alternative disposal routes such as incineration should be used rather than landfill; drummed wastes should not normally be landfilled. (7.19).

*13.56 Planning and licensing authorities should include among site licence conditions means for ensuring site aftercare. (7.22).

*13.57 Waste disposal authorities should ensure that they are imposing appropriate conditions on all sites in their areas, whether their own or those of independent operators. (7.23).

*13.58 The Department of the Environment should set up an Incineration Practices Review Group, whose report would lead to the preparation of standards for the operation of incineration plants. (7.28).

13.59 We are concerned that there may soon be insufficient and inadequately distributed merchant incinerator capacity to burn all waste chemicals for which incineration is the BPEO, with the consequence that more will be consigned to less appropriate disposal such as landfill. (7.31).

13.60 We outline the requirements for the incineration of toxic industrial waste and suggest an enhancement of the chemical industry's responsibilities. We commend this approach to the industry. (7.29-7.34).

13.61 Incineration at sea, under the strict conditions prescribed, is an acceptable option for some liquid wastes, provided that the critical incineration parameters are continuously measured and recorded and the records kept. (7.39).

*13.62 The development of alternative methods of straw disposal should be further encouraged by financial support from Government for research and development, perhaps in the form of Department of Trade and Industry funding on a joint basis; the Government should put forward these methods as eligible candidates for European Community grants. (7.45).

*13.63 As recommended in the Tenth Report, the Government should announce the introduction of a legislative ban on straw burning on stubble fields to take effect in five years' time; the legislation should be introduced now and come into effect on the prescribed date without the need for subsequent statutory instruments or commencement orders. (7.46).

*13.64 This legislative ban should be extended to the burning of all field crop residues. (7.46).

*13.65 As recommended in the Tenth Report, full implementation of the recommendations of the Working Party on Sewage Disposal should be achieved to an agreed timetable. (7.48).

*13.66 Water authorities should consult the relevant industries in their areas with a view to increasing the removal of metals from industrial discharges at source and reducing the metal content of sewage. (7.49).

*13.67 In view of the importance to the UK of international acceptance of economic methods of sludge disposal, the Government should consider ways and means of assisting the further reduction of the heavy metals load in sewage sludge. (7.49).

13.68 Deep burial is appropriate for the disposal of materials that have been immobilised and for which the BPEO is their return to the earth's crust. (7.51).

*13.69 Details of wastes disposed of by deep burial should be recorded on the Land Register as a local land charge and waste disposal authorities should make such recording a condition of the licence. (7.52).

13.70 We believe that chemical fixation systems are satisfactory provided that they are properly managed and that inappropriate materials are not included. (7.54).

*13.71 The Department of the Environment should continue to include provision for research into immobilisation of hazardous wastes in its research programme. (7.55).

*13.72 Implementation of sections 12-14 and the enactment of Regulations under sections 12(3) and 30(4) of the Control of Pollution Act 1974 should be completed without further delay. (8.6).

*13.73 The Department of the Environment, the Home Office and others as appropriate should review the enforcement of the law on litter and identify what changes in the law and procedures are needed to improve the efficiency and effectiveness of this enforcement. (8.11).

*13.74 The Control of Pollution Act 1974 should be amended to provide:

(a)   that producers of controlled wastes have a duty of care to take all reasonable steps, having regard to the hazards presented by their wastes, to ensure that their wastes are subsequently managed and disposed of without harm to the environment;

(b)   that the steps that it is reasonable for the waste producer to take in different circumstances to discharge his duty of care shall be contained in a code of practice issued by the Secretary of State; and

(c)   that producers of commercial, industrial and certain domestic wastes who engage contractors to transport their wastes remain liable for the proper disposal of those wastes unless they use a contractor registered as a waste transporter in accordance with our later recommendation and provide him in writing with an unambiguous indication of the nature of the wastes and clear instructions for their disposal. (8.21).

*13.75 The Department of the Environment should set up a working party to review the information needs of waste disposal authorities and the adequacy of the existing sources of information available to them. (8.24).

*13.76 The existing system of licensing for the operators of heavy goods vehicles should be supplemented by a system of registration for the operators of all vehicles, irrespective of weight, carrying controlled wastes for hire or reward. (8.29).

*13.77 Each vehicle covered by a registration should display a conspicuous sign which immediately identifies that vehicle as such. (8.35).

*13.78 The Control of Pollution Act 1974 should be amended:

(a)   to make clear that a breach of waste disposal site licence conditions is an offence in its own right, unrelated to any deposition of waste;

(b)   to empower waste disposal authorities to have regard to the qualifications and previous conduct of applicants when determining site licence applications;

(c)   to provide that, unless otherwise agreed by the parties concerned, an appellant against a decision of a waste disposal authority in respect of a disposal site licence shall have three months in which to present his case to the Secretary of State, failing which the authority's decision shall take effect;

(d)   to make clear that waste disposal authorities are entitled to impose site licence conditions that relate to periods additional to those during which waste is being deposited at a site; and

(e)   to provide that the holder of a waste disposal licence shall be permitted to surrender that licence only if the waste disposal authority or, on appeal, the Secretary of State is satisfied that adequate arrangements have been made for the continued safe management or aftercare of the site. (8.46).

*13.79 Crown immunity should cease to apply to the National Health Service, and incineration and other waste disposal facilities operated by or on behalf of the NHS should, in consequence, be subject to exactly the same controls and standards as similar facilities operated by other organisations. (8.49).

*13.80 The Lord Chancellor should arrange for formal advice to be given to magistrates of the serious and possibly long-term damage to the environment that can be caused by improper handling and disposal of waste and of the need to sentence offenders accordingly. (8.54).

13.81 We conclude that landfill capacity is already a scarce resource in some parts of the country and will become increasingly so in others. It should therefore be conserved by being used only for the disposal of wastes for which it clearly constitutes the best practicable environmental option. The conservation of landfill capacity where it is needed is a matter to which Government policy should be directed. (9.7; 12.12).

*13.82 All non-Metropolitan waste disposal authorities should complete their waste disposal plans forthwith, and new or revised plans covering waste disposal in Metropolitan areas and Greater London should be completed by 31 March 1987; all waste disposal plans should be regularly updated. (9.9).

*13.83 If doubt persists about the adequacy of arrangements for waste regulation and disposal in any part of the United Kingdom, the Government should give further consideration to the scope for reorganising these arrangements on a regional basis. (9.15).

*13.84 The Government should review the present system of land registration with a view to establishing whether it would be desirable and feasible for the fact that land is contaminated to be registered as a local land charge. (9.20).

*13.85 If Department of the Environment's review of its application of section 6(2) of the Control of Pollution Act 1974 suggests that the sub-section does not permit the imposition of insurance or bonding requirements as conditions of waste disposal site licences, the sub-section should be amended to make clear that such requirements can be so imposed; model insurance and bonding requirements should be developed and embodied in appropriate codes of practice. (9.28).

13.86 We do not support the adoption of a 'Superfund' solution to the problem of cleaning up pollution which has already occurred. (9.31).

*13.87 The Government should examine the appropriateness and feasibility of adapting UK law and administrative procedures to provide for some form of discretionary compensation or inducement to individuals or communities affected by waste handling and disposal sites, such that the costs fall ultimately on those who generate the waste. (9.32).

*13.88 The Government should introduce arrangements that would allow for the monitoring of specialist facilities which are the responsibility of a national pollution control inspectorate to be undertaken by local authorities on an agency basis. (9.36).

*13.89 The complement of technical staff in the Department of the Environment's Land Waste and Toxic Substances Divisions should be reinforced. (9.38).

*13.90 The Department of the Environment should strengthen, on a permanent basis, its arrangements for liaison between the Divisions responsible for policy on minerals extraction, waste management and land reclamation and should ensure that local authorities are likewise advised on the importance of co-ordinating their responsibilities in these areas. (9.39).

*13.91 The remit of the Hazardous Waste Inspectorate should be formally designated as concerning all controlled waste. (9.40).

*13.92 The Hazardous Waste Inspectorate should be made a statutory body with powers of enforcement over the actions of waste disposal authorities. (9.41).

*13.93 The Hazardous Waste Inspectorate should remain firmly as part of the Department of the Environment. (9.41).

*13.94 The Industrial Air Pollution Inspectorate should be returned to the Department of the Environment and should there form the nucleus of a unified Pollution Inspectorate embracing also the Hazardous Waste Inspectorate, the Radiochemical Inspectorate and those concerned with the protection of fresh and sea water. (9.47).

*13.95 An appropriate hazard and operability or similar study should be undertaken as a standard part of the design procedure for all installations handling, processing and disposing of wastes which might present significant hazards. (10.11).

*13.96 The British Standards Institution should review equipment and procedures for the management and disposal of wastes and the treatment of contaminated land, including existing standards, with a view to developing new standards and codes of practice in this field. (10.13).

13.97 We hope that the Institute of Waste Management and the chartered institutes in engineering, chemistry and environmental health will continue and intensify their professional interests in waste management, handling, treatment and disposal. (10.14).

*13.98 The Department of the Environment in consultation with local authority associations, industry and other relevant organisations should seek to establish national standards of competence and qualifications for all those involved in the management of waste. (10.26).

13.99 We consider that the Department of the Environment should keep under regular review the balance between centrally funded research and development and local initiatives which have potential applications nationally. (11.4).

*13.100 Joint funding for engineering research and development in the waste industry should be encouraged and should become an area for priority funding by the Department of Trade and Industry. (11.5).

13.101 It is important to give continued high priority to research on co-disposal in order to reduce the uncertainties about the degradative mechanisms involved. (11.10).

*13.102 The Department of the Environment should continue and where possible expand its support for research in the field of microbial breakdown of wastes. (11.11).

13.103 It is important that the Department of the Environment's survey of the incidence of dioxins and furans in soils should cover all types of waste management operation and should be supported by adequate measurements of background concentrations. (11.13).

*13.104 Further research should be undertaken on waste fixation techniques to improve scientific understanding and control of the processes involved and to enable waste disposal authorities to devise effective tests for the acceptance of the solidified wastes in landfill. (11.16).

13.105 We endorse the priorities which the Department of the Environment has identified for research on contaminated land. (11.17).

13.106 It will be important, as application of the concept of BPEO develops, for the Department of the Environment to inject a greater degree of economic analysis into its research programme. (11.18).

13.107 Measures to encourage recycling and reclamation of waste materials are valuable because they help to demonstrate to the public that every effort is being made by those in positions of responsibility to reduce the size of the waste stream. (12.11).

13.108 We consider that public acceptability of waste handling and disposal practices is essential. The process of seeking it has four necessary components:

Information for the public
Involvement of the community
Incentives for the community
Implementation of high standards and their enforcement. (12.14-12.16).

13.109 There is a need for the systematic investigation of cases where an unusual illness appears to occur in a cluster in the neighbourhood of factories or other installations handling substances about which there is scientific uncertainty as to their toxic effects at very low levels in the environment. We suggest a number of steps which such an investigation must go through. (12.23-12.24).

13.110 Rational decisions on the siting of a particular facility, such as a specialised waste treatment or disposal plant, are best made within a broader geographical rather than a purely local context. (12.25).

13.111 The annual report of the new unified pollution inspectorate would provide an important regular review of the state of pollution control in the United Kingdom. (12.26).

13.112 The higher standards that will follow from acceptance of our recommendations will ensure that the United Kingdom participates in the international waste management market: waste management must not remain the Cinderella of government and industry. (12.28).

Acknowledgement

We would like, in closing, first to express our appreciation to the very large number of individuals and organisations who have been so generous with their time in helping us with this study. We have sought to list them comprehensively in Appendix 2, whilst conscious that such a list cannot do justice to individual effort behind the scenes. We hope that all who have contributed in so many different ways will accept our grateful thanks. Secondly, we must record our thanks to our consultants for the helpful analysis in their report. Finally, we are immensely indebted to our small Secretariat, every one of whom has provided unflagging advice, assistance and support throughout our study. Their first-rate team effort has ensured timely completion of the many stages of distilling evidence, drafting and editing of this complex Report, and with their help we have been able to improve on the target we originally set ourselves for publication.

ALL OF WHICH WE HUMBLY SUBMIT FOR YOUR MAJESTY'S GRACIOUS CONSIDERATION

> Richard Southwood (Chairman)
> Cranbrook
> Nathan
> Barbara Clayton
> Gordon Fogg
> Lancelot Gilling
> Jeremy Pope
> Albert Archer
> Christopher Blake
> Henry Charnock
> Gordon Conway
> John Edmonds
> David Newland
> Charles Suckling
> Martin Vessey

T.E. Radice   (Secretary)

P.V. Green
J.M. Wilkinson   (Assistant Secretaries)

November 1985

175

APPENDIX 1

MEMBERS OF THE COMMISSION
during the period of study leading to the present Report

Chairman:

*PROFESSOR SIR RICHARD SOUTHWOOD, MA, PhD, DSc, ARCS, FIBiol, FRS
   Linacre Professor of Zoology, University of Oxford
   Fellow of Merton College, Oxford and Imperial College, London
   A.D. White Professor at Large, Cornell University, United States
   Honorary Foreign Member, American Academy of Arts and Sciences
   Chairman, National Radiological Protection Board (from November
     1985)
   Honorary Vice-President, Institution of Environmental Health Officers
   Vice-President, Zoological Society, London
   Member of the Council for Science and Society

Members:

*A. ARCHER, ESQ, MBE, FIEH
   Past-President, Institution of Environmental Health Officers
   Vice-President, National Society for Clean Air
   Environmental Health Consultant

*PROFESSOR C. BLAKE, MA, PhD, FRSE
   Bonar Professor of Applied Economics, University of Dundee
   Treasurer, Royal Society of Edinbugh
   Member, Environment and Planning Committee, Economic and Social
     Research Council
   Member, Council for Applied Science in Scotland
   Chairman, William Low & Co plc
   Director, Alliance Trust plc

PROFESSOR H. CHARNOCK, MSc, DIC, FRS
   Professor of Physical Oceanography, University of Southampton
   Chairman, Research Sub-Committee, Royal Meteorological Committee
   Chairman, British National Committee on Oceanic Research (Royal
     Society)

PROFESSOR B. E. CLAYTON, CBE, MD, PhD, DSc, FRCP, FRCPE, PRCPath
   Professor of Chemical Pathology and Human Metabolism, and Dean of the Faculty of Medicine University of Southampton
   President, Royal College of Pathologists
   Honorary Consultant to the Southampton and South West Hampshire Health Authority
   Member, General Medical Council
   Chairman, MRC Advisory Group on Lead and Neuropsychological Effects in Children
   Chairman, DHSS Committee on Medical Aspects of the Contamination of Air, Soil and Water
   Deputy Chairman, DHSS Committee on Toxicity of Chemicals in Food, Consumer Products and the Environment
   Member, DHSS Standing Medical Advisory Committee
   Member, British Paediatric Association

PROFESSOR G. R. CONWAY, PhD, DipAgriSci, DTA, FIBiol
   Professor of Environmental Technology, Imperial College of Science and Technology, University of London
   Consultant, Aga Khan and Ford Foundations, USAID and the World Bank
   Member, Southern Zone Research Committee, Royal Society

THE RT. HON. THE EARL OF CRANBROOK, MA, PhD, FLS, FRSA
   Member, House of Lords Select Committee on Science and Technology
   Member, Natural Environment Research Council
   Trustee, British Museum (Natural History)
   Vice-President, National Society for Clean Air

J. W. EDMONDS, ESQ, MA
   Industrial Officer and Secretary General designate, General Municipal Boilermakers and Allied Trades Union
   Member, TUC Public Services, Local Government and Health Services Committees

*PROFESSOR G. E. FOGG, CBE, BSc, PhD, ScD, Hon LLD, FIBiol, FRS
   Former Professor of Marine Biology, University College of North Wales
   Chairman, Scientific Advisory Committee, British Antarctic Survey
   Trustee, Royal Botanic Gardens, Kew
   Trustee, British Museum (Natural History)

L. C. G. GILLING, ESQ, OBE, BSc, FIBiol FRAgS
  Chairman, Executive Committee, Yorkshire Agricultural Society
  Chairman of the Council, Yorkshire Philosophical Society
  Vice-Chairman, Yorkshire Museum Sub-Committee, Libraries
    Archives and Museums Committee, North Yorkshire County Council
  Member, Minister of Agriculture, Fisheries and Food's Northern
    Regional Panel
  Member, Agriculture and Veterinary Advisory Committee, British
    Council
  Former Principal, Askham Bryan College of Agriculture and
    Horticulture

THE RT. HON. LORD NATHAN, MA, FSA, FRSA, FRGS
  Senior Partner, Herbert Oppenheimer Nathan & Vandyk, Solicitors
  Chairman, Sub-Committee G (Environment), House of Lords Select
    Committee on the European Communities
  Vice-President, and member of the Environment Committee, Royal
    Society of Arts
  Member, Watt Committee on Energy

PROFESSOR D. E. NEWLAND, MA, ScD, FEng, FIMechE
  Professor of Engineering, Cambridge University
  Fellow of Selwyn College, Cambridge
  Consulting Engineer
  Member of Council, Fellowship of Engineering
  Member, Board of the Engineering Sciences Division, Institution of
    Mechanical Engineers
  Consultant Editor, Proceedings of the Institution of Mechanical
    Engineers, Part C - Mechanical Engineering Science

J. J. R. POPE, ESQ, OBE, MA
  Joint Managing Director, Eldridge Pope & Co plc (Brewers and Wine
    Merchants)
  Chairman, Winterbourne Hospital plc
  Former Chairman, CBI Smaller Firms Council
  Former Member, National Economic Development Council

C. W. SUCKLING, ESQ, PhD, DSc, DUniv, CChem, FRSC, FRS
  Consultant in Science, Technology and Innovation
  Non-executive Director, Albright and Wilson Ltd
  Visiting Professor, University of Stirling
  Member, Science Consultative Group, British Broadcasting Corporation
  Member, Biosciences Sub-Committee, University Grants Committee
  Member, Electricity Supply Research Council
  Treasurer and Vice-Chairman of the Council, Royal College of Art

PROFESSOR M. P. VESSEY, MA, MD, FRCP(Ed), FFCM, FRCGP
   Professor of Social and Community Medicine, Oxford University
   Fellow of St Cross College, Oxford
   Honorary Specialist in Community Medicine, Oxford Regional and
      District Health Authorities
   Member, Committee on Safety of Medicines
   Adviser, WHO Special Programme of Research, Development and
      Research Training in Human Reproduction

* Members whose terms of office end with the publication of this Report.

While this Report was in press it was announced that Professor Sir Jack
Lewis FRSC FRS, Professor of Inorganic Chemistry in the University of
Cambridge and Warden of Robinson College, had been appointed to the
Chairmanship in succession to Sir Richard Southwood.

APPENDIX 2

ORGANISATIONS AND INDIVIDUALS CONTRIBUTING TO THE STUDY

Listed below are those organisations and individuals who gave written evidence or assisted the Commission in other ways during this study. Those marked * gave oral evidence at formal Commission meetings; those marked + gave oral evidence during visits by the Commission, details of which are listed at the end of this Appendix.

Government Departments

Department of Agriculture and Fisheries for Scotland
Department of Energy
Department of the Environment *
Department of the Environment for Northern Ireland
Department of Trade and Industry (including Warren Spring
    Laboratory +)
Department of Transport
Foreign and Commonwealth Office (including posts in Bonn,
    Düsseldorf, Tokyo and Washington)
Lord Chancellor's Department
Ministry of Agriculture, Fisheries and Food
Scottish Development Department
Scottish Home and Health Department
Welsh Office

Other Organisations

Agricultural and Food Research Council
Amey Roadstone Corporation Limited
Association of Consulting Engineers
Association of County Councils
Association of District Councils
Association of District Councils (Welsh Office)
Association of Local Authorities of Northern Ireland
Association of Metropolitan Authorities
Association of Public Analysts
Aston University

Basildon District Council
Bayer AG, Leverkusen, Federal Republic of Germany +

Bedfordshire Against Nuclear Dumping
Biffa Waste Services Ltd
Billingham Against Nuclear Dumping
Birmingham City Council +
Blue Circle Industries plc
Bristol Polytechnic
British Aggregate Construction Materials Industries
British Ecological Society
British Gas Corporation
British Hydrological Society
British Nuclear Fuels plc
British Paper and Board Industry Federation
British Railways Board
British Reclamation Industries Confederation
British Steel Corporation
British Waterways Board

Central Electricity Generating Board
Chemical Industries Association *
Cleanaway Ltd +
Commission of the European Communities +
Committee of Vice Chancellors and Principals
Confederation of British Industry *
Conservation Foundation, Washington DC
Convention of Scottish Local Authorities
Cornish Chamber of Mines
Council for Environmental Conservation
Council for the Protection of Rural England
Council of Environmental Advisors, Federal Republic of Germany
Council of Scottish Agricultural Colleges
County Planning Officers Society
Country Surveyors' Society
Cremer and Warner Ltd

Dames and Moore International
District Planning Officers Society
Duracell Batteries Limited
Durham University
Düsseldorf City Council +

ECOTEC Research and Consulting Ltd
Environmental Defense Fund, Washington DC

Farnborough College of Technology
Federal Ministry of the Interior (including Federal Environmental
    Agency), Federal Republic of Germany +

Fellowship of Engineering
Food Manufacturers' Federation
Forestry Commission
Friends of the Earth

Glass Manufacturers' Federation
Greater London Council +
Greater Manchester Council
Greenwich Borough Council

Hales Industrial Services Ltd
Hammersmith and Fulham Borough Council
Health and Safety Executive (including Industrial Air Pollution
    Inspectorate *)
Highland River Purification Board
Hillingdon Borough Council
Humberside County Council

ICI Fibres
Imperial College of Science and Technology
Industrial Gas Cleaning Association
Industrial Waste Panel (Scotland)
Industry Committee on Packaging and the Environment
Institute of Biology
Institute of Fisheries Management
Institute of Hospital Engineering
Institute of Wastes Management
Institute of Water Pollution Control
Institution of Chemical Engineers
Institution of Civil Engineers
Institution of Environmental Health Officers
Institution of Environmental Sciences
Institution of Geologists
Institution of Mechanical Engineers
Institution of Mining and Metallurgy
Institution of Public Health Engineers
Institution of Water Engineers and Scientists
Italian Embassy, London

Keep Britain Tidy Group
Kempen Town Council, Federal Republic of Germany +

Lawyers' Ecology Group
Leigh Interests plc +
Liberal Party Environmental Panel
Liverpool University
Local Authority Associations' Joint Minerals and Reclamation Group
London Boroughs Association
Loughborough University of Technology
Luton College of Higher Education

Magistrates Association
Maryland State Waste Management Administration, USA
Medical Research Council
Merseyside Chamber of Commerce and Industry
Metal Packaging Manufacturers Association
Mid Anglian Waste Disposal Consortium
Middlesbrough Borough Council
Mining Association of the United Kingdom
Ministry of Food, Agriculture, Environment and Forestry, Baden-
    Württemberg, Federal Republic of Germany
Ministry of Labour, Environment and Social Affairs, Hesse, Federal
    Republic of Germany
3M Company

National Association of Waste Disposal Contractors
National Coal Board
National Farmers' Union
National Radiological Protection Board
National Society for Clean Air
National Trust for Scotland
Natural Environment Research Council
Nature Conservancy Council
North West Water Authority
Northumbrian Water Authority
Nottingham University
Nuclear Industry Radioactive Waste Executive

Open University

Packington Estate Enterprises Ltd +
Plymouth Polytechnic
Polytechnic of Central London
Pozzolanic Lytag Ltd
Prince of Wales' Committee

Queen Mary College, University of London

Re-Chem International Ltd +
Road Haulage Association
Royal Environmental Health Institute of Scotland
Royal Society of Chemistry
Royal Society of Health
Royal Town Planning Institute

Sand and Gravel Association
Schönmackers GmbH, Kempen, Federal Republic of Germany +
Science and Engineering Research Council
Scottish River Purification Boards' Association *
Severn-Trent Water Authority
Sheffield City Council
Sheffield University
Shell International Chemical Company Ltd
South of Scotland Electricity Board
South West Water Authority
South Yorkshire Metropolitan County Council
Southern Water Authority
Standing Technological Committee of European Local Authorities
Stirling University
Survey Research

Taunton Think Tank Ltd
Teesside and District Chamber of Commerce and Industry
Thames Water Authority
Torfaen Borough Council
Town and Country Planning Association
Trienekens, Neuss, Federal Republic of Germany
Tyne and Wear Metropolitan County Council +

United Kingdom Atomic Energy Authority
United Kingdom Petroleum Industry Association
United States Congress Office of Technology Assessment
United States Council on Environmental Quality
United States Environmental Protection Agency
University of East Anglia

Walsall Metropolitan Borough Council +
Warmer Campaign
Waste Disposal Engineers Association
Water Authorities Association *
Water Research Centre
Welsh Counties Committee

Welsh Water Authority
West Glamorgan Joint Environmental Pollution Committee
West Midlands County Council +
West Yorkshire Industrial Waste Panel
West Yorkshire Metropolitan County Council
Westminster City Council
J M Whelan Ltd, Birmingham +

Yorkshire Water Authority

Individuals

Professor D J P Barker (MRC Environmental Epidemiology Unit, Southampton)
Mr C Burford (Lancashire County Council) *
Mr T Burke (The Green Alliance) *
Mr E E Finnecy (Environmental Safety Group, AERE, Harwell) *
Mr R Grove-White (Council for the Protection of Rural England) *
Dr L D Guruswamy (Clare Hall, Cambridge)
Mr R G P Hawkins *
Mr J R Holmes (GIS Waste Services Ltd)
Mr G Lean (The Observer) *
Professor P Matthews FRS (Radioactive Waste Management Advisory Committee) *
Professor K Mellanby *
Mr J Porritt (Friends of the Earth) *
Mr J Taylor (North Yorkshire County Council)
Mr R K Turner (University of East Anglia)
Mr H Watt (Orsett)

VISITS

During the course of this study Members of the Commission visited the facilities and met representatives of the organisations listed below:

5 April 1984 : **Greater London**

GLC : Solid waste incineration plant, Edmonton

GLC : Transport Avenue solid wastes rail transfer station, Brentford

5 July 1984 : **Essex**

Cleanaway Ltd : Pitsea and Ockendon landfill sites

GLC : Aveley landfill site and methane recovery plant

19-21 September 1984 : **West Midlands**

West Midlands County Council : Coventry waste reduction unit, Bickenhill civic amenity site, Queslett and other landfill sites and areas of contaminated and reclaimed land

Leigh Interests plc : Empire Works hazardous waste treatment and disposal centre, Walsall

J.M. Whelan Ltd : toxic waste treatment plant, Birmingham

Walsall Metropolitan Borough Council

Packington Estate Enterprises Ltd : landfill site, Warwickshire

An open meeting for members of the public was held in Birmingham.

17 January 1985

Department of Trade and Industry : Warren Spring Laboratory, Stevenage

15-18 April 1985 : **Federal Republic of Germany**

Council of Environmental Advisors

Federal Ministry of the Interior

Federal Environment Office

Düsseldorf City Council : domestic waste incinerator

Bayer AG : Leverkusen waste treatment centre

Kempen Town Council

Kempen : Schönmackers resource recovery plant

Neuss : Trienekens waste recycling and landfill site

19 April 1985 : **Brussels**

Commission of the European Communities

3 May 1985

Re-Chem International : chemical waste incineration plant, Hythe

3 June 1985

Tyne and Wear Metropolitan County Council : Byker reclamation plant

APPENDIX 3

THE COMMISSION'S INVITATION FOR EVIDENCE, APRIL 1984

I am writing to invite your organisation to submit written evidence for consideration by the Royal Commission in its next study.

As you probably know, the standing Royal Commission has been in existence since 1970 and was appointed 'to advise on matters, both national and international, concerning the pollution of the environment; on the adequacy of research in this field; and the future possibilities of danger to the environment.' It has published ten reports; the most recent, published in February 1984, was entitled 'Tackling Pollution - Experience and Prospects' and contained a wide-ranging review of priorities for the future and the action that is needed to combat new or growing forms of pollution.

The Commission has decided that its new study will be on pollution by wastes, including the problem of land contamination. This is a very wide field and aspects of it have been covered in studies by other bodies and, indeed, by the Commission itself in past Reports. The Commission therefore, in building on this work, does not intend to undertake a comprehensive survey of all forms of wastes but will review best practicable environmental options for handling and disposal of wastes in the future and will identify particular issues of pollution and land contamination which are likely to arise. Having examined the various options, it would expect to draw some conclusions about the major waste disposal problems facing us today.

The term 'wastes' is to be understood in a wide sense including, for example, household, trade and industrial wastes, toxic and hazardous wastes, radioactive wastes and mining spoils. The Commission will not be concerned in this study with gaseous emissions except insofar as they are the result of the handling and disposal of other wastes or represent alternatives to other disposal options.

As a guide to areas which you may wish to consider covering in your evidence, Annex 1 contains a list of issues which the Commission has already identified as likely to be of particular importance in this study. The list is not meant to be exhaustive or to inhibit the form in which evidence is presented. We hope that you will not hesitate to draw the Commission's attention to any other issues which you consider to be important within the broad framework of the study; on the other hand we are not expecting that you will necessarily wish to comment on every area covered by the list.

* The Commission has not yet decided the extent to which its new study should give further consideration to pollution by agricultural wastes. Such wastes were dealt with in detail in the Commission's Seventh Report, to which the Government responded in December 1983. The Tenth Report noted, however, that agriculture was the one major area in which the Commission could not discern clear evidence of the general trend to reduction of pollution. The Commission would, therefore, welcome views on whether there are aspects of pollution by agricultural wastes that continue to give rise to concern and which may have been inadequately considered or acted upon in the past.

* With regard to radioactive wastes, I wish to draw your attention to the passages from the Commission's Tenth Report which are reproduced in Annex 3. Besides serving as a reminder of the comprehensive nature of the Commission's 'watch dog' role, these passages indicate the Commission's views on the place of nuclear power in the present environmental context, on the current administrative arrangements for waste management, and on the continuing validity of the principles and recommendations contained in the Sixth Report. Against the background of those views, the main purpose of the Commission's inquiries at this stage will be to familiarise itself with current policies and with developments since the Sixth Report. You may find it helpful to have these considerations in mind when framing your evidence.

With regard to timing, it would be very helpful to the Commission if your evidence could reach us by the end of June. If this presents problems, or if you would like to discuss the form or content of your evidence, please do not hesitate to contact me. I should in any case be pleased to hear from you, as soon as possible, whether you are able to respond to this invitation.

Annex 2† contains a list of people and organisations who are initially being invited, in similar terms to those of this letter, to submit evidence to the Commission. The list will doubtless need to be added to as the study proceeds, and if you have any further names to suggest we should be very pleased to have them.

Signed by the Secretary to the Commission

---

* The first or second of these paragraphs was included in the invitations sent to addressees with particular interests in agriculture and the nuclear industry respectively. Annex 3, which is not reproduced, consisted of paragraphs 2.12-2.14, 3.42-3.45 and 5.137-5.139 of the Commission's Tenth Report.

† The list of addressees is not reproduced.

Annex 1 to the Commission's invitation for evidence

LIST OF ISSUES ALREADY IDENTIFIED AS BEING OF
INTEREST TO THE COMMISSION

1. **Surface Disposal and Landfill**
   The future of availability of suitable sites. Landfill as a positive means of
     land reclamation.
   Problems of nuisances during tipping operations.
   Contamination of ground water and surface water.
   Potential of energy production from methane.

2. **Deep Burial**
   Mines. Subterranean structures.

3. **Processing and Storage**
   Storage versus disposal. Potential for future recovery and use.
   Treatment to reduce toxicity or facilitate disposal.

4. **Incineration**
   Air pollution and nuisances from incineration plants.
   Potential of incineration for energy production.
   Incineration of toxic wastes at sea.

5. **Sea Disposal**
   Suitability of the sea and sea-bed for disposal of different types of wastes.
   Adequacy of international conventions.

6. **Recycling of Wastes**
   Potential for recycling of domestic and trade wastes.
   Problems associated with the use of toxic wastes as chemical feedstocks.
   Potential of low-waste technology.

7. **Transport of Wastes**
   Environmental aspects of transport of different types of wastes.
   Nuisances associated with transfer stations.
   Problems associated with transfrontier movements of wastes.

8. **Land Contamination**
   Avoidance of future land contamination problems from existing industrial
     activity and on-site waste disposal and storage.
   Problems of decommissioning and of business failures.
   Technical problems relating to the legacy of existing contamination.
   Avoidance of future land contamination problems from mining activities.

9. **Economic Implications**
   Quantitative assessments of financial and energy costs of different handling
     and disposal options.

10. **The Future**
    Predictions of trends in waste quality and quantity.
    Future problems of pollution by wastes.
    New methods for wastes handling and disposal. Export potential.

APPENDIX 4

Abolition of the Greater London and Metropolitan County Councils - waste disposal arrangements: correspondence with the Secretary of State for the Environment, June 1984 and February/March 1985

**Royal Commission
on Environmental Pollution**

Church House
Great Smith Street
London SW1P 3BL

From the Chairman
Professor Sir Richard Southwood FRS

Telephone 01-212 8710

The Rt Hon Patrick Jenkin MP
Secretary of State for the Environment
Department of the Environment
2 Marsham Street
LONDON
SW1P 3EB

1 June 1984

Dear Secretary of State,

METROPOLITAN WASTE DISPOSAL ARRANGEMENTS

The effectiveness of pollution control arrangements, including the organisational aspects, is an essential element of any study undertaken by the Royal Commission, and our new study of pollution by wastes is no exception. Although this study is still at an early stage, we have already been able to give some consideration to the implications for waste management of the proposals in the White Paper "Streamlining the Cities". We find that, as we become more acquainted with the subject, these proposals give us grounds for some concern, which is shared by many from industrial and scientific as well as local authority circles with whom we have had preliminary discussions. We are of course aware that this concern has been similarly expressed to the Government and doubtless we shall see the arguments rehearsed in greater detail in the formal written evidence which will start to arrive next month.

Although it is inevitable that we should be drawn into this debate, the timing is awkward in relation to our programme of study. In the normal course of things, we would not presume to offer an opinion on such an important matter before we had had an opportunity to study the underlying issues with some care. In any case, it seemed to us when we first embarked on our new study that we could not possibly offer comments on the Department's consultation document of November 1983 before the specified deadline of 31 January 1984. Since then, it has become apparent

190

that firm proposals for waste disposal arrangements in the
metropolitan areas are not likely to emerge for at least another
month, and having now formed a preliminary view on the matter the
Commission felt that it should convey it to you in the hope that
it might be helpful to you and your colleagues in taking what we
know will be some difficult decisions.

I hope you will understand that if this letter appears to
concentrate on the arrangements in the London conurbation rather
than in the metropolitan counties it is partly because we have
not yet had an opportunity to consider the position in the latter
counties, but also. because of the sheer size and complexity of
the waste disposal task in London. Having seen at first hand
some of the waste disposal facilities in London, and having
discussed with officers of the GLC Department of Public Health
Engineering and one of their leading private contractors the
nature of their responsibilities, the problems that can arise in
planning new facilities, and the extremely long lead-times
involved, we have the greatest difficulty in conceiving how these
activities can continue effectively under the aegis of purely
voluntary consortia of borough councils. We believe that the
pressures of "not in my back yard" will in many cases prove
overwhelming and that sensible decisions in the interests not
only of London but also of much of South East England will become
very much more difficult to achieve. We strongly suspect that
much the same would apply in the other metropolitan areas. The
complexity, sophistication and scale of waste disposal operations
in large metropolitan areas require central management, although
we are not suggesting for future administrative purposes these
areas need necessarily coincide with existing GLC or metropolitan
county council boundaries.

Whilst acknowledging that we have had to reach this view with
more haste than we would normally consider desirable, we are very
concerned lest the manner in which the Government's policy is
implemented should have the effect of damaging the environment
and of reversing much of the progress of the past twenty years.
We also fear that it may undermine the principles of waste
management which your Department has been actively promoting and
which are inherent in the present pattern of county waste
disposal authorities throughout England and in particular in
Greater London. We are, of course, aware of the proposed reserve
powers and of your assurances that these would be used in the
event of failure by district or borough councils to come to
suitable voluntary arrangements. We feel, however, that the
needs of metropolitan waste disposal are such that some kind of
statutory central arrangement is likely to prove essential.

We appreciate that there are wider political aspects of this
problem which fall outside our remit. Nevertheless we felt bound
to draw these environmental considerations to your notice whilst
the detailed organisational arrangements are still the subject of
deliberation within Government.

Yours sincerely,

Richard Southwood

191

T R E SOUTHWOOD

Appendix 4

2 MARSHAM STREET
LONDON SW1P 3EB

01-212 3434

My ref:

Your ref:

29 June 1984

Dear Sir Richard,

Thank you for your letter of 1 June about the arrangements to be made for waste disposal in London and the other metropolitan areas after the abolition of the GLC and metropolitan county councils.

I share your concern that there should be effective arrangements for waste disposal following abolition, and you are absolutely right to stress the scale and nature of what is involved for Greater London. But the circumstances and problems of different areas vary greatly. I am less pessimistic than you that we can in due course get effective arrangements for voluntary cooperation between the borough and district councils to whom these functions will be transferred; nor should we overlook the benefits in these areas of integrating refuse collection and waste disposal.

We are currently seeking to launch discussions with local authorities in each area so as to establish the most effective means of securing the necessary cooperation. Unfortunately, a number of authorities are dragging their feet but I hope that before long they will appreciate the sense of starting to plan as soon as possible for the consequences of abolition.

As you note, I intend to seek reserve powers to impose a solution, if need be. I hope that this will not be necessary. It is far better that authorities should voluntarily cooperate in schemes developed on their own initiative according to their individual problems and needs. But I shall not hesitate to use any reserve powers given me if I think the situation warrants.

Yours ever

PATRICK JENKIN

Sir Richard Southwood FRS

192

**Royal Commission
on Environmental Pollution**
Church House
Great Smith Street
London SW1P 3BL

From the Chairman   Telephone 01-212 8710
Professor Sir Richard Southwood FRS

The Rt Hon Patrick Jenkin MP
The Secretary of State for the Environment
Department of the Environment
2 Marsham Street
LONDON
SW1P 3EB   14 February 1985

Dear Secretary of State,

WASTE DISPOSAL IN METROPOLITAN AREAS

I wrote to you on 1 June 1984 to express the Commission's concern
about the implications for waste management of the Government's
proposals for reorganising local government in Greater London and
the metropolitan counties, and you replied on 29 June. Since
then, the Commission has received and studied a number of
submissions on this subject, written from a variety of
viewpoints, and has had discussions with a representative range
of people, some of them during an extended visit to the West
Midlands last September.

We have also noted the discussion which took place in the House
of Commons Standing Committee G on Tuesday 29 January, in
particular Mr Baker's comments (column 872) on the Government's
readiness to consider further views from the Commission on this
matter.

The evidence received during our study has impressed upon us the
importance of safe and efficient waste disposal and the potential
penalties in terms of cost, amenity and public safety if waste
disposal is not carried out properly. The confidence of the
public is also essential. If this is lost through inept
management, the costs of regaining it can be considerable.

We remain concerned that waste disposal should be planned and operated on a sufficiently large scale to ensure that environmental damage is minimised, for instance by the correct choice and location of facilities and by making maximum use of the opportunities which exist for waste reduction at source and resource recovery. Experience has shown that decisions based entirely on local factors, particularly if they are swayed by parochial pressures, do not necessarily result in the best practicable environmental option being chosen.

Successful waste disposal depends on a multi-disciplinary approach and requires a high degree of technical and managerial expertise. Since the supply of persons possessing appropriate technical expertise in the disciplines relevant to waste disposal is always likely to be at a premium, co-operative arrangements between authorities, as the Government has recognised, will be necessary to ensure that the best use is made of their skills.

Whilst the collection and disposal of much household and commercial waste is relatively straightforward, the maintenance of proper standards both in landfill sites and in the operation of incinerators requires expert technical management. The difficulties that many district councils experience in providing this are illustrated by the problems that arose in England prior to the reorganisations of 1965 and 1974; and it is apparent from the evidence we have received that they continue to arise in Scotland, Wales and Northern Ireland. Indeed, as far as Wales is concerned, we note that the Secretary of State for Wales stated a year ago that there was considerable room for improvement in the way in which the waste disposal function was carried out in Wales, and we understand that legislation to transfer responsibility for waste disposal from district to county councils remains a possibility.

The cycle of excavation, landfill, reclamation and management should be seen as an integrated process, and considerable technical and managerial resources are needed to co-ordinate it. There is an important interaction between waste disposal and mineral planning, to which similar considerations apply. We note the comment in your Department's evidence to us that there is likely to be an overall trend towards fewer, but larger, and more professionally operated landfill sites.

Another task which demands a high level of technical expertise is the efficient utilisation of domestic and commercial wastes for energy production and resource recovery. Your Department's evidence, after referring to the problems of older municipal incinerators installed by smaller authorities in the 1960s and early 1970s, emphasises that even with well designed and well constructed modern incinerators, it is essential to employ high calibre operators and supervisors in order to achieve good results from the handling of waste of variable composition and of a largely unpredictable nature. Moreover there is a minimum efficient scale in most resource recovery technologies. For all but the simplest forms of recycling, district and borough councils will need to act jointly, and in this task they will require appropriate technical support.

Finally, the control and safe disposal of hazardous wastes, and the consistent application of proper standards, will need very careful consideration in the context of the proposed reorganisation of waste disposal functions. Whilst we recognise, and welcome, the important role of the Hazardous Waste Inspectorate in this field, its success will depend to a very large extent on the level of technical competence within the local authority teams with whom the Inspectorate has dealings.

Many district and borough councils do not have adequate landfill sites within their boundaries, while across the country as a whole only a limited number of the more specialised facilities are required (e.g. for incineration of toxic industrial wastes). Local authorities will face considerable political difficulties in accepting the siting and licensing of waste disposal facilities for other authorities within their boundaries. Private waste disposal contractors have been particularly emphatic in expressing this view to us. We feel that this "not in my back yard" difficulty could be ameliorated in the proposed new arrangements if district and borough councils were serviced by well respected, expert teams, who were in a position to take an objective view of waste disposal needs over wider areas. Their advice would also be invaluable in negotiations with the Regional Water Authorities on conditions for site licences.

Thus we are convinced that local authorities will need support and guidance on a day-to-day basis on how to achieve appropriate standards in these activities. From our present knowledge we do not believe that, in terms of either size or remit, the present Hazardous Waste Inspectorate would be adequate for the task. Nor do we believe that the availability of published guidance from your Department, valuable though it is, is a substitute for in-house expertise of the kind we have described.

We have been impressed by the expertise of existing teams at county level and by the range of sophisticated laboratory facilities at their disposal, such as those which we have seen in London and the West Midlands. The continued existence and location of what are undeniably centres of excellence cannot prudently be left to chance. We would therefore urge you, when reviewing the proposals made by borough and district councils for the discharge of their new responsibilities, to give positive consideration to ways in which they can continue to draw at first hand on the wealth of in-house technical and managerial expertise which has been so carefully built up over a decade or more.

In view of the importance we attach to the subject, it is our intention at some stage (assuming you have no objection) to publish this correspondence, together with our earlier exchange, possibly as an Appendix to our next Report.

Yours sincerely,

T R E SOUTHWOOD

2 MARSHAM STREET
LONDON SW1P 3EB

01-212 3434

My ref:

Your ref:

\ ९ March 1985

Dear Sir Richard,

WASTE DISPOSAL IN METROPOLITAN AREAS

Thank you for your letter of 14 February about the arrangements
to be made for waste disposal following enactment of the Local
Government Bill.

I entirely agree on the importance of ensuring that waste disposal
is properly organised when borough and district councils take
over these responsibilities in April next year. That, as you
say, must depend on planning being done on a sufficiently large
scale, and on effective deployment of the necessary expertise
particularly in relation to incineration and energy recovery.
But I do not think that this necessitates retention of the GLC
and the metropolitan county councils. What it does necessitate,
and what I am seeking to ensure, is a proper measure of coordination
between authorities sharing the same facilities and disposal
outlets. That we made clear in the special consultation paper
which we published in 1983, when we asked successor authorities
to bring forward cooperative proposals for carrying out the
new functions.

I am happy to say that most London Boroughs are now bringing
forward such proposals, and they currently have it in mind to
work together in a series of sectoral groupings focussed on
the key facilities and disposal routes which tend to form a
radial pattern. I regret that we have not yet received comprehensive
proposals for the metropolitan counties but proposals have been
received from a number of individual authorities, and useful
discussions held with them. I am currently considering what
further guidance I might usefully give to hasten the planning
process. While I am prepared to use the reserve powers in the
Bill, if need be, to ensure satisfactory arrangements, I regard
this as a last resort. It is far more preferable for authorities
to get together on their own initiative in ways best suited
to their circumstances.

You refer to the problems that many English district councils
experienced prior to 1974 in maintaining proper standards for
landfill sites and operating incinerators. But the 1974
re-organisation did, of course, producer larger, stronger district
councils; and the improvements which have been made over the
last 10 years in facilities, techniques and standards will not
be lost. There is no question in London or in the metropolitan
counties of reverting to the earlier situation. With proper
coordination where needed I am confident that the borough and
district councils can discharge their responsibilities successfully

and indeed make further improvements. They will in particular
be able to integrate the advantages of collection and disposal
services in a way which is not now possible. This in turn can
facilitate recycling where this is dependent on special collection
arrangements as in the particular case of glass.

You will not, I am sure, expect me to comment on the merits
of the organisation of waste disposal in Scotland, Wales and
Northern Ireland (to which you refer). These arrangements are
not within my responsibility and I would in any event be cautious
about drawing comparisons in this respect between English
metropolitan boroughs and districts and districts in other countries
of the United Kingdom.

You rightly make the important point that excavation, landfill,
reclamation and management should be seen as an integrated process.
But the co-location of minerals control, general planning
responsibilities and waste disposal functions in the lower tier
authorities will promote rather than hamper an integrated approach.

You finally refer to the problem of hazardous wastes, and the
wider strategic issues involved in siting of disposal facilities.
I am entirely at one with you on the need to retain the benefit
of existing expertise. As Kenneth Baker has made clear at the
Committee Stage of the Bill we shall be looking in all counties
for arrangements for coordinating emergency services and controls
relating to hazardous wastes. The sort of arrangement we have
in mind is the employment of a single unit of staff by one authority
whose services will be made available to other authorities on
a repayment basis. While my hazardous Waste Inspectorate will
certainly be available to advise authorities, I agree that it
is not a substitute for an adequate expert team of their own.
In addition, we are looking to all authorities to coordinate
their long term planning and other regulatory activities. This
will help to counteract any tendency to resort to
"not-in-my-backyard" policies.

In conclusion, I would like to say how much I value the constructive
comments you have made in your letter. It seems to me that there
is no difference between us on the underlying considerations,
and I shall certainly bear in mind your key points of concern.
I look forward to seeing in due course the Commission's report
of their wider review of waste disposal matters.

I am happy for you to publish your letter and my reply, as also
the earlier exchange between us.

PATRICK JENKIN

Professor Sir Richard Southwood FRS

REFERENCES

1. ROYAL COMMISSION ON ENVIRONMENTAL POLLUTION (1984). Tackling pollution - experience and prospects. *Tenth Report, Cmnd.9149.* HMSO, London.
2. ENVIRONMENTAL RESOURCES LIMITED (ERL). (In press). Resource recovery: a report for the Royal Commission on Environmental Pollution. DoE, London.
3. HOLDGATE, M.W. (1979). *A Perspective of Environmental Pollution.* Cambridge University Press, Cambridge.
4. DEPARTMENT OF THE ENVIRONMENT (1978). Co-operative programme of research on the behaviour of hazardous waste in landfill sites. *Final Report of the Policy Review Committee. (Chairman: Mr J Sumner).* HMSO, London.
5. HOUSE OF LORDS SELECT COMMITTEE ON SCIENCE AND TECHNOLOGY (1981). Hazardous waste disposal. *First report, Session 1980-81.* HMSO, London.
6. DEPARTMENT OF THE ENVIRONMENT (1985). Report of a review of the Control of Pollution (Special Waste) Regulations 1980. DOE, London.
7. DEPARTMENT OF THE ENVIRONMENT (In press). Landfilling wastes. Report of the Landfill Practices Review Group.
8. WILSON, D.C. (1981). *Waste Management: Planning, Evaluation, Technologies.* Oxford University Press, Oxford.
9. HOLMES, J.R. (Editor) (1983). *Practical Waste Management.* John Wiley and Sons, Chichester.
10. SUESS, M.J., AND HUISMANS, J.W. (Editors) (1983). *Management of Hazardous Waste.* WHO Regional Publications, European Series No.14. WHO, Copenhagen.
11. ROYAL COMMISSION ON ENVIRONMENTAL POLLUTION (1981). Oil pollution of the sea. *Eighth Report, Cmnd.8358.* HMSO, London.
12. SOCIAL AND COMMUNITY PLANNING RESEARCH. Jowell, R. and Witherspoon, S. (Editors) (1985). *British social attitudes: the 1985 Report.* Gower Publishing Company Limited, Aldershot.
13. KESSEL, H. (1984). Environmental awareness in the Federal Republic of Germany, England and the United States. *Discussion Paper 84-4. International Institute for Environment and Society.* Wissenschaftszentrum, Berlin (W).
14. DUNLAP, R.E. (1985). Public opinion: behind the transformation. *EPA Journal,* **11** (July/August).
15. HOUSE OF COMMONS TRADE AND INDUSTRY COMMITTEE (1984). The wealth of waste. *Fourth Report, Session 1983-84.* HMSO, London.
16. DEPARTMENT OF THE ENVIRONMENT (1985). Public access to information held by pollution control authorities. *A discussion paper circulated by DoE to interested organisations, August 1985.*
17. THE HAZARDOUS WASTE INSPECTORATE (1985). Hazardous waste management - an overview. *HWI First Report.* Department of the Environment, London.
18. NATIONAL RESEARCH COUNCIL OF CANADA. ASSOCIATE COMMITTEE ON SCIENTIFIC CRITERIA FOR ENVIRONMENTAL QUALITY (1984). Polychlorinated dibenzo dioxins. Criteria for their effects on man and his environment. *Publication NRCC 18574.*
19. INTERNATIONAL AGENCY FOR RESEARCH ON CANCER (1978). Polychlorinated biphenyls and polybrominated biphenyls. **18.** *Monographs on the evaluation of the carcinogenic risk of chemicals to humans.* IARC.
20. OUW, H.K., SIMPSON, G.R. AND SIYALI, D.S. (1976). Use and health effects of Aroclor 1242, a polychlorinated biphenyl, in the electrical industry. *Arch Environ Health* **31**, 189-94.

21. FISCHBEIN, A., WOLFF, M.S., LILIS, R., THORNTON, J. AND SELIKOFF, I.J. (1979). Clinical findings among PCB-exposed capacitor manufacturing workers. *Ann NY Acad Sci* **320**, 703-15.

22. WARSHAW, R., FISCHBEIN, A., THORNTON, J., MILLER, A., AND SELIKOFF, I.J. (1979). Decrease in vital capacity in PCB-exposed workers in a capacitor manufacturing facility. *Ann NY Acad Sci* **320**, 277-83.

23. KUWABARA, K., YAKUSHIJI, T., WATANABE, I., YOSHIDA, S., KOYAMA, K., KUNITA, N., & HARA, I. (1978). Relationship between breast feeding and PCB residues in blood of the children whose mothers were occupationally exposed to PCBs. *Int Arch Occup Environ Hlth* **41**, 159-197.

24. YAKUSHIJI, T., WATANABE, I., KUWABARA, K., TANAKA, R., KASHIMOTO, T., KUNITA, N. AND HARA,I. (1984). Post natal transfer of PCBs from exposed mothers to their babies: influence of breast feeding. *Archives of Environmental Health* **39** (5) 368-375.

25. HARA, I. (1985). Health status and PCBS in blood of workers exposed to PCBS and of their children. *Environmental Health Perspectives,* **59**, 85-90.

26. RAWLS, R.L. (1983). Dioxin's human toxicity is most difficult problem. *Chemical and Engineering News* **61** (23) 37-48.

27. LOWRANCE, W.W. (1983). (Editor). *Public health risks of the dioxins.* Symposium held in New York City, October, 1983.

28. DUNEA, G. (1985). Sense and senselessness - letter from Chicago. *British Medical Journal* **290**, 776-777.

29. ROYAL COMMISSION ON ENVIRONMENTAL POLLUTION (1972). Pollution in some British estuaries and coastal waters. *Third Report, Cmnd.5054.* HMSO, London.

30. ROYAL COMMISSION ON ENVIRONMENTAL POLLUTION (1976). Air pollution control: an integrated approach. *Fifth Report, Cmnd.6371.* HMSO, London.

31. ROYAL COMMISSION ON ENVIRONMENTAL POLLUTION (1976). Nuclear Power and the Environment. *Sixth Report, Cmnd.6618.* HMSO, London.

32. ROYAL COMMISSION ON ENVIRONMENTAL POLLUTION (1979). Agriculture and pollution. *Seventh Report, Cmnd.7644.* HMSO, London.

33. MINISTRY OF HOUSING AND LOCAL GOVERNMENT: SCOTTISH DEVELOPMENT DEPARTMENT. Technical Committee on the Disposal of Toxic Solid Wastes (Chairman: Dr A Key) (1970). Disposal of solid toxic wastes. HMSO, London.

34. DEPARTMENT OF THE ENVIRONMENT. Working Party on Refuse Disposal (Chairman: Mr J Sumner) (1971). Refuse disposal. HMSO, London.

35. ROYAL COMMISSION ON ENVIRONMENTAL POLLUTION (1972). Three issues in industrial pollution. *Second Report, Cmnd.4894.* HMSO, London.

36. DIRECTIVE 75/442/EEC on Waste. *Official Journal of the European Communities.* **L194**, 39-41, 25 July 1975.

37. DIRECTIVE 78/319/EEC on Toxic and Dangerous Waste. *Official Journal of the European Communities.* **L84**, 43-47, 31 March 1978.

38. HAIGH, N. (1984). *EEC Environmental Policy and Britain - an Essay and Handbook.* Environmental Data Services Ltd., London.

39. FINNECY, E.E. (Editor) (1985). Pollution by wastes. *Atomic Energy Research Establishment Report No. R 11649.* AERE, Harwell.

40. THIRD ACTION PROGRAMME ON THE ENVIRONMENT. *Official Journal of the European Communities.* **C46** 1-6. 17 February 1983.

41. DEPARTMENT OF THE ENVIRONMENT (1984). Digest of environmental protection and water statistics. HMSO, London.

42. For example: SCOTTISH DEVELOPMENT DEPARTMENT (1984). Environmental Monitoring for Radioactivity in Scotland, 1980-83. *Statistical Bulletin, No.4, November 1984.*

43. MINISTRY OF AGRICULTURE, FISHERIES AND FOOD: DIRECTORATE OF FISHERIES RESEARCH (1985). Radioactivity in surface and coastal waters of the British Isles, 1983. *Aquatic Environment Monitoring Report, No.12.* MAFF, Lowestoft.

References

44. i. CHARTERED INSTITUTE OF PUBLIC FINANCE AND ACCOUNTANCY: STATISTICAL INFORMATION SERVICE. (1985). Waste disposal statistics 1983-84 actuals. *SIS ref 63.85*. CIPFA, London.

    ii. CHARTERED INSTITUTE OF PUBLIC FINANCE AND ACCOUNTANCY: STATISTICAL INFORMATION SERVICE (1984). Waste disposal statistics 1984-85 estimates. *SIS ref 64.85*. CIPFA, London.

    iii. CHARTERED INSTITUTE OF PUBLIC FINANCE AND ACCOUNTANCY: STATISTICAL INFORMATION SERVICE. (1985). Waste collection statistics 1983-84 actuals. *SIS ref 62.85*. CIPFA, London.

    iv. CHARTERED INSTITUTE OF PUBLIC FINANCE AND ACCOUNTANCY: STATISTICAL INFORMATION SERVICE. (1985). Waste disposal statistics 1985-86 estimates. *SIS ref 64.86*. CIPFA, London.

45. WATER RESEARCH CENTRE. Evidence to the Royal Commission.

46. THE OSLO AND PARIS COMMISSIONS (1984). *The First Decade*. Oslo and Paris Commissions, London.

47. DEPARTMENT OF THE ENVIRONMENT, SCOTTISH DEVELOPMENT DEPARTMENT AND WELSH OFFICE: Advisory Committee on Aggregates (Chairman: Sir Ralph Verney) (1976). Aggregates: the way ahead. HMSO, London.

48. COMMISSION ON ENERGY AND THE ENVIRONMENT (1981). Coal and the environment. HMSO, London.

49. DEPARTMENT OF THE ENVIRONMENT, DEPARTMENT OF ENERGY, SCOTTISH OFFICE, WELSH OFFICE (1983). Coal and the environment: the Government's response to the Commission on Energy and the Environment's Report. *Cmnd.8877*. HMSO, London.

50. WRITTEN ANSWER. *House of Commons Official Report*, 8 July 1985. Column 331.

51. ADAS FARM WASTE UNIT (1984). A report on the 1983 survey of water pollution incidents caused by farm wastes in England and Wales. Ministry of Agriculture, Fisheries and Food.

52. ADAS FARM WASTE UNIT (1985). A report on the 1984 survey of water pollution incidents caused by farm wastes in England and Wales. Ministry of Agriculture, Fisheries and Food.

53. DEPARTMENT OF THE ENVIRONMENT (1983). Agriculture and pollution: the Government response to the Seventh Report of the Royal Commission on Environmental Pollution. *Pollution Paper 21*. HMSO, London.

54. PROPOSAL FOR A COUNCIL DIRECTIVE on the Use of Sewage Sludge in Agriculture. *Official Journal of European Communities*. **C.264**, 3-7, 8 October 1982.

55. HEALTH AND SAFETY COMMISSION (1982). The Safe Disposal of Clinical Wastes. HMSO, London.

56. ICRCL Guidance Notes Include:

    i. Notes on the redevelopment of landfill sites   ICRCL 17/78
    ii. Notes on the redevelopment of gasworks sites ICRCL 18/79
    iii.Notes on the redevelopment of sewage works and farms ICRCL 23/79
    iv.Notes on the redevelopment of scrap yards and similar sites ICRCL 42/80
    v. Guidance on the assessment and redevelopment of contaminated land ICRCL 59/83
    vi.Notes on the fire hazards of contaminated land ICRCL 61/84
      DoE, London.

57. BECKETT, M.J. AND SIMMS, D.L. (1985). Assessing contaminated land: UK policy and practice. *Paper presented at the 1st International Conference on Contaminated Soils, Utrecht, 11-15 November 1985*. TNO, Netherlands.

58. SIMMS, D.L. AND BECKETT, M.J. (1985). Risk analysis and safety margins. *Paper presented at the 1st International Conference on Contaminated Soils, Utrecht, 11-15 November 1985*. TNO, Netherlands.

59. SMITH, M.A. (Editor) (1985). *Contaminated Land: Reclamation and Treatment. Nato Committee on the Challenges to Modern Society*. Plenum Press, London.

60. DEPARTMENT OF THE ENVIRONMENT, WELSH OFFICE (1984). Memorandum on Structure and Local Plans. *DOE Circular 22/84 and WO Circular 43/84*. HMSO, London.

61. DEPARTMENT OF THE ENVIRONMENT, WELSH OFFICE (1973). Planning and Noise. *DOE Circular 10/73 and WO Circular 16/73.* HMSO, London.

62. DEPARTMENT OF THE ENVIRONMENT (1982). Air pollution control. *Pollution Paper 18.* HMSO, London.

63. *S.I. 1985 No.1065,* The Building Regulations, 1985.

64. CONFEDERATION OF BRITISH INDUSTRY (1982). Guidelines on the responsible disposal of waste. CBI, London.

65. EUROPEAN COUNCIL OF CHEMICAL MANUFACTURERS' FEDERATIONS (1985). *Industrial Waste Management.* CEFIC, Brussels.

66. ORGANISATION FOR ECONOMIC COOPERATION AND DEVELOPMENT (1985). Identification of responsibilities in hazardous waste management. OECD, Paris.

67. GURUSWAMY, L.D. (1985). Waste management planning. *Journal of Environmental Management.* **21** (1) 69-84, July 1985.

68. CHEMICAL INDUSTRIES ASSOCIATION. Evidence to the Royal Commission.

69. DEPARTMENT OF TRADE AND INDUSTRY. Evidence to the Royal Commission.

70. IDEAS. *3 M Fact Sheets about innovations within the company which reduce waste arisings or prevent pollution.* 3M, Minnesota, USA.

71. BUSINESS ROUNDTABLE ENVIRONMENTAL INFORMATION PROGRAM (1984). Formula for progress: imagination, cooperation, practicality. *3rd Report of BREIP.* Washington, DC.

72. ERL LIMITED (1983). Cleaner technologies in the chemical industry. *Report EUR 8443 EN.* Commission of the European Communities: Environment and quality of life.

73. ERL LIMITED (1983). Clean technologies in the EEC cement industry. *Report EUR 8394 EN.* Commission of the European Communities: Environment and quality of life.

74. D'ARCY, B.J. AND WITHER, A.W. (1983). Reductions in effluent loads achieved during a period of economic recession. *Paper given to N.W. Branch of Industrial Water Society on 11 October 1983.* North West Water, Rivers Division. Ref. No. RI 84/1. 31 October 1984

75. ECOTEC RESEARCH AND CONSULTING LTD (1985). Clean technologies and innovation. *A pilot study on a clean technologies information centre/network, being carried out for the EC Commission.*

76. ASTON UNIVERSITY. Evidence to the Royal Commission.

77. OFFICIAL GAZETTE OF THE REPUBLIC OF ITALY - No.356. 29 December 1984.

78. DIRECTIVE 85/339/EEC on Containers and Liquids for Human Consumption. *Official Journal of the European Communities,* **L.176,** 18-21, 6th July 1985.

79. MELINAR PET GROUP OF ICI FIBRES. Evidence to the Royal Commission.

80. ANON. (1985). The improving prospect for PET recycling. *ENDS Report 128,* September 1985

81. COOK, R. (1981). The environmental threat to packaging. *In PRI International Conference Advances in Blow Moulding II, held 20-21 May 1981 in London.* Plastics and Rubber Institute, London.

82. ANON. (1984). Survey findings: consumers want packaging that offers convenience. *Packaging Today,* May 1984.

83. TRON, A.R., RAY, D.J., COUSINS, H.E. (1981). The United Kingdom Waste Materials Exchange. *Conservation and Recycling* 4 (2) 99-107.

84. UK Waste Material Exchange Bulletin no.20. 1979. Warren Spring Laboratory, Stevenage.

85. WEST MIDLANDS COUNTY COUNCIL. Evidence to the Royal Commission.

86. ANON. (1985). The Chemical Recovery Association. *ENDS Report, No.125,* June 1985.

87. WILLING, E. (1984). Materials recovery and recyling - German development trends. *Paper delivered at a one day seminar, Waste Processing and Resource Recovery; 25 October 1984.* Institute of Wastes Management, London.

88. BUSINESS ROUND TABLE ENVIRONMENT INFORMATION PROGRAM. (1983). Business and the environment: challenge and commitment. *2nd Report of BREIP.* Washington, DC.

References

89. ANON. (1985). Batteries: EEC proposal soon on recycling. *European Report, No.1158,* 14 September 1985.

90. BARTON, J.R., POLL, A.J., WEBB, M. AND WHALLEY, L. (In Press). *Waste Sorting and RDF Production in Europe.* Elsevier Applied Science Publications, London.

91. ANON. (1984). Government Laboratory Studies RDF Emissions. *Warmer Bulletin* 1 (4) December 1984.

92. DAVIS, B.J. AND CLAYTON, P. (1984). The combustion of waste derived fuel. *WSL Report LR 491 (AP).* Warren Spring Laboratory, Stevenage.

93. ANON. (1985). Domestic smoke control. *Environmental Health* **93,** July 1985.

94. DIRECTIVE 75/439/EEC on the Disposal of Waste Oils. *Official Journal of the European Communities,* **L194,** 23-24, 25 July 1975.

95. PEREIRA, M.B.R., SCOTT, D.W., SIMMONDS, A. AND ZOLGHADR, M. (1983). The combustion of waste oil and emission measurements. *WSL Report LR 479(AP).* Warren Spring Laboratory, Stevenage.

96. ANON. (1984). Processes to solve Britain's scrap tyre disposal problems. *ENDS Report, No.111,* April 1984.

97. DEPARTMENT OF THE ENVIRONMENT (1985). Alternatives for waste disposal No.2: Waste and scrap tyres. *NAWDC News,* August 1985.

98. ANON. (1985). Old tyres for oil? *Europe 85,* May 1985.

99. GREATER MANCHESTER COUNCIL. Evidence to the Royal Commission.

100. INSTITUTION OF CHEMICAL ENGINEERS. Evidence to the Royal Commission.

101. HOUSE OF COMMONS TRADE AND INDUSTRY COMMITTEE (1985). *Second Special Report, Session 1984-85.* HMSO, London.

102. KEEP BRITAIN TIDY GROUP. Evidence to the Royal Commission.

103. MASON, D. (1985). Beach refuse - an urgent case for tighter control. *Surveyor,* 5 September 1985.

104. AUDIT COMMISSION (1984). Securing further improvements in refuse collection. *A review by the Audit Commission.* HMSO, London.

105. INSTITUTE OF SOLID WASTE MANAGEMENT (1980). *Contract Refuse Collection: guidelines for local authorities.* ISWM. September 1980.

106. BRITISH STANDARDS INSTITUTION (1985). B.S. Specification for disposable plastic refuse sacks made from polyethylene. *British Standard 6642:1985* B.S.I. London.

107. For example:
    ARCHER, A. (1984). The town that cleaned up in the sweep stakes - a study in collective savings. *Municipal Journal,* **92,** 31 August 1984.

108. DEPARTMENT OF TRANSPORT (1985). Code of practice for routine maintenance of motorways and all-purpose trunk roads; trunk road management and maintenance notice. DTp, London.

109. RITCHIE, J.P. (1982). MacDonald's commitment to food hygiene. *IEHO 89th Environmental Health Congress, Scarborough, 20-23 September 1982.*

110. WESTMINSTER CITY COUNCIL. Evidence to the Royal Commission.

111. The London Standard, 26 September 1985

112. LIFT WORKING PARTY (1984). Report of the London-wide Initiative on Fly Tipping Working Party. GLC, London.

113. THE WORKING PARTY ON THE DISPOSAL OF CLINICAL WASTES IN THE LONDON AREA (1983). Final Report.

114. OAKLAND, D. AND HOOPER, J. (1985). The disposal of clinical waste in London. *London Environment Bulletin,* **3,** 1, Summer 1985.

115. DEPARTMENT OF THE ENVIRONMENT (1983). Clinical Wastes. *Waste Management Paper No.25.* HMSO, London.

116. For example:
    i.   CENTRAL ELECTRICITY GENERATING BOARD (1984). CEGB proves its point. CEGB, London.
    ii. The Guardian, 18 July 1984.
    iii. The Times, 18 July 1984.

117. CENTRAL ELECTRICITY GENERATING BOARD. Press Notice - Greenpeace retracts crash test allegations. 28 May 1985.

118. BOND, M. & CAMPBELL, D. (1984). CEGB crash stunt hides chronic spills. *New Statesman,* 20 July 1984.

119. IMO (1981). International Maritime Dangerous Goods Code. IMO, London.

120. For example:
    i.   DEPARTMENT OF TRADE (1981). Carriage of dangerous goods in ships. *Merchant Shipping Notice M956.* DoT, London.
    ii. DEPARTMENT OF TRADE (1982). Emergency procedures for ships carrying dangerous goods in packaged form. *Merchant Shipping Notice M1023.* DoT, London.

121. IMO. *International Conference on Marine Pollution (1973), including the International Convention for the Prevention of Pollution from Ships, 1973.* IMO, London.

122. DEPARTMENT OF TRADE (1976). Disposal of out-of-date pyrotechnics. *Merchant Shipping Notice No.M787.* DOT, London.

123. DEPARTMENT OF THE ENVIRONMENT (1984). Controlling pollution: principles and prospects. The Government's response to the Tenth Report of the Royal Commission on Environmental Pollution. *Pollution paper 22.* HMSO, London.

124. DIRECTIVE 84/631/EEC on the Supervision and control within the European Community of the transfrontier shipment of hazardous waste. *Official Journal of the European Communities.* L.326, 31-36, 13 December 1984.

125. ANON. (1985). Towards an international treaty on hazardous waste shipments. *ENDS Report 123,* April 1985.

126. ANON (1985). OECD Ministers agree to tackling emerging environmental problems. *ENDS Report 125,* June 1985.

127. ORGANISATION FOR ECONOMIC COOPERATION AND DEVELOPMENT (1985). *Transfrontier movements of hazardous wastes.* OECD, Paris.

128. SAWHNEY, B.L. AND KOZLOSKI, R.P. (1984). Organic pollutants from landfill sites. *Journal of Environmental Quality.* 13 (3) 349-352.

129. HARRIS, R.C. AND LOWE, D.R. (1984). Changes in the organic fraction of leachate from two domestic refuse sites on the Sherwood Sandstone, Nottinghamshire. *Quarterly Journal of Engineering Geology,* 17 (1) 57-70.

130. REINHARD, M., GOODMAN, N.L. AND BARKER, J.F. (1984). Occurrence and distribution of organic chemicals in two landfill leachate plumes. *Environmental Science and Technology.* 18 (12) 953-961.

131. VENKATARAMAUI, E.S., AHLERT, R.C. AND CARBO, P. (1984). Biological treatment of landfill leachates. *Critical Reviews in Environmental Control* 14 (4) 333-376.

132. GHASSEMI, M., QUINLAIVAN, S. AND BACKMAIER, J. (1984). Characteristics of leachates from hazardous waste landfills. *J. Environmental Science and Health.* A.19 (5) 579-620.

133. NATIONAL SOCIETY FOR CLEAN AIR (1985). Last year's harvest burn. *The NSCA Survey of straw/stubble burning in 1984.* NSCA, Brighton.

134. ANON. (1985). Do landfills pose a threat to Britain's aquifers? *ENDS Report No.129,* October 1985.

135. STEVENS, C. (1984). Landfill lining and capping. *Atomic Energy Research Establishment Report No. 11506. AERE Harwell.*

136. MONTAGUE, P. (1982). Hazardous waste landfills: some lessons from New Jersey. *Civil Engineering - ASCE,* (September 1982) 53-56.

References

137. FRASER, J.A.L. AND TYTLER, N.B. (1983). Operational experience using H_2O_2 in landfill leachate treatment. *Effluent and Water Treatment,* April 1983.

138. ANON. (1984). Update on landfill gas. *ENDS Report 116,* September 1984.

139. ANON. (1985). Enthusiasm flares for landfill gas. *ENDS Report 128,* September 1985.

140. PECKSEN, G. (1983). London's first gas field comes on stream. *London Environment Bulletin,* 1 (2) Autumn 1983.

141. MOSS, H. (1984). Making the best use of landfill. *Municipal Journal,* 17th August 1984, 1278-1280.

142. ADER, G. (1982). Methane from landfill. *Report ETSU-B-1066,* Energy Technology Support Unit, Harwell.

143. ASPINWALL, R. (1985). Technical and economic planning, control and monitoring for the modern landfill. *Paper presented at a joint DOE/IWM/NAWDC symposium, London, March 1985.*

144. PACKINGTON ESTATE ENTERPRISES LIMITED. Evidence to the Royal Commission.

145. DÜSSELDORF CITY COUNCIL. Evidence to the Royal Commission.

146. BRITISH EMBASSY, TOKYO. Data gathered for the Royal Commission.

147. DAMES AND MOORE INTERNATIONAL. Evidence to the Royal Commission.

148. MR. T. BURKE. Evidence to the Royal Commission.

149. CLAYTON, P. (1984). The incineration of municipal refuse. *WSL Report LR498(AP).* Warren Spring Laboratory, Stevenage.

150. SCOTTISH HOME AND HEALTH DEPARTMENT. Independent Review Group (Chairman: Professor J Lenihan) (1985). Bonnybridge/Denny morbidity review. SHHD, Edinburgh.

151. THE WELSH OFFICE (1985). The incidence of congenital malformations in Wales, with particular reference to the district of Torfaen, Gwent. Welsh Office.

152. For example:

   i. WRITTEN ANSWER. *House of Commons Official Report,* 26 June 1984. Columns 401-406.

   ii. DEBATE. *House of Commons Official Report,* 2 July 1985. Columns 306-312.

   iii. WRITTEN ANSWER. *House of Commons Official Report,* 24 July 1985. Column 561.

   iv. WRITTEN ANSWER. *House of Commons Official Report,* 21 October 1985, Columns 95-98.

   v. WRITTEN ANSWERS. *House of Commons Official Report,* 23 October 1985, Columns 176-177.

   vi. WRITTEN ANSWERS. *House of Commons Official Report,* 24 October 1985, Columns 231-236.

153. LARSSON, P. (1984). Sedimentation of polychlorinated biphenysl (PCBs) in limnic and marine environments. *Water Research* 18 (11) 1389-94.

154. GEYER, H., FREITAG, D. AND KORTE, F. (1984). Polychlorinated biphenyls (PCBs) in the marine environment, particularly in the Mediterranean. *Ecotoxicology and Environmental Safety,* 8, 129-151.

155. WASTE MANAGEMENT BRANCH, EPS, CANADA. (1978). Guideline on the management of waste materials containing polychlorinated biphenyls (PCBs). *Report EPS 1-EC-78-1.*

156. WASTE MANAGEMENT BRANCH, EPS, CANADA. (1978). Guideline on central collection and storage facilities for waste materials containing polychlorinated biphenyls (PCBs). *Report EPS 1-EC-78-8.*

157. BAXTER, R.M. AND SUTHERLAND, D.A. (1984). Biochemical and photochemical processes in the degradation of chlorinated biphenyls. *Environmental Science and Technology* 18, (8) 608-610.

158. CZUCZWA, J.M., MCVEETY, B.D. AND HITES, R.A. (1984). Polychlorinated dibenzo dioxins and dibenzo furans in sediments from Siskiwit Lake, Isle Royale (Lake Superior). *Science* 226, 568-9.

159. CLEVERLY, D.M. Chlorinated dibenzo dioxins and furans in incineration of municipal solid waste. *Paper presented at a symposium in the United States.*

160. CHOUDHRY, G.C., OLIE, K. AND HUTZINGER, O. (1982). Mechanisms in the thermal formation of chlorinated compounds including polychlorinated dibenzo dioxins. *In Chlorinated Dioxins and Related Compounds. (Editors: O. Hutzinger et. al.)* Pergammon Press, Oxford and New York.

161. OLIE, K., BERG, M.V.D., AND HUTZINGER O. (1983). Formation and fate of PCDD and PCDF from combustion processes. *Chemosphere* 12 (4/5) 627-636.

162. INDUSTRIAL AIR POLLUTION INSPECTORATE (1985). Industrial air pollution: health and safety 1984. HSE, London.

163. FUHR. H. (1984). Hazardous waste incineration at Bayer AG, FRG. General approach and special solutions. *2nd International Symposium on Operating European Centralized Hazardous (Chemical) Waste Management Facilities, Odense, Denmark. September 1984.*

164. RICH, L.A. (1985). Burning of toxics faces rising protests worldwide. *Chemical Week,* 22 May 1985.

165. BUSINESS ROUNDTABLE ENVIRONMENT INFORMATION PROGRAM (1985). Toward a cleaner America: a progress report. *1st Report of BREIP.* Washington, DC.

166. BUSINESS ROUNDTABLE ENVIRONMENT INFORMATION PROGRAM (1985). Toward a cleaner environment. *4th Report of BREIP.* Washington, DC.

167. MINISTRY OF AGRICULTURE, FISHERIES AND FOOD. Evidence to the Royal Commission.

168. EUROPEAN COUNCIL OF CHEMICAL MANUFACTURERS' FEDERATIONS (CEFIC). (1985). Incineration at sea: history, state of the art and outlook. *Paper presented by CEFIC for the consideration of the Scientific Group of the London Dumping Convention at the March 1985 meeting.*

169. US ENVIRONMENTAL PROTECTION AGENCY (1985). Proposed regulations for incineration at sea. *US Federal Register.* 28 February, 1985, 8222-8288.

170. US ENVIRONMENTAL PROTECTION AGENCY (1985). Incineration at sea – research strategy. *US EPA.* 19 February, 1985.

171. SUTTER H. (1984). Trends in burning chlorinated hydrocarbons at sea (in German). *Müll und Abfall* 4 (84) 89-93.

172. WATT, H. (1985). Talking point. *Farmers Weekly,* 11 October 1985.

173. LARKIN, S.B.C., LEE, M., MCINNES, G., SHARP, U. and SIMMONDS, A.C. (1985). The measurement of air pollution and other factors relating to the practice of straw and stubble burning. *WSL Report LR 518(AP).* Warren Spring Laboratory, Stevenage.

174. INDUSTRIAL AIR POLLUTION INSPECTORATE (1985). Industrial air pollution: health and safety 1983. HSE. London.

175. MINISTRY OF AGRICULTURE, FISHERIES AND FOOD (1984). Straw disposal and utilisation, a review of knowledge. MAFF, London.

176. PROPOSED DIRECTIVE on the Dumping of Waste at Sea, submitted to Council 13 August 1985 *Official Journal of the European communities.* C.245, 23-41, 26 September 1985.

177. WRITTEN ANSWER. *House of Commons Official Report.* 11 April 1984. Column 249.

178. Report of the Independent Review of Disposal of Radioactive Waste in the North East Atlantic. (Chairman: Professor F.G.T. Holliday) (1985). HMSO, London.

179. *House of Lords Official Report.* 22 April 1985. Columns 953-975.

180. The Hon. William Waldegrave MP, addressing the Campaign for Lead Free Air, 25 September 1985.

181. ANON. (1985). Algae/waste removal. *Environment Report,* 13 September 1985.

182. SEGAR, D.A., STANMAN, D. AND DAVIS, P.G. (1985). Beneficial use of municipal sludge in the ocean. *Marine Pollution Bulletin,* 6 (5) 186-191.

183. ANON (1985). Sewage transforms barren sand pits to fertile lakes. *New Scientist,* 105, 28 March 1985.

184. HOATHER, H.A. (1985). In-house waste disposal. *Waste Management Bulletin No.9,* August 1985.

References

185. CLARK, A.I. AND PERRY, R. (1984). Cement-based stabilisation/solidification processes for the disposal of toxic wastes. *Department of Civil Engineering,* Imperial College, London.

186. DEBATE: *House Commons Official Report,* 4 April 1985. Columns 1402-1407.

187. DALTON, H. AND STIRLING, E.I. (1982). Co-metabolism. *Philosophical Transactions of the Royal Society.* **B.297,** 481-496.

188. WRITTEN ANSWER. *House of Commons Official Report,* 7 March 1985. Column 548.

189. DEPARTMENT OF THE ENVIRONMENT (1985). Control of Pollution Act 1974, sections 12-14 - review of costs of implementation. DoE, London.

190. BAILEY, G. AND HAWKINS, R.G.P. (1983). The future of rubbish. Conservative Political Centre, London.

191. WRITTEN ANSWER. *House of Commons Official Report,* 14 March 1985. Column 215.

192. ORAL ANSWER. *House of Commons Official Report,* 4 July 1985. Columns 510-511.

193. WRITTEN ANSWER. *House of Commons Official Report,* 4 April 1985. Column 759.

194. i. NEW YORK TIMES, 24 April 1984.
     ii. NEW YORK TIMES, 3 June 1984.

195. IMPERIAL COLLEGE OF SCIENCE AND TECHNOLOGY , LONDON. Evidence to the Royal Commission.

196. ASSOCIATED PRESS REPORT, 31 August 1985, from World Reporter Ninety Day Newsfile.

197. ROBINSON V. BEACONSFIELD RDC. (1911). 2 ch. p.188.

198. ANON (1985). Industry urged to review safety of long-term chemical storage. *ENDS Report 128,* September 1985.

199. HOUSE OF LORDS SELECT COMMITTEE ON SCIENCE AND TECHNOLOGY (1985). Opinion of the Committee on the Review of the Control of Pollution (Special Waste) Regulations 1980. *Sixth Report, Session 1984-85.* HMSO, London.

200. HOUSE OF LORDS SELECT COMMITTEE ON SCIENCE AND TECHNOLOGY (1985). Hazardous waste disposal: Government response. *Third Report, Session 1984-85.* HMSO, London.

201. HEALTH AND SAFETY EXECUTIVE (1985). *News releases E26 (21 March) and E61 (5 July).* HSE, London.

202. ROYAL SOCIETY OF ARTS (1984). Examinations for the certificates of professional competence in road transport. RSA, Orpington.

203. DEPARTMENT OF THE ENVIRONMENT (1976). The licensing of waste disposal sites. *Waste Management Paper No.4,* HMSO, London.

204. *S.I. 1985 No.698.* The Town and Country Planning (Compensation for Restriction of Mineral Working) Regulations 1985

205. INDUSTRIAL AIR POLLUTION INSPECTORATE (1984). Notes on Best Practicable Means for Chemical Incineration Works. *BPM11.* HMSO, London.

206. Nottingham No.1 Area Hospital Management Committee V. Owen, 1958, 1 QB 50; 1957, 3 A11 ER 358.

207. INSTITUTION OF ENVIRONMENTAL HEALTH OFFICERS (1985). *Annual Report 1984.* IEHO, London.

208. BRITISH PEST CONTROL ASSOCIATION (1985). Hospitals can damage your health. BPCA, London.

209. LORD HAILSHAM OF SAINT MARYLEBONE (1983). Speech to Nottinghamshire magistrates, 4 March. The Magistrate, April 1983.

210. LORD HAILSHAM OF SAINT MARYLEBONE (1983). Presidential Address to the Magistrates' Association, 14 October. The Magistrate, December 1983.

211. HORSMAN, E.R. (1984). Presentation of cases in magistrates' courts. *Law Society Gazette,* 18 October 1984.

212. MACRORY, R. AND WITHERS, S.M. (1985). The application of administrative and criminal punishments with regard to toxic and hazardous wastes in EEC Member Countries - The United Kingdom. *Research Report prepared for the Commission of the European Communities.*

213. UNITED STATES GENERAL ACCOUNTING OFFICE (1985). Illegal disposal of hazardous waste: difficult to detect or deter. GAO, Washington DC.

214. DIRECTIVE 85/337/EEC on the Assessment of the Effects of Certain Public and Private Projects on the Environment. *Official Journal of the European Communities* **L175** 40-48, 5 July 1985.

215. DEPARTMENT OF THE ENVIRONMENT (1984). Survey of land for mineral workings in England, 1982. DoE, London.

216. STREAMLINING THE CITIES. *Cmnd.9063, 1983.*

217. DEPARTMENT OF THE ENVIRONMENT (1983). Consultation paper on waste management aspects of 'Streamlining the Cities'.

218. HOUSE OF LORDS SELECT COMMITTEE ON SCIENCE AND TECHNOLOGY (1985). Local Government Bill - Scientific and technical services. *Fourth Report, Session 1984-85.* HMSO, London.

219. DEBATE *House of Lords Official Report,* 9 May 1985. Columns 739-783 and 788-789.

220. DEBATE *House of Lords Official Report,* 8 July 1985. Columns 803-816.

221. WRITTEN ANSWER. *House of Commons Official Report,* 25 October 1985. Columns.266-267.

222. WRITTEN ANSWER. *House of Commons Official Report,* 24 February 1984, Columns 640-641.

223. GARNER, (Editor) *Pollution Control Encyclopaedia.* Butterworths, London.

224. LOOMIS, C.J. (1985). Naked came the insurance buyer. *Fortune,* 67-71, 10 June 1985.

224. SKINNER, J.H. (1983). Hazardous waste management in the United States. *Industry and Environment, Special Issue 1983,* 66-69. U.N.E.P.

226. WALGATE, R. (1985). Dump it here, please. *Nature,* **314,** 396.

227. SWARTZMAN, D., CROKE, K. AND SWIBEL, S. (1985). Reducing aversion to living near hazardous waste facilities through compensation and risk reduction. *Journal of Environmental Management.* **20,** 43-50.

228. LEE, J.R., BROWN, J., HENDERSON, J., McDERMID, C. AND WHITE, H. (1985). Nuclear waste management. *Nature,* **317,** 570.

229. ANON. (1985). Staff shortages still hampering environmental policy making. *ENDS Report No.127,* August 1985.

230. REPORT OF THE COMMITTEE ON SAFETY AND HEALTH AT WORK (Chairman: Lord Robens) (1972), *Cmnd. 5034.* HMSO, London.

231. SIMMONS, R.F. AND TYLER, B.J. (1984). Hazard assessment techniques used in the chemical industry and their possible uses elsewhere. *Fire and Materials,* **8** (4) 199-205, December 1984.

232. ANON (1983). One company's experience of a HAZOP study. *Loss Prevention Bulletin, No.49,* 1-6.

233. BENDIXEN, L.M., AND ONEILL J.K. (1984). Chemical plant risk assessment using HAZOP and fault tree methods. *Plant/operations Progress,* **3** (3) 179-184.

234. KLETZ, T.A. (1983). Loss prevention. HAZOP and HAZAN : Notes on the identification and assessment of hazards. Institution of Chemical Engineers, Rugby.

235. MARSHALL, V.C. (1982). Hazard and risk analysis - a forward. *Loss Prevention Bulletin, No.46,* 1-4.

236. ANON. (1985). Broken branches in the fault tree. *New Scientist,* **108,** 19, 31 October 1985.

237. ROYAL COMMISSION ON ENVIRONMENTAL POLLUTION (1971). *First Report, Cmnd.4585.* HMSO, London.

238. ROYAL COMMISSION ON ENVIRONMENTAL POLLUTION (1974). Pollution control: progress and problems. *Fourth Report, Cmnd.5780.* HMSO, London.

239. ELKINGTON, J. (1982). Seven bridges for the future. *In the Conservation and Development Programme for the UK.* Kogan Page, London.

240. IMPERIAL COLLEGE CENTRE FOR ENVIRONMENTAL TECHNOLOGY (1984). Training for pollution control in industry. *Final Report to the Commission of the European Communities.* Imperial College of Science and Technology, London.

References

241. ECOTEC RESEARCH AND CONSULTING LTD. (1985). Training and advice requirements in the environmental field in the European Community. *Final Report to the Commission of the European Communities.* ECOTEC, Birmingham.

242. INSTITUTION OF ENVIRONMENTAL SCIENCES AND CENTRE FOR EXTENSION STUDIES (LOUGHBOROUGH UNIVERSITY OF TECHNOLOGY). Evidence to the Royal Commission.

243. The Hon. William Waldegrave, MP. Speech at the 1985 Conservation Awards Ceremony.

244. ANON. (1985). Rockware reclamation : recycling comes of age. *ENDS Report 127,* August 1985.

245. GOOD, I. (1985). Recycling : get on your bikes! *Municipal Journal,* **93,** 16 August 1985.

246. SLATER, J.H. AND BULL, A.T. (1982). Environmental microbiology, biodegradation. *Philosophical Transactions of the Royal Society.* **B.297,** 575-597.

247. PADHY, R.N. (1985). Cyanobacteria employed as fertilisers and waste disposers. *Nature,* **317,** 10 October 1985.

248. LORD GREGSON (1983). Disposal needs more than optimism. *Waste Management Bulletin, No.2.* April 1983.

249. ROYAL SOCIETY (1983). Risk assessment. *Report of a Royal Society study group.* Royal Society, London.

250. OTWAY, H. (1980). The perception of technological risks - a psychological perspective. *In Technological Risk. (Editors: Dierkes, M., Edwards, S. and Coppock, R.).* Commission of the European Commission. Oelgeschlager, Gunn and Hain, Cambridge Massachusetts.

251. OTWAY, H. AND THOMAS, K. (1982). Reflections on risk perception and policy. *Risk analysis.* **2** (2).

252. PROFESSOR D.J.P. BARKER. Evidence to the Royal Commission.

253. SOUTHWOOD, T.R.E. (1985). The roles of proof and concern in the work of the Royal Commission on Environmental Pollution. *Marine Pollution Bulletin,* **16** (9) 346-350.

254. JESSOP, E.G. AND HORSLEY, S.D. (1985). Multiple myeloma in south Cumbria 1974-84: problems of health analysis in small communities. *Journal of Epidemiology and Community Health.* **39** (3) 231-236.

255. LATHROP, P. (1985). Responding to a cancer scare. *EPA Journal,* **11,** June.

208

INDEX

b-denotes information box
n-denotes footnote

See also contents pages (v-xiii) for a guide to the discussion of subjects in this Report.

Index

Control of Pollution (Special Waste) Regulations 1980, 2.9–2.10, 2.17, 2.20, 2.42, 2.53b, 6.35, 8.2, 8.15, 8.22, 8.37, 13.3, 13.45
   review of, 2.10, 3.7, 8.16, 8.22–8.24, 8.28, 8.38, 8.43, 9.38, 13.7
Crown immunity, 7.41, 8.48–8.49, 13.79

Deep burial of waste, 7.50ff, 13.68–13.69
Definitions:
   pollution, 1.3
   special waste, 2.9
   waste, 1.5, 2.15ff, 2.21b
   waste management 1.25
Denmark, 7.25
Department of Energy, 7.14, 11.9
Department of the Environment:
   Circular 'Planning and Noise', 2.55
   co-operative programme of research on behaviour of
   hazardous wastes in landfill sites, 7.17
   Digest of Environmental Pollution and Water Statistics, 2.24
   discussion paper on secrecy, 1.17
   guidance on hospital wastes, 6.29, 6.32, 8.4, 13.43
   guidance to waste collection authorities, 6.9(b)
   implementation of European Community policies, 4.12, 13.17
   mineral extraction, 8.43, 9.39, 13.90
   research programme, 11.1ff, 13.99, 13.102, 13.103, 13.105, 13.106
   research on incinerator emissions, 7.28, 13.58
   staff resources, 2.49, 9.37–9.39, 13.89
   Waste Management Papers, 1.4, 2.12, 8.40, 9.28
   (See also:
      Hazardous Waste Inspectorate
      Interdepartmental Committee on the Redevelopment of Contaminated Land
      Landfill Practices Review Group)
Department of Trade and Industry, 4.12, 5.32–5.33, 13.17, 13.100
   Warren Spring Laboratory, 5.5, 11.12, 11.15
Department of Transport, 6.11, 6.13, 6.26, 6.43, 8.32, 9.41, 13.22, 13.41, 13.48
Deposit of Poisonous Waste Act 1972, 2.4, 2.8–2.9
Design, 10.7ff, 13.14
Development control, 9.3ff
Dioxins and furans, 1.18–1.20, 1.19b, 5.24, 7.27b, 11.13, 11.19, 13.1, 13.103
Disposers of waste, responsibilities of, 8.38ff (See also Duty of care)
Drummed waste, 7.19, 13.52
Dumping at Sea Act 1974, 2.11, 7.49
Dustbins, 6.4ff, 11.14, 13.31
Duty of care, 1.12, 3.4ff, 5.7, 8.12ff, 12.3, 13.10, 13.74(a)

ECOTEC Research and Consulting Ltd, 10.18
Energy from waste, 5.22ff, 13.24
Environmental Resources Ltd, 1.2, 5.3
European Community:
   definitions of waste, 2.17, 2.22
   recycling of batteries, 5.19
   research on effects of dioxins, 1.20, 11.13, 13.1
   Third Action Programme on the Environment, 4.5, 4.9, 4.12, 13.2, 13.13, 13.16
   training for environmental specialists, 10.17–10.18, 10.26
European Community legislation:
   Directives on:
      Containers of liquids for human consumption, 4.9b, 4.12, 5.12, 13.17
      Toxic and dangerous wastes, 2.13, 2.17, 8.22
      Transfrontier shipment of hazardous wastes, 6.48
      Waste, framework Directive, 2.13, 2.17
      Waste oil, 5.26
   Regulation on Farm Structures, 2.40, 13.6
   Proposed legislation:
      Amending Directive on waste oil, 5.27
      Directive on dumping of waste at sea, 7.47
      Directive on use of sewage sludge in agriculture, 2.45
European Council of Chemical Manufacturers' Federations (CEFIC), 3.6b, 7.33, 13.11

Index

Printed for Her Majesty's Stationery Office by Commercial Colour Press, London E7. 11/85, C45, Dd.601675.